Metal-Polymer Multi-Material Structures and Manufacturing Techniques in Transportation

Metal-Polymer Multi-Material Structures and Manufacturing Techniques in Transportation

Special Issue Editor

Sergio T. Amancio-Filho

MDPI • Basel • Beijing • Wuhan • Barcelona • Belgrade • Manchester • Tokyo • Cluj • Tianjin

Special Issue Editor
Sergio T. Amancio-Filho
Graz University of Technology
Austria

Editorial Office
MDPI
St. Alban-Anlage 66
4052 Basel, Switzerland

This is a reprint of articles from the Special Issue published online in the open access journal *Materials* (ISSN 1996-1944) (available at: https://www.mdpi.com/journal/materials/special_issues/ metal_polymer_multi_material).

For citation purposes, cite each article independently as indicated on the article page online and as indicated below:

LastName, A.A.; LastName, B.B.; LastName, C.C. Article Title. *Journal Name* **Year**, *Article Number*, Page Range.

ISBN 978-3-03936-150-2 (Pbk)
ISBN 978-3-03936-151-9 (PDF)

Cover image courtesy of Sergio T. Amancio-Filho.

Contents

About the Special Issue Editor

Sergio T. Amancio-Filho is a professor and the deputy head of the Institute of Materials Science, Joining and Forming at Graz University of Technology (TU Graz), Austria, where he chairs the 'Austrian Ministry for Climate Action, Environment, Energy, Mobility, Innovation and Technology (BMK) Endowed Professorship for Aviation'. The focus of Prof. Amancio's work is on the process development and materials science of new additive manufacturing and joining techniques for lightweight hybrid structures. Before joining TU Graz, Sergio Amancio was a group leader at Helmholtz-Zentrum Geesthacht (HZG), Germany, and an assistant professor at the Hamburg University of Technology (TUHH), Germany. He is the main inventor of several patents on new manufacturing processes and has co-authored over 160 technical publications.

Preface to "Metal-Polymer Multi-Material Structures and Manufacturing Techniques in Transportation"

The demand for lightweight structures has been growing across a wide range of engineering solutions, for transport, renewable power generation and construction industries, where both weight savings and increased energy efficiency are pursued. The use of high-performance engineering polymers and composites (e.g. glass- and carbon-fiber reinforced polymers) has gained considerable importance in hybrid, multi-material structures. In addition to their advantage in specific strength, composites possess outstanding corrosion resistance, high strength and fatigue performances, and thermal stability. Furthermore, the development of advanced metal alloys, such as aluminum, titanium, magnesium and high strength steel alloys, helps to reduce the overall weight of a structure while maintaining high mechanical performance. Therefore, the observed trend for achieving weight reduction is a mixed material design.

The field of metal–polymer multi-material structures has been growing at an increasing and particularly fast pace in recent years. Several techniques have been or are being developed with the aim of being used for additively manufacturing or joining dissimilar materials in cost efficient manners. Despite the benefits of using metals, high-performance polymers and their respective composite materials in a hybrid structure, the manufacturing of these dissimilar materials presents a great challenge, due to their distinct thermal and physical properties.

Recently, new joining techniques have been developed, including adhesive bonding, mechanical fastening, welding-based technologies or combinations of one or more of these individual techniques—known as hybrid joining technologies. Moreover, a new manufacturing field has been created to directly assemble metal-composite structures. These technologies involve the hybridization of metallic parts with polymer processing—such as injection over molding—or composite lamination techniques. Therefore, the fabrication of complex parts with improved mechanical performance and strength-to-weight ratios are possible. Within this scope, one field that has great disruptive potential for contributing to the rise of hybrid structures is additive manufacturing. The possibility of using new materials and their combinations to additively manufacture hybrid components with complex geometries has gained momentum across several industries.

This book—published based on the correlating Special Issue (https://www.mdpi.com/journal/materials/special_issues/metal_polymer_multi_material)— presents recent developments in the state of the art of advanced manufacturing and the joining of metal–polymer multi-material structures in transportation (i.e., aircraft and automotive industries). The chapters of this book mainly focus on the correlations between the microstructure, process, properties and mechanical performance of metal-polymer/composite hybrid structures.

Chapters 1 and 2 addresses the new additive manufacturing method AddJoining, developed for layered metal-polymer and metal-polymer composite hybrid structures. The chapter reports on the material combination composed of aluminum 2024-T3 and acrylonitrile butadiene styrene. The influence of the isolated process parameters on the mechanical properties and microstructure of these multi-material builds is reported. The work explains, via microstructural analysis and mechanical testing, that proper mechanical interlocking was achieved between the metal and polymer parts.

Chapter 3 introduces thin-ply hybrid laminates—a recent new novel category of fiber metal laminates. Generally speaking, thin-ply laminates exhibit a higher degree of freedom in design and altered failure behavior, and therefore, an increased strength for unnotched laminates in comparison to thick-ply laminates. It is well known that the static strength is strongly decreased for notched laminates; this is caused by a lack of stress relaxation through damage, which leads to a higher stress concentration and premature, brittle failure; for instance, around pre-drilled roles for mechanical fasteners. This chapter reports on the influence of different metal volume fractions in thin-ply metal–carbon fiber-reinforced polymer laminates, in areas with high stress concentrations in open holes. The main achievements of this fiber metal laminating strategy were an increase of approximately 60% in open hole tensile strength, as well as an increase of over 30% in specific strength.

Chapter 4 evaluates the importance of metal surface micro-structuring in the adhesive bonding of polymer–metal hybrid structures. Mechanical interlocking and chemical etching/conversion have been proven to be effective bonding mechanisms for dissimilar material structures, such as polymers and metals. The chapter assesses the influence of different surface pretreatments for the metallic part on the interlaminar strength and the corresponding surface roughness parameters. Investigated surface pretreatments are blasting, chemical etching (stand-alone and combined), thermal spraying, and laser structuring. This chapter provides an important insight on the role of the metal-polymer interface in controlling the global mechanical performance of layered structures.

Chapter 5 presents a comprehensive study on the effects of a novel polymer staking technique —the friction-based injection clinching joining (F-ICJ) process—on the microstructure and local properties of polymer–metal staked overlap joints. Focus is given to the polymer stake head formation mechanisms, which are evaluated by the microhardness map and cross-polarized transmitted-light optical microscopy (CP-TLOM), and size exclusion chromatography (SEC) analysis. Special attention is given to the process-related thermomechanical changes in local mechanical properties (i.e., in microhardness) of the created stake head. A detailed analysis of correlations between these local changes and the global mechanical performance (under shar and tensile loading) is presented for overlap joints. This chapter provides a better understanding of the relationships between processing, microstructure, and properties for the staking of polymer–metal hybrid structures.

Chapters 6 and 7 introduce the friction riveting process. This revolutionary mechanical fastening process allows for a rapid and efficient way of similarly and dissimilarly joining thermoplastics and thermosets, as well as their fiber-reinforced combinations, and metal–polymer/composite hybrid structures. Chapter 6 presents a systematic study on the correlations between process parameters and rivet plastic deformation, while in Chapter 7, the correlation between energy efficiency and the global mechanical performance of hybrid aluminum–thermoplastic hybrid joints produced by a force-controlled friction riveting process variant. Bell-shaped rivet plastic deformation—meaning high mechanical interlocking—resulted from moderate energy inputs, allowing for the high tensile resistance of friction-riveted joints. An energy efficiency threshold, up until which energy input displayed good linear correlations with joint mechanical performance, was reported, whereby additional process energy did not significantly contribute toward increasing joint mechanical performance. A correlation between friction parameters was established for the first time, to maximize mechanical response while minimizing energy usage in Firction Reveting.

Chapter 8 reports the application of friction riveting on a woven carbon fiber reinforced polymer joined with titanium rivets. It is well known that mechanical fastening is a pre-requisite in the process of the certification of composite and metal-composite aircraft structures. Therefore, friction riveting has the potential to substitute conventional riveting processes. Focus, in this chapter, is given to investigating the influence of pre-set clamping pressure on the joint formation and mechanical strength of direct-friction-riveted overlap joints. The results show the important role of pre-set clamping pressure, whereby its increase for joints produced with a low friction force did not affect joint strength. However, the combined effect of a high-friction force and clamping pressure induced a lower anchoring efficiency, and the delamination of the composite performance. All in all, the chapter introduces important process knowledge based on microstructural and mechanical characterization, thereby improving the state of the art of friction riveting of composite laminates.

Chapters 9 and 10 tackle the advanced friction spot joining process for aluminum–polymer composite joints. This process is an efficient and weight-saving joining process, applied as a substitution to adhesive bonding. Joints are achieved without filler materials, by application of frictional heat and pressure created by a non-consumable tool. Chapter 9 evaluates aluminum alloy 7075-T6 and carbon-fiber-reinforced polyphenylene sulfide (CF-PPS) single-lap joints for future aircraft structures. Macro- and micro-mechanical interlocking were identified as the main bonding mechanisms, along with adhesion forces at the metal-composite interface. Ultimate lap shear forces which were superior/similar to adhesive bonding were achieved, with shorter joining times. Chapter 10 investigates the durability of the single-lap shear aluminum-composite friction spot joints and their behavior under harsh accelerated aging and natural weathering conditions. Four aluminum, surface pre-treatments were selected to be performed: sandblasting (SB), conversion coating (CC), phosphoric acid anodizing (PAA), and PAA with the subsequent application of a primer (PAA-P). Most of the pre-treated specimens retained approximately 90% of their initial as-joined strength after accelerated aging experiments; an excellent performance when compared with adhesively bonded metal–composite parts. Under outside natural weathering (i.e., wind, rain, sun, snow, minus and plus temperature variations), PAA-P surface pre-treated specimens demonstrated the best performance, with a retained strength of more than 80% after one year, due to the tight adhesion and chemical bonding, which reduced the weakening of the metal–composite interface by humidity penetration.

I am indebted to all chapter authors, who contributed the chapters of this exciting book project:

- André B. Abibe, Natalia Manente André

- Lucian A. Blaga, Natascha Z. Borba

- Leonardo B. Canto, Gonçalo Pina Cipriano

- Axel Dittes

- Rielson Falck, Bodo Fiedler

- Seyed M. Goushegir

- Julian Karsten, Johann Körbelin, Benedikt Kötter, Thomas Lampke, Thomas Lindner,

- Erik Saborowski, Jorge F. dos Santos, Ingolf Scharf, Nico Scharnagl, Andreas Schubert, Marilia Sônego, Philipp Steinert

- Pedro Vilaça

I would also like to gratefully acknowledge the financial support received from the Austrian aviation program "TAKE-OFF" and from the Austrian Ministry for Climate Action, Environment, Energy, Mobility, Innovation and Technology (BMK).

I hope that this book will help complement your technical knowledge in materials science and manufacturing. I hope that you enjoy reading it!

Sergio T. Amancio-Filho
Special Issue Editor

Article

Microstructure and Mechanical Performance of Additively Manufactured Aluminum 2024-T3/Acrylonitrile Butadiene Styrene Hybrid Joints Using an AddJoining Technique

Rielson Falck [1], Jorge F. dos Santos [1] and Sergio T. Amancio-Filho [2,*]

[1] Helmholtz-Zentrum Geesthacht, Center for Materials and Coastal Research, Institute of Materials Research, Materials Mechanics, Solid State Joining Processes, 21502 Geesthacht, Germany; rielson.falck@hzg.de (R.F.); jorge.dos.santos@hzg.de (J.F.d.S.)

[2] Institute of Materials Science, Joining and Forming, BMVIT Endowed Professorship for Aviation, Graz University of Technology—TU Graz, Kopernikusgasse 24/1, Graz 8010, Austria

* Correspondence: sergio.amancio@tugraz.at; Tel.: +43-316-873-1610 (ext. 7184)

Received: 20 February 2019; Accepted: 11 March 2019; Published: 14 March 2019

Abstract: AddJoining is an emerging technique that combines the principles of the joining method and additive manufacturing. This technology is an alternative method to produce metal–polymer (composite) structures. Its viability was demonstrated for the material combination composed of aluminum 2024-T3 and acrylonitrile butadiene styrene to form hybrid joints. The influence of the isolated process parameters was performed using the one-factor-at-a-time approach, and analyses of variance were used for statistical analysis. The mechanical performance of single-lap joints varied from 910 ± 59 N to 1686 ± 39 N. The mechanical performance thus obtained with the optimized joining parameters was 1686 ± 39 N, which failed by the net-tension failure mode with a failure pattern along the $45°$ bonding line. The microstructure of the joints and the fracture morphology of the specimens were studied using optical microscopy and scanning electron microscopy. From the microstructure point of view, proper mechanical interlocking was achieved between the coated metal substrate and 3D-printed polymer. This investigation can be used as a base for further improvements on the mechanical performance of AddJoining hybrid-layered applications.

Keywords: AddJoining; FDM; additive manufacturing; aluminum 2024-T3; ABS; metal–polymer

---

1. Introduction

The substitution of conventional metals with lightweight materials is inevitable. Weight reduction and reliable mechanical performance are the driving forces in core industries, i.e., automotive and aerospace, to search for the next generation of materials and innovative production technologies.

The employment of multi-materials in a structure, where material, design, and manufacturing technique are the essential characteristics of the development of any engineering structural application, is a challenge. Joining technologies and additive manufacturing techniques complement the successful integration of material, design, and manufacturing technique [1]. Traditional joining methods, such as adhesive bonding and mechanical fastening, face technological limitations when joining dissimilar materials, such as metals and composites. For instance, the relatively long curing time of adhesive is a significant drawback in adhesive bonding. In recent years, new joining techniques have been investigated to develop hybrid joints to overcome the limitations of traditional joining methods. These include friction riveting [2], friction spot joining [3,4], injection clinching joining [5,6], ultrasonic joining [7,8], ultrasonic welding [9,10], and induction-heated joining [11].

An increased interest in the recent advances in the field of additive manufacturing (AM) is the flexibility to produce complex geometric parts, which are net-shaped with mechanical functionalities, such as in sandwich structures with AM honeycomb cores [12,13]. Combining the principles of joining and the polymeric AM, Falck et al. [14] recently introduced the AddJoining technology as an alternative method to produce metal–polymer (composite) layered structures. This technique is a patent application developed at Helmholtz-Zentrum Geesthacht, Germany (DE 102016121267A1). The process is inspired by AM and joining technology principles, where the new technique uses polymer 3D printing, e.g., fused deposition modeling (FDM), to add layers of polymer or composite on a metal substrate. Some of the advantages of AddJoining are geometric flexibility, such as honeycomb cores, a wide range of material combinations, and the production of complex parts. In the early phase of this technology, it is necessary to understand the adhesion forces and interactions between the metal and the polymer. In a previous publication [14], the authors briefly discussed the main bonding mechanisms that occur during the process, which are adhesion forces and mechanical interlocking at the metal–polymer interface.

The current work aims to evaluate the influence of different process parameters on the mechanical behavior of hybrid joints made by AddJoining. This exploratory study facilitates the first insights into the understanding and improvement of hybrid joints using AM means. Therefore, two well-established materials were selected for this study: aluminum alloy 2024-T3 and acrylonitrile butadiene styrene (ABS). The geometry selected to perform mechanical testing (lap shear test) was single-lap joint configuration. The one-factor-at-a-time (OFAT) approach and analysis of variance (ANOVA) were used to evaluate the significance of the selected parameters on the mechanical strength of the joints. Moreover, the microstructure of the joints and the fracture morphology of the specimens after failure were studied using optical microscopy (OM), laser confocal scanning microscope (LCSM), microcomputed tomography (μCT), and scanning electron microscopy (SEM).

AddJoining Principles

In the AddJoining method, fused deposition modeling (FDM) is used to form the polymeric part, where parts can be produced with complex geometries by depositing extruded material layer by layer on a substrate. This manufacturing technique is divided into three mains steps (Figure 1) [14]. Prior to starting to produce the metal–polymer hybrid part, AddJoining begins by slicing 3D CAD (Computer-Aided Design) data into layers. The first phase starts by fixing the metallic substrate on the build platform (Figure 1a). Subsequently, the polymer material is uncoiled slowly and guided to the extrusion head, where the resistive heated part is located closer to the nozzle. This is heated to high temperatures (above glass transition temperature or melting temperature) to decrease material viscosity. At this stage, the softened or molten material flows smoothly through the extrusion nozzle where the polymer material is deposited to form a full layer on top of the metal substrate (Figure 1b). Following each sequence, the building platform is lowered down by the thickness of one layer (in the Z-direction), while the extrusion head moves in a horizontal plane (the X-Y plane). The process is repeated, adding polymer layers on top of the previously consolidated polymer, until the final thickness of the polymeric part is achieved (Figure 1c). Finally, the metal–polymer layered joint is removed from the building platform (Figure 1d). Additional post-printing steps (e.g., thermomechanical treatment), such as hot isostatic pressing, may be applied to eliminate intrinsic voids in the layered component. This technique is usually used for metals and ceramics, but has been used as a possible technique to produce a homogeneous and defect-free material for 3D-printed polymers as well [15]. Note that post-processing was not considered in this work.

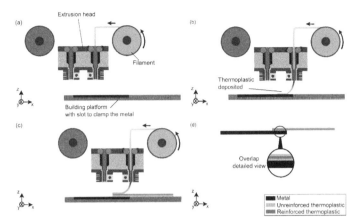

Figure 1. Schematic representation of the AddJoining process for layered metal–polymer composite hybrid structures: (**a**) initial setup, (**b**) deposition of the first polymer layer on the metal substrate, (**c**) deposition of the subsequent polymer layers, (**d**) final layered metal-polymer hybrid structure. Reproduced from Reference [14].

The AddJoining has five controllable parameters, with four of these depending on the 3D printer selected. In this study, there are five controllable parameters: printing temperature (PT), road thickness (RT), deposition speed (DS), and number of contours (NC). The fifth controllable parameter is the ABS coating concentration (AC), where a homogeneous coating layer using the respective unreinforced filament materials is deposited on the metallic surface to promote better adhesion between the metal and subsequent printed polymer layers. Although only single-lap joints were evaluated in this study, AddJoining was conceived to produce rather complex 3D hybrid parts with integrated functionalities or optimized topologies. Figure 2a,b presents schematics of potential AddJoining parts, and Figure 2d shows an net-shape demonstrator part, which can be used in future topology and strength-to-weight optimized aircraft under floor beams (Figure 2c).

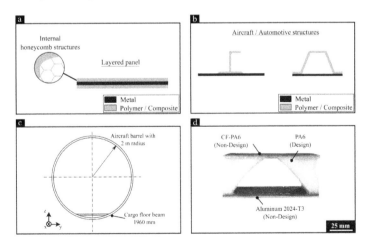

Figure 2. Example of potential AddJoining applications in transportation hybrid structures: (**a**) layered panel with internal honeycomb cores, (**b**) skin-stringer or B pillars for aircraft and automotive structures. Also, (**c**) schematic view of the fuselage barrel of a mid-size aircraft with (**d**) a topology-optimized 3D-printed cargo floor beam (scale 1:20).

2. Materials and Methods

2.1. Aluminum 2024-T3

The aluminum alloy 2024-T3 used in this work was a rolled sheet with a thickness of 2 mm from Constellium, Issoire, France [16]. The metal alloy was selected thanks to its excellent mechanical properties and applicability in the transportation industry. Such material belongs to the 2xxx series of precipitation hardening aluminum alloy, where copper and magnesium are the major alloying elements. The physical and mechanical properties of the aluminum 2024-T3 used in this study are shown in Table 1.

Table 1. Primary physical and mechanical properties of aluminum 2024-T3 at room temperature [17].

Coeff. of Thermal Expansion (μm/m·°C)	Thermal Conductivity (W/m·K)	Melting Temperature (°C)	Elastic Modulus (GPa)	Tensile Strength (MPa)
24.7	121	500–638	72	480

2.2. Acrylonitrile Butadiene Styrene (ABS)

An unreinforced thermoplastic was selected and supplied by VShaper, Jasionka, Poland, in a spool with a filament 1.75 mm in diameter. The amorphous thermoplastic was ABS, which is a terpolymer with glass transition temperature of 105 °C [18–20]. Table 2 highlights some of the physical and mechanical properties of ABS. This polymer is a potential material for engineering applications to fulfill impact resistance, strength, and stiffness [21,22].

Table 2. Primary physical and mechanical properties of ABS at room temperature [18–20].

Coeff. of Thermal Expansion (μm/m·°C)	Thermal Conductivity (W/m·K)	Glass Transition Temperature (°C)	Elastic Modulus (GPa)	Tensile Strength (MPa)
10.1	0.21	94	2.4	26

2.3. Surface Preparation

A pre-processing was necessary before AddJoining the parts, where the aluminum surface was treated to increase the roughness for better adhesion between the joining parts. The aluminum alloy was sandblasted with corundum (Al_2O_3), with the particle size ranging from 100 to 150 μm, with a pressure of six bar. The metal was located at an angle of 45° from the blasting nozzle and with a work distance of 200 mm. The surface pre-treatment was applied in the overlap area (12.5 mm × 25.5 mm) within 10 s. The pretreated samples were cleaned using pressurized air and immersed in ethanol for three minutes in an ultrasonic bath. The peak-to-valley distance surface roughness (Rz) were measured using LCSM. The average surface roughness of the aluminum part prior to sandblasting was 7 ± 0.8 μm. After this surface pre-treatment, the average Rz of the aluminum part 89 ± 0.3 μm increased up to 91% in comparison to the as received specimen surface. In other words, the sandblasting pre-treatment increased the surface roughness creating crevices, which support the formation of micro-mechanical interlocking between the deposited ABS coating layer and the Al 2024 surface.

After sandblasting, a coating was applied to the aluminum surface to increase the adhesion between the printed ABS and the sandblasted aluminum surface during the AddJoining process. Three different concentrations of ABS filament were evaluated, namely 5 wt.%, 15 wt.%, and 25 wt.%. To perform the coating, first ABS filament was dissolved in pure acetone at room temperature for 24 h. The solution was applied with a customized tool to spread it manually on the aluminum surface.

The samples were subsequently dried in the horizontal position for five minutes at room temperature. The nominal coating thickness was measured after the AddJoining process using OM.

In this work, two phenomena occurred during the process. First, the applied coating formed a mechanical interlocking within the metallic sandblasted surface, where the polymer flowed and filled in the cavities. Second, the deposited polymer layer formed a bond with the coating layer [14].

2.4. Manufacturing Procedure

In this exploratory study, printing temperature, road thickness, deposition speed, ABS coating concentration, and the number of contours were selected as process parameters to produce aluminum 2024-T3/ABS hybrid joints using VShaper PRO (VShaper, Jasionka, Poland). Two parameters were constant along the OFAT, such as road angle in [−45°,45°] and building surface temperature at 115 °C. The first means the road deposition directions alternated for different layers between −45° and 45°. The five controllable process parameters are described as follows:

1. Printing temperature (PT) refers to the working temperature at the extruder head (Figure 3a), which was above the glass transition temperature or melting temperature, respectively, for amorphous and semi-crystalline thermoplastics.
2. Road thickness (RT) is the thickness of the consolidated road, which is the vertical distance between each layer (Figure 3b).
3. Deposition speed (DS) means the speed of the extruder head during operation (Figure 3c).
4. ABS coating concentration (AC) is the polymer concentration applied as the coating on the metallic surface.
5. The number of contours (NC) refers to the enclosed loops of road deposition in the filled-perimeter region (Figure 3d).

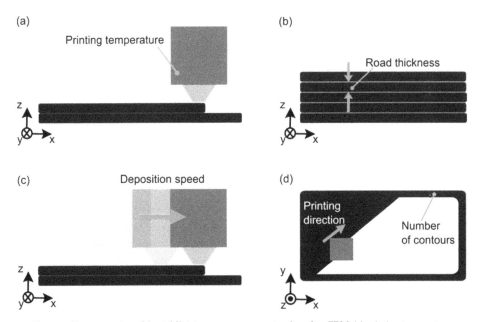

Figure 3. Representation of the AddJoining process parameters based on FDM: (**a**) printing temperature, (**b**) road thickness, (**c**) deposition speed, and (**d**) number of contours.

Table 3 shows the ranges for each process parameter. There were 11 combinations of process parameters for the OFAT approach. A total number of 33 aluminum 2024-T3/ABS hybrid joints were manufactured to investigate the ultimate lap shear force (ULSF). For each condition, three replicates were made, and the ULSF were averaged. With the similar process parameters, the mechanical performance of the aluminum 2024-T3/ABS hybrid joints was compared with the stand-alone printed ABS as the base material (BM) using FDM (hereafter, referred to ABS BM FDM).

Table 3. AddJoining process parameters range for the OFAT.

Factor	Abbreviation	Unit	Level 1	Level 2	Level 3
Printing temperature	PT	°C	230	255	280
Road thickness	RT	mm	0.1	0.2	0.3
Deposition speed	DS	mm/s	20	40	60
ABS coating concentration	AC	wt.%	5	15	25
Number of contours	NC	-	2	12	22

2.5. Mechanical Performance

The joints were evaluated under quasi-static loading to assess the mechanical performance. Based on ASTM D3163-01, the single-lap shear test was performed in the universal testing machine Zwick/Roell 1478 (Zwick Roell, Ulm, Germany) at room temperature with a transverse speed of 1.27 mm/min. The AddJoining hybrid joint configuration had the specimen geometry of 101.6 mm × 25.5 mm × 2 mm with an overlap area of 12.5 mm × 25.5 mm (Figure 4a). For the comparison with the AddJoining hybrid joint, (Figure 4b), ABS BM FDM was produced, based on the total length (109.7 mm) from the single-lap joint configuration.

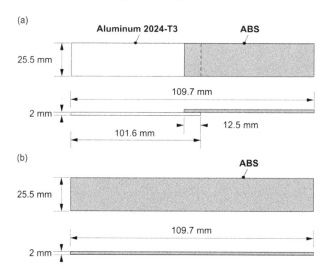

Figure 4. Scheme from the specimen geometry for the (**a**) AddJoining hybrid joints and (**b**) ABS BM FDM.

2.6. Microstructural and Fracture Surface Analysis

OM (DM IR microscope, Leica, Wetzlar, Germany) was used to analyze the microstructure of the joints. ImageJ, an open source software (Version 1.8, Public Domain), used for the images generated from the OM to evaluate the sizes of the pores in the printed polymer generated during the process.

Fracture morphology and surface coating formed on the metallic substrate were investigated using SEM (Quanta FEG 650, FEI, Hillsboro, OR, USA) for the optimum parameter combination with maximum ULSF. To eliminate charging effects beforehand, a vacuum sputter (Q150R ES, Quorum,

Lewes, UK) was used to coat the sample with a layer of gold alloy before analysis. The sample was exposed for 30 s to a current of 65 mA.

2.7. Statistical Analysis of Mechanical Performance

The influence of the process parameters was evaluated using the one-factor-at-a-time (OFAT) approach. This approach was used to identify the range of process parameters in the early stage of a new process. It was conducted to evaluate the isolated effects of the process parameters. The parameters used to assess their influence on the selected response (ULSF) along with their corresponding levels are listed in Table 3. The effect of the process parameters on the response was performed using analysis of variance (ANOVA). Abibe et al. [6] used OFAT and ANOVA to investigate the influence of the injection clinching process parameters on the mechanical performance of Aluminum 2024-T351 and polyamide 6,6 reinforced with 30% short glass fibers.

A one-way ANOVA was conducted via use of the F-test, carried out on Minitab 14 software (Minitab Inc., State College, PA, USA). This method allows the rejection of the null hypothesis for the factors with no statistical significance on the response. Using this technique, the p-value < 0.05 (confidence level of 95%) was chosen as an indication of the significance of the parameter and the f-value was used to evaluate the effect of the process parameters.

2.8. Non-Destructive Testing

Microcomputed tomography (μCT) is a 3D computed tomography technique used to investigate damage and porosity analysis for additive manufacturing parts [23]. In this work, the internal structural information, e.g., pore size and pore distribution, were evaluated using YXLON Cougar EVO (Yxlon, Hamburg, Germany), which is a microcomputed tomography method for seven conditions (condition one to condition seven from Table 4) only for the ABS BM FDM. There are two reasons for this initial approach. First, the presence of a metallic part in the hybrid joint led to insufficient resolution and mistaken identification within the polymeric volume. Further investigation needs to be performed to identify the ideal radiation source. For this initial evaluation, only the ABS BM FDM was considered to understand the influence of the process parameter on the internal structural formation. The outcome of this investigation can aid our understanding of the impact of the process parameter on the mechanical performance of AddJoining hybrid joints. The scanned volume considered was nearly 125,000 mm^3; however, the physical volume size was 25 mm $\times$ 30 mm $\times$ 2 mm, excluding the air surrounding the sample. The specimen was fixed on a rotational stage, and the distance between the rotation axis and the radiation source was set to approximately 10 mm. The X-ray tube voltage was set to 40 kV, and X-ray tube current was set to 40 μA for all the specimens. An image was acquired per degree during X-ray projection images, and the 3D image was reconstructed using the image processing unit of the X-ray CT system. VGStudio Max 3.1 (Volume Graphics, Heidelberg, Germany) was used and a Gaussian filter was applied to remove the noise from the scanning method.

Table 4. Summary of the ULSF and DaB for all 11 conditions for ABS BM FDM.

Condition	PT (°C)	RT (mm)	DS (mm/s)	AC (wt.%)	NC (-)	ULSF (N)	DaB (mm)
C1	230	0.2	40	15	2	1228 ± 132	4.7 ± 0.7
C2	255	0.2	40	15	2	1209 ± 95	5.1 ± 0.3
C3	280	0.2	40	15	2	1259 ± 128	5.7 ± 0.5
C4	280	0.1	40	15	2	1401 ± 30	4.8 ± 0.3
C5	280	0.3	40	15	2	1152 ± 75	4.2 ± 0.2
C6	280	0.1	20	15	2	1142 ± 33	4.5 ± 0.6
C7	280	0.1	60	15	2	1410 ± 71	6.2 ± 0.9
C8	280	0.1	60	5	2	1410 ± 71	6.2 ± 0.9
C9	280	0.1	60	25	2	1410 ± 71	6.2 ± 0.9
C10	280	0.1	60	25	12	1412 ± 104	3.8 ± 0.1
C11	280	0.1	60	25	22	1682 ± 63	4.7 ± 0.7

3. Results

3.1. Influence of the AddJoining Process Parameters on the ULSF

Single-lap joints are typically affected by the eccentricity on the load path. Eccentric load means a nonsymmetrical concerning the central axis, thereby producing a bending moment during the loading. Thus, a single lap joint in tension leads to large deflections, and the relationship between the bending moment in cross-section and the applied tensile force is nonlinear. With an increase in the tensile loading, stress analysis of the single lap joint becomes highly nonlinear. Hence, the state of the stress in the aluminum 2024-T3/ABS hybrid joints is not purely axial stress but shear and peel stresses also appear. In contrast, for ABS BM FDM, the axial stress is uniform as a result of the load application direction. Therefore, it is expected that ABS BM FDM leads to higher ductility than aluminum 2024-T3/ABS hybrid joints. ULSF is the primary response in the OFAT. However, to help with the discussions, the displacement at break (DaB) for each condition was also taken into account to compare the ductility between the aluminum 2024-T3/ABS hybrid joints (Table 5) and the ABS BM FDM (Table 4). Nevertheless, the ULSF values were added to the strength for condition eight and condition nine, based on ABS BM FDM from condition seven because of the similarity in the process parameters (Table 4). Note that in this case, no direct comparison was made between the strength of the joint with the base material because no solution was necessary to produce ABS BM using FDM.

Table 5. Summary of the ULSF and DaB for the 11 conditions in the aluminum 2024-T3/ABS hybrid joints.

Condition	PT (°C)	RT (mm)	DS (mm/s)	AC (wt.%)	NC (-)	ULSF (N)	DaB (mm)
C1	230	0.2	40	15	2	1058 ± 89	1.2 ± 0.3
C2	255	0.2	40	15	2	1121 ± 94	1.3 ± 0.2
C3	280	0.2	40	15	2	1159 ± 50	1.3 ± 0.2
C4	280	0.1	40	15	2	1267 ± 27	1.5 ± 0.5
C5	280	0.3	40	15	2	1062 ± 39	1.3 ± 0.3
C6	280	0.1	20	15	2	910 ± 59	0.9 ± 0.1
C7	280	0.1	60	15	2	1340 ± 47	1.8 ± 0.3
C8	280	0.1	60	5	2	1142 ± 35	0.8 ± 0.4
C9	280	0.1	60	25	2	1486 ± 36	1.9 ± 0.2
C10	280	0.1	60	25	12	1686 ± 39	2.3 ± 0.4
C11	280	0.1	60	25	22	1464 ± 77	2.0 ± 0.7

The ANOVA technique was used to assess the effects of the process parameters. Based on the OFAT design, the parameters studied were evaluated independently for aluminum 2024-T3/ABS hybrid joints (Table 6) and ABS BM FDM (Table 7). For the mechanical performance, all parameters except PT were statistically significant within the confidence level, where the probability value (p-value) was below 0.05. According to the F-test in ANOVA, the order of significance is different for single-lap joint and ABS BM FDM. For aluminum 2024-T3/ABS hybrid joints, the order of relevance is based on the f-value, where the highest significant parameter was DS, followed by AC, NC, and RT having the lowest significance. The order was slightly different for ABS BM FDM, where NC, DS, and RT were, respectively, had the highest to the lowest order of relevance. In the following section, the influence of each process parameter on the ULSF is discussed separately.

Table 6. ANOVA results for ULSF for aluminum 2024-T3/ABS hybrid joints.

Factor	Unit	Level 1	Level 2	Level 3	f-Value	p-Value
PT	°C	230	255	280	2.15	1.34×10^{-1}
RT	mm	0.1	0.2	0.3	5.73	8.0×10^{-3}
DS	mm/s	20	40	60	32.38	1.24×10^{-6}
AC	wt.%	5	15	25	29.42	2.43×10^{-5}
NC	-	2	12	22	15.64	1.46×10^{-5}

Table 7. ANOVA results for ULSF for ABS BM FDM.

Factor	Unit	Level 1	Level 2	Level 3	F-Value	*p*-Value
PT	°C	230	255	280	1.28	2.97×10^{-1}
RT	mm	0.1	0.2	0.3	5.65	1.0×10^{-2}
DS	mm/s	20	40	60	14.09	1.78×10^{-6}
NC	-	2	12	22	17.19	2.32×10^{-5}

3.1.1. Printing Temperature

Figure 5 shows the cross-section of the joint for each printing temperature that was investigated. A detailed view of the polymeric part was considered to highlight the presence of pores. The pore surface area of the polymeric cross-sectional view was investigated to evaluate the average pore size. From the images, increasing the printing temperature from 230 °C (Figure 5a) to 280 °C (Figure 5c) led to a decrease of 320% in the void area from 1314 ± 81 μm^2 (Figure 5a (1)) to 314 ± 27 μm^2 (Figure 5c (1)). In the additive manufacturing of amorphous thermoplastics such as ABS, the primary bonding mechanisms between the printed layers are by thermal fusion and interlayer bonding. Mendelson [24] correlated the melt viscosity dependence of ABS with temperature. The author reported that a variation in temperature reduced the melt viscosity up to 50% (4600 Pa·s (230 °C) and 2500 Pa·s (260 °C)), where the bonding between the layers is thermally driven by the polymer viscous flow process [25]. Keeping the temperature above the glass transition temperature assured us that there would be good bonding between successively deposited layers.

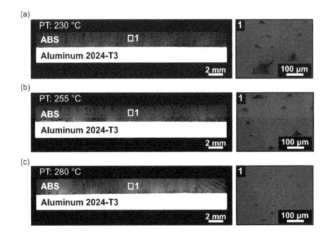

Figure 5. Microstructure of the aluminum 2024-T3/ABS hybrid joints manufactured with different printing temperatures, with detailed view of the pores formed within the ABS part for (**a**) condition one, PT: 230 °C, (**b**) condition two, PT: 255 °C, and (**c**) condition three, PT: 280 °C (the following parameters RT: 0.2 mm, DS: 40 mm/s, AC: 15 wt.%, and NC: 2 were fixed for the conditions investigated).

The formation of the pores was analyzed using a non-destructive test to determine the pores content within the 3D-printed parts, their distribution, and size. By changing the PT, the distribution of the pore volume of the polymeric part was affected. The formation of the pores was investigated in the scanned volume for condition one (PT: 230 °C, Figure 6a), condition two (PT: 255 °C, Figure 7a), and condition three (PT: 280 °C, Figure 8a). Each graph contains a highlighted section against a gray background, where it corresponds to a highlighted graph with pore frequencies (from 0 to 10) and pore volume (from 0 mm^3 to 1 mm^3). This scale range was selected to conduct a qualitative comparison across all conditions investigated in this work.

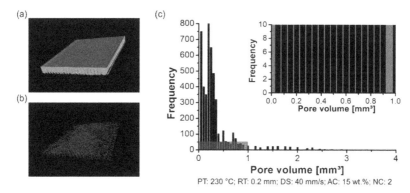

Figure 6. Pore distribution on the 3D-printed ABS for condition one (PT: 230 °C, RT: 0.2 mm, DS: 40 mm/s, AC: 15 wt.%, and NC: 2): (**a**) scanned volume, (**b**) pores distribution, and (**c**) pore volume histogram.

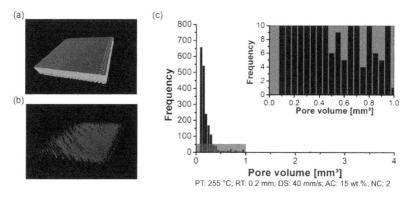

Figure 7. Pore distribution on the 3D-printed ABS for condition one (PT: 255 °C, RT: 0.2 mm, DS: 40 mm/s, AC: 15 wt.%, and NC: 2): (**a**) scanned volume, (**b**) pores distribution, and (**c**) pore volume histogram.

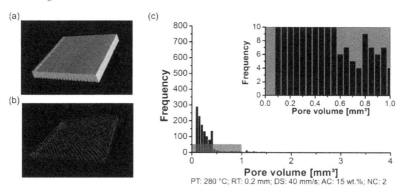

Figure 8. Pore distribution on the 3D-printed ABS for condition one (PT: 280 °C, RT: 0.2 mm, DS: 40 mm/s, AC: 15 wt.%, and NC: 2): (**a**) scanned volume, (**b**) pores distribution, and (**c**) pore volume histogram.

For the three conditions mentioned here, it reveals pores within the scanned 3D-printed polymeric part (Figures 6b, 7b and 8b). Notably, the amount of average pore volume size decreased by nearly 40%

by increasing the PT from 230 °C (0.05 mm³ to 2.5 mm³) to 255 °C (0.05 mm³ to 1.25 mm³). Moreover, the pore volume size did not experience abrupt changes by increasing the PT from 255 °C to 280 °C, i.e., the voids kept constant in the range of 0.05 mm³ to 1.25 mm³. The pores were generally smaller and less frequent by increasing the PT from 230 °C (Figure 6c) to 280 °C (Figure 8c). It reflects the fact that part density, which is the ratio between the total pore volume and total material volume for each condition, is influenced by changing the PT. Preliminary results showed a decrease in the pore content from 4 ± 1% (at 230 °C) to 1 ± 0.4% (at 280 °C).

The strength of the AddJoining part was influenced by the presence of voids in the 3D-printed polymeric part. The aluminum 2024-T3/ABS hybrid joints demonstrated an increase of 9% on increasing the PT from 230 °C (ULSF: 1058 ± 89 N) to 280 °C (ULSF: 1159 ± 50 N), as shown in Figure 9a. An increase in the PT increased the mechanical performance of ABS BM FDM by 5%, where the condition with 230 °C (condition one) achieving 1228 ± 132 N and 280 °C (condition three) achieving 1259 ± 128 N. The difference in the ductility between aluminum 2024-T3/ABS hybrid joints and ABS BM FDM was previously explained. As shown in Table 5, the average DaB of the aluminum 2024-T3/ABS hybrid joints increased (approximately 8%) by changing the PT from 230 °C (DaB: 1.2 ± 0.3 mm) to 280 °C (DaB: 1.3 ± 0.2 mm). However, ABS BM FDM deformation increased by nearly 20%, respectively from 4.7 ± 0.7 mm to 5.7 ± 0.5 mm, and respectively from 230 °C to 280 °C (Table 4). The variations in ductility and strength were correlated with the reduction in the voids content in the 3D-printed polymeric part (Figure 9b). Preliminary results showed a decrease in the pore content from 4 ± 1% (at 230 °C) to 1 ± 0.4% (at 280 °C).

For polymer materials in the 3D-printed part, the increase in printing temperature allows chain diffusion and polymer entanglement across the interface formed between adjacent consolidated roads or layers, leading to a stronger bonding formation [26].

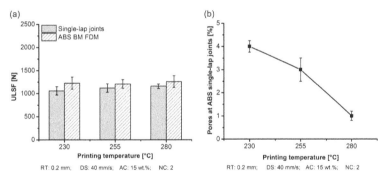

Figure 9. Influence of the printing temperature on the aluminum 2024-T3/ABS hybrid (single-lap joints) and ABS BM FDM (**a**) ULSF and (**b**) pores formation at the ABS part; (condition one, PT: 230 °C; condition two, PT: 255 °C; condition three, PT: 280 °C; the following parameters RT: 0.2 mm, DS: 40 mm/s, AC: 15 wt.%, and NC: 2 were fixed for the conditions investigated).

3.1.2. Road Thickness

PT was fixed at 280 °C, as observed from the previous section. The following parameters—DS: 40 mm/s, AC: 15 wt.%, and NC: 2—were also fixed to continue with the investigation on the mechanical performance (ULSF). RT is a parameter used to investigate the influence on the mechanical performance by varying in 0.1 mm (condition four), 0.2 mm (condition three), and 0.3 mm (condition five). The bonding between the adjacent roads and layers influenced the strength of a 3D-printed part. As previously commented on PT, for polymer materials, a sintering process occurred at the interface during the road deposition. Hence, the bonding mechanism was primarily caused by adhesion between the roads and layers.

The surface quality was evaluated to influence the RT in the surface roughness (Figure 10a). It is possible to identify a trend on the surface roughness, where in the thicker RT (0.3 mm), a lack of bonding typically existed, also known as air gaps (Figure 10b), with an average surface roughness of 240 ± 22 µm. In contrast, a thinner RT (0.1 mm) resulted in a smooth surface with nearly no gaps visible. By decreasing the RT from 0.3 mm to 0.1 mm, this decreased the average surface roughness by 67% (from 240 ± 22 µm to 80 ± 17 µm). This result is in qualitative agreement with the findings of Anitha et al. [27] where the authors found that decreasing the road thickness decreases the surface roughness and impacts the surface quality.

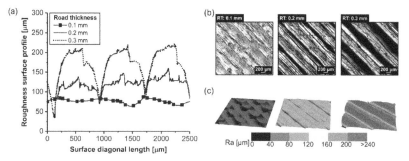

Figure 10. Influence of the surface roughness on the 3D-printed ABS for different road thicknesses (**a**) roughness surface profile, (**b**) surface image, and (**c**) 3D-image from the surface (condition four, RT: 0.1 mm; condition three, RT: 0.2 mm; condition five, RT: 0.3 mm; the following parameters PT: 280 °C, DS: 40 mm/s, AC: 15 wt.%, and NC: 2 were fixed for the conditions investigated).

By measuring the pore volume in each RT condition, cited here, it was possible to correlate the pore content with the surface roughness. The scanned volume for condition three (RT: 0.2 mm) has been previously commented on in PT condition (Figure 8a). Moreover, condition four (RT: 0.1 mm) and condition five (RT: 0.3 mm) are respectively displayed in Figures 11a and 12a. For the three conditions cited here, it revealed no concentrated area of pores, but instead a random distribution across the scanned volume for the formation of pores (RT: 0.1 mm, Figure 11b; RT: 0.2 mm, Figure 8b; RT: 0.3 mm, Figure 12b). The pore volume drastically decreased by 55% by decreasing the RT from 0.3 mm (0.05 mm^3 to 2.25 mm^3; Figure 12c) to 0.1 mm (0.05 mm^3 to 1.25 mm^3, Figure 11c). Moreover, it is relevant to comment that the frequency of pores was reduced by decreasing the RT. It reflects the point that part density—in this study, this is the ratio between the total pore volume and total material volume for each condition—was influenced by changing the RT. It indicated that the thinner RT (0.1 mm) was compactly stacked together, leading to a better interlayer bonding when compared to a thicker RT (0.3 mm).

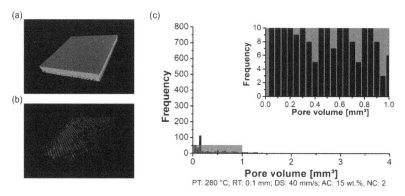

Figure 11. Pore distribution on the 3D-printed ABS for condition four (PT: 280 °C, RT: 0.1 mm, DS: 40 mm/s, AC: 15 wt.%, and NC: 2): (**a**) scanned volume, (**b**) pores distribution, and (**c**) pore volume histogram.

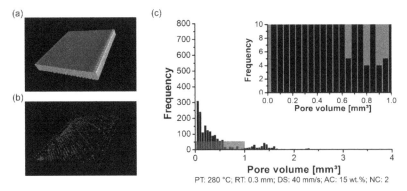

Figure 12. Pore distribution on the 3D-printed ABS for condition four (PT: 280 °C, RT: 0.3 mm, DS: 40 mm/s, AC: 15 wt.%, and NC: 2): (**a**) scanned volume, (**b**) pores distribution, and (**c**) pore volume histogram.

As discussed earlier, increasing the RT increased the surface roughness in the external part and pore accumulation in the internal structure. Hence, it could be expected that because of the presence of pores in between the layers, this could lead to stress concentration and a possible location to form cracks. Therefore, Figure 13 depicts the relationship between RT and the mechanical performance of aluminum 2024-T3/ABS hybrid joints and ABS BM FDM, which were highly influenced by the RT parameter. The difference in the mechanical performance between the single-lap joint and tensile specimen was explained in the first few sections. For aluminum 2024-T3/ABS hybrid joints, reducing the RT from 0.3 mm (ULSF: 1267 ± 27 N) to 0.1 mm (ULSF: 1062 ± 39 N) improved the mechanical performance by 19%. A similar trend was observed for the ABS BM FDM, where an improvement of 22% in the mechanical performance was achieved by changing the RT from 0.3 mm (ULSF: 1152 ± 75 N) to 0.1 mm (ULSF: 1401 ± 30 N). Table 4 shows that the average DaB of the aluminum 2024-T3/ABS hybrid joints decreased (approximately 15%) by changing the RT from 0.1 mm (DaB: 1.5 ± 0.5 mm) to 0.3 mm (DaB: 1.3 ± 0.3 mm). A similar reduction in ductility was observed for ABS BM FDM of nearly 14% (4.8 ± 0.3 mm to 4.2 ± 0.2 mm) from 0.1 mm to 0.3 mm, respectively.

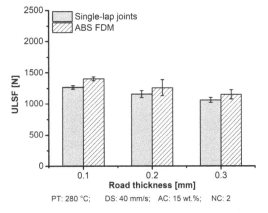

Figure 13. Influence of the road thickness on ULSF for aluminum 2024-T3/ABS hybrid joints (single-lap joints) and ABS BM FDM; (condition four, RT: 0.1 mm; condition three, RT: 0.2 mm; condition five, RT: 0.3 mm; the following parameters PT: 280 °C, DS: 40 mm/s, AC: 15 wt.%, and NC: 2 were fixed for the conditions investigated).

3D-printed part integrity is primarily conceived through bonding with subsequent layers. Thus, the results show that smaller road thicknesses led to small pore formation, where the thickness of the polymer improved the interfacial bonding strength, with a lower layer thickness contributing to dissipate the stress in an easier manner. It, therefore, aids our understanding of the improvement in mechanical performance within the parameter conditions studied in this work. Sood et al. [28] concluded that an increase of around 15% in mechanical performance could be achieved when building with thinner road thickness. Wu et al. [29] and Shubahm et al. [30] observed that the presence of microvoids was smaller for thinner road thickness. Ning et al. [31] also observed a similar effect, where the lower thickness led to considerable inter-bonding strength.

3.1.3. Deposition Speed

Considering the effect of PT and RT fixed at 280 °C and 0.1 mm, respectively, because of high mechanical performance and low presence of pores in the internal structure of the 3D-printed polymer, the following parameters—AC: 15 wt.% and NC: 2—were also fixed to continue with the investigation on the mechanical performance (ULSF). In this work, DS is a parameter used to investigate the influence on the mechanical performance by varying at 20 mm/s (condition six), 40 mm/s (condition four), and 60 mm/s (condition seven).

The surface quality was evaluated to understand the influence the DS had on the surface roughness (Figure 14a). Within the parameter range studied, a lower DS (20 mm/s) led to gaps between the roads (Figure 14b) with an average surface roughness of 302 ± 77 µm. In contrast, DS equal to and above 40 mm/s resulted in a smooth surface, with nearly no gap visible (DS: 40 mm/s; 80 ± 17 µm) and (DS: 60 mm/s; 70 ± 3 µm). Hence, by increasing the DS from 20 mm/s to 60 mm/s, the average surface roughness decreased four-fold. It is important to emphasize that the road was deposited into the coated metal substrate, neighboring consolidated road, and on top of the consolidated layer. Typically, the road could lose the heat via conduction to the consolidated neighboring road and the road below and by convection to the surrounding air in the envelope environment. Hence, the road was cooling, and the viscosity increased until a solid state was reached. However, the consolidated road temperature increased when a new road was deposited. The effect of DS associated with RT could increase adhesion forces because a thinner RT increased the interfacial bonding strength and stress flow was dissipated through the interface easier [32].

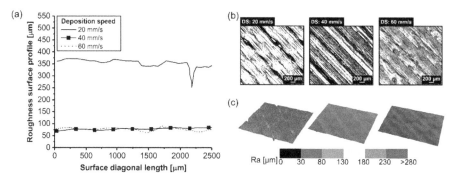

Figure 14. Influence of the surface roughness on the 3D-printed ABS for different deposition speeds (**a**) roughness surface profile, (**b**) surface image, and (**c**) 3D-image from the surface (condition six, DS: 20 mm/s; condition four, DS: 40 mm/s; condition seven, DS: 60 mm/s; the following parameters PT: 280 °C, RT: 0.1 mm, AC: 15 wt.%, and NC: 2 were fixed for the conditions investigated).

As presented in previous sections, the measurements of the pore volume in each DS condition are cited here. The scanned volume for condition four (DS: 40 mm/s) has been previously commented on regarding the RT condition (Figure 11a). In this section, the following condition six (DS: 20 mm/s,

Figure 15a) and condition seven (DS: 60 mm/s, Figure 16a) showed no presence of a preferable concentrated area of pores in the polymeric part (DS: 20 mm/s, Figure 15b; DS: 40 mm/s, Figure 11b). In contrast, the condition with a high DS at 60 mm/s showed a low concentration of pores in the volume edge of the 3D-printed polymer part (Figure 16b). Figure 17a shows the orientation in odd and even layers in the XY-plane to explain the concentration of pores in the edges. A detailed schematic view in Figure 17b shows the nozzle trajectory, where the infill road deposition at 45° created a region with a lack of material when it reached the outer contour. Eiliat and Urbanic [33] reported a similar observation, and, by applying an algorithm to change the road deposition trajectory, it was possible to minimize the voids in the preferable regions.

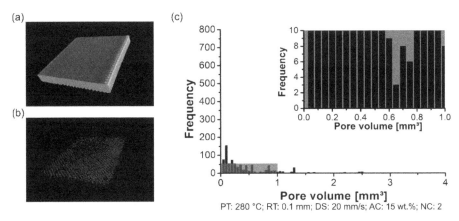

Figure 15. Pore distribution on the 3D-printed ABS for condition six (PT: 280 °C, RT: 0.1 mm, DS: 20 mm/s, AC: 15 wt.%, and NC: 2): (**a**) scanned volume, (**b**) pores distribution, and (**c**) pore volume histogram.

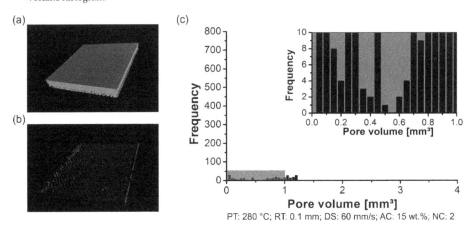

Figure 16. Pore distribution on the 3D-printed ABS for condition seven (PT: 280 °C, RT: 0.1 mm, DS: 60 mm/s, AC: 15 wt.%, and NC: 2): (**a**) scanned volume, (**b**) pores distribution, and (**c**) pore volume histogram.

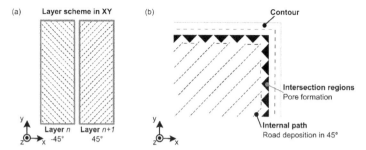

Figure 17. (**a**) Schematic view of typical 3D-printed layers with (**b**) a detail schematic on the pore formation in the intersection region between road deposition at 45° and contour.

Furthermore, for all conditions cited in this section, the pore volume was kept constant in the range of 0.05 mm^3 to 1.25 mm^3. However, it is significant to note that the number of pores was reduced drastically for higher DS (condition seven, Figure 16c), with no pore frequency above 50. In the literature described [18,34], the temperature of the road decay on a time scale of two seconds for ABS was near to the glass transition temperature for the FDM process. Seppala et al. [35] observed that interlayer bonding is sensitive to the printing temperature and associated with the deposition speed; this can increase the interface bonding layer between polymer and polymer. As presented in this section, and considering the parameter range, it reveals that a higher DS does not give enough time to the deposited road for consolidation before depositing the following road. Hence, the previous road remains softened upon the deposition of the subsequent road. It facilitates the intermolecular diffusion in nearby roads. Therefore, it enables a better interlayer bonding in the interface polymer-to-polymer, consequently reducing the microvoids.

It has been shown that DS reduces pore accumulation due to high interlayer bonding formation. It intrinsically plays a significant role in the mechanical performance (Figure 18). For aluminum 2024-T3/ABS hybrid joints and ABS BM FDM, increasing the DS led to high mechanical performance. For the aluminum 2024-T3/ABS hybrid joints, the ULSF increased 33% from 910 ± 59 N to 1340 ± 47 N when the DS was increased from 20 mm/s (condition six) to 60 mm/s (condition seven). For tensile specimens, an improvement of 24% was achieved by changing the DS from 20 mm/s (ULSF: 1142 ± 33 N) to 60 mm/s (ULSF: 1410 ± 71 N). As shown in Table 5, the average DaB of the aluminum 2024-T3/ABS hybrid joints decreased by 50% at lower DS (20 mm/s; DaB: 0.9 ± 0.1 mm) in comparison to higher DS (60 mm/s; DaB: 1.8 ± 0.3 mm). For the ABS BM FDM (Table 4), the ductility was also improved by 37%, changing in DS from 4.5 ± 0.6 mm to 6.2 ± 0.9 mm for 20 mm/s to 60 mm/s, respectively.

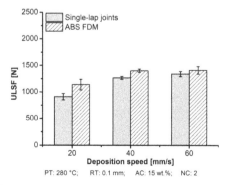

Figure 18. Influence of the deposition speed on ULSF for the aluminum 2024-T3/ABS hybrid joints (single-lap joints) and ABS BM FDM (condition four, RT: 0.1 mm; condition three, RT: 0.2 mm; condition five, RT: 0.3 mm; the following parameters PT: 280 °C, DS: 40 mm/s, AC: 15 wt.%, and NC: 2 were fixed for the conditions investigated).

3.1.4. ABS Coating Concentration

The fourth parameter, AC, was studied after fixing PT at 280 °C, RT at 0.1 mm, and DS at 60 mm/s, which improved the mechanical properties of the aluminum 2024-T3/ABS hybrid joints. AC varied as follows: 5 wt.% (condition eight), 15 wt.% (condition seven), and 25 wt.% (condition nine).

The aluminum 2024-T3/ABS hybrid joint achieved the highest ULSF for condition nine (AC: 25 wt.% ABS) (Figure 19a). Based on the experiment, it resulted in an improvement of 30% in the mechanical aspect by increasing the AC from 5 wt.% (ULSF: 1142 ± 35 N) to 25 wt.% (ULSF: 1486 ± 36 N). The ULSF values were added to the strength for condition eight, and condition nine was added, based on ABS BM FDM from condition seven due to the similarity with the process parameters (Table 4). Please note that in this case, no direct comparison was made between the strength of the joint with the base material because no solution was necessary to produce ABS BM using FDM. Table 5 shows that the ductility was compromised with a low concentration of ABS (5 wt.%), where a premature failure of the joint occurred (DaB: 0.8 ± 0.4 mm). Contrariwise, a high concentration of ABS in the coating allowed for a high deformation in the joint (DaB: 1.9 ± 0.2 mm).

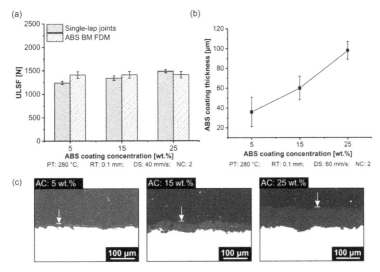

Figure 19. Influence of the ABS coating concentration on the aluminum 2024-T3/ABS hybrid (**a**) ULSF, (**b**) ABS coating thickness, and (**c**) detailed view from the ABS film formation (condition eight, AC: 5 wt.%; condition seven, AC: 15 wt.%; condition nine, AC: 25 wt.%; the following parameters PT: 280 °C, RT: 0.1 mm, DS: 60 mm/s, and NC: 2 were fixed for the conditions investigated).

The thickness of the ABS coating on the metallic surface was measured. In this experiment, the thinnest AC (5 wt.% ABS) reached a coating thickness of 36 ± 15 μm, approximately 63% lower than the thickest AC (25 wt.% ABS), which achieved 98 ± 9 μm (25 wt.% ABS) (Figure 19b). The mechanical performance decreased for coating thicknesses below 100 μm. This thickness dependency is not exclusive for AddJoining principles, where the results of this work give a hint that the AC coating layer behaved similarly to adhesive bonding in the single-lap joint. Typically, the stress distribution acting in the interface is associated with axial and bending stress. Hence, the thinner coating layer (5 wt.% ABS) led to higher stresses because of the lower mass interaction in the interface. On the contrary, a thicker coating layer (25 wt.% ABS) had more mass to deform in the interface metal-polymer, leading to plastic deformation; this may have resulted in low shear and peel stresses.

The effect of the ABS coating thickness can be considered similar to an adhesive thickness on the mechanical performance of single-lap joint (Figure 19c). Objois et al. [36] observed that a lower adhesive thickness below 50 μm led to sudden decreases in mechanical performance. The authors reported that local stress concentration caused by the non-uniform stress distribution in the adhesive layer led to the premature adhesive failure of the joint. Hence, the stress levels increase with decreasing adhesive thickness. In fact, the thinner coating layer probably causes local stress concentration, because of the non-uniformity in the coating layer, which resulted in the roughness of the metallic part (Figure 20b) with 75% average roughness from purely sandblasted (SB) aluminum surface (Figure 20a). On increasing the AC concentration from 5 wt.% (Ra: 2.7 ± 0.3 µm) to 15 wt.% (Ra: 1.2 ± 0.3 µm), the presence of cavities was visually reduced (Figure 20c). Furthermore, at the highest level of AC concentration considered in this work (25 wt.%), the average roughness decreased by 58%, changing from 1.2 ± 0.3 µm to 0.7 ± 0.2 µm. At this level, the surface was smoother (Figure 20d); this probably helped transfer the stress from the 3D-printed part to the aluminum part, decreasing the local stress concentration, where it led to changes in the failure mode to net-tension. Such a failure mode was along the 45° deposition orientation for these specimens. For the previous conditions investigated, an adhesive failure mode occurred. Hence, as discussed earlier, higher AC improved the mechanical performance of aluminum 2024-T3/ABS hybrid joints.

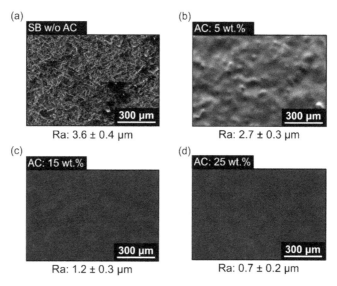

Figure 20. Surface roughness on the sandblasted aluminum surface: (**a**) without coating, (**b**) with 5 wt.% (condition eight), (**c**) with 15 wt.% (condition seven), and (**d**) with 25 wt.% (condition nine); (the following parameters PT: 280 °C, RT: 0.1 mm, DS: 60 mm/s, and NC: 2 were fixed for the conditions investigated).

3.1.5. Number of Contours

After fixing PT at 280 °C, RT at 0.1 mm, DS at 60 mm/s, and AC at 25 wt.%, NC was evaluated in this section. Increasing NC from its lowest level (condition nine, NC: 2) to the highest level (condition eleven, NC: 22) changed the road distribution arrangement and, consequently, the mechanical performance. Primarily, the infill road orientation was fixed at +45°/−45°; however, with increases in NC, the contribution of the overall road area in 45° was reduced, and the orientation at 0° and 90° increased. The latter two orientations were responsible for the closed loop in the infill pattern, as explained in the previous section (Figures 3 and 17). In the single-lap joint, the force was applied in a tensile direction, which was collinear with the road here referred to as 0°. The overlap area fraction was extracted in the overlap area on the surface of the ABS 3D-printed. Figure 21a shows a schematic view highlighting each of the contributions from 0°, 45°, and 90° road depositions. As the infill road was orientated at +45°/−45°, it contributed positively to the mechanical performance in a similar matter as a 0°-orientated road, a well-known behavior found in traditional composite laminates. The contribution at 0° and 45° are considered together because this orientation represents the positive influence on the mechanical performance. Road aligned with the axis of the load application can help increase the greatest mechanical performance [37,38]. Figure 21b shows that the overlap area fraction for two contours (condition nine) with 0° and 45° reached 4% and 94%, respectively, and 2% for 90°. By increasing to 12 contours (condition ten), the overlapping area fraction increased the contribution of the road deposition in 0° and 90° by 27% and 30%, respectively. At the highest NC (condition eleven), the overlap area fraction was distributed into 40% and 19% for 0° and 45°, respectively, and 41% to 90°.

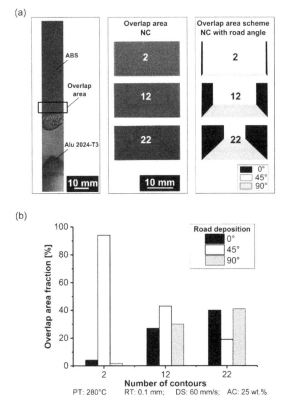

Figure 21. Correlation with the overlap area and road deposition angle on the aluminum 2024-T3/ABS hybrid joints (**a**) schematic, (**b**) overlap area fraction (condition nine, NC: 2; condition ten, NC: 12; condition eleven, NC: 22; the following parameters PT: 280 °C, RT: 0.1 mm, DS: 60 mm/s, and AC: 25 wt.% were fixed for the conditions investigated).

The effect of the NC parameter influenced the mechanical performance of aluminum 2024-T3/ABS hybrid joints, and consequently also changed the failure mode. Figure 22 shows that increasing the NC increased the mechanical performance of the single-lap joint. Condition ten (NC: 12) reached the maximum performance (ULSF: 1686 ± 39 N) across the other conditions mentioned. However, by increasing NC further to 22 (Condition 11), a slight decrease in the mechanical performance was observed for the single-lap joint. The explanation lies in the road orientation distribution, where the road deposition at 90° was inevitably formed in the overlap area, and therefore perpendicular to the testing loading direction, which is known to be detrimental.

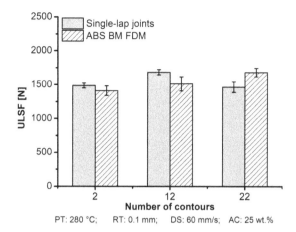

Figure 22. Influence of the number of contours on ULSF for the aluminum 2024-T3/ABS hybrid joints (single-lap joints) and ABS BM FDM (condition nine, NC: 2; condition ten, NC: 12; condition eleven, NC: 22; the following parameters PT: 280 °C, RT: 0.1 mm, DS: 60 mm/s, and AC: 25 wt.% were fixed for the conditions investigated).

For the ABS BM FDM, it showed a clear trend of increasing by 17% in the mechanical performance when increasing the number of contours from two (ULSF: 1410 ± 71) to 22 (ULSF: 1682 ± 63). In this work, the average DaB for single-lap joints and a tensile specimen within their range did not statistically change; 2 mm for aluminum 2024-T3/ABS hybrid joints (Table 5) and ABS BM FDM (Table 4) deformed 95% more (3.9 mm). For ABS BM FDM, the road deposition in 90° was inside the grips during mechanical testing, which was far from the carrying loading area. Hence, the influence of road deposition in 90° did not directly influence the performance in the ABS BM FDM.

For the aluminum 2024-T3/ABS hybrid joints, this isolated parameter was the only one with a different failure mode. The previous conditions failed in the interface with a typical adhesive failure (condition one to condition eight from Table 5). Figure 23 shows the different failure mode results influenced by changing NC. For the two contours (Figure 23a,b) and 12 contours (Figure 23c,d), the mode changed to a net-tension failure, where the specimen failure along the 45° degrees was along the road bonding line. The similar pattern at 45° also occurred for the ABS BM FDM. Increasing the number of contours to 22 contributed to a wider contour width area (as shown in Figure 21), which increased the contribution at the 0° orientation by 40%, and primarily the main part to carry the load than by infilling roads. Nevertheless, it also reduced the effectiveness of the load transfer, because it reached 41% of the overlap area with 90° orientation. Hence, for this condition (NC: 22), the contribution for the 90° orientation was weakening the mechanical performance of the single-lap joint. Moreover, the failure mode reached the adhesive failure for the highest level (NC: 22) (Figure 23e,f).

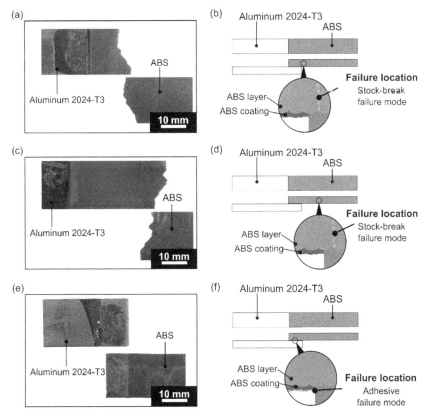

Figure 23. Aluminum 2024-T3/ABS hybrid joint failed joint under a quasi-static lap shear test with its failure mode: (**a**,**b**) NC: 2, (**c**,**d**) NC: 12, and (**e**,**f**) NC: 22 (respectively condition nine, condition ten, and condition eleven; the following parameters PT: 280 °C, RT: 0.1 mm, DS: 60 mm/s, and AC: 25 wt.% were fixed for the conditions investigated).

3.2. Optimum Condition Based on Maximum ULSF

In this section, a condition was selected based on the maximum ULSF for the aluminum 2024-T3/ABS hybrid joints (ULSF: 1686 ± 39 N) from the OFAT (condition ten; PT: 280 °C; RT: 0.1 mm; DS: 60 mm/s; AC: 25 wt.%; NC: 12). Consequently, the joint was analyzed regarding the microstructural features and fracture analysis. The cross-section of the aluminum 2024-T3/ABS hybrid joints is shown in Figure 24. Different features are present in the cross-sectional image, where a detailed analysis was performed using optical microscopy. Voids in the ABS coating can be observed in Figure 24a, with the average cross-sectional area of 2583 ± 1124 μm^2, due to evaporation of the remaining acetone from the solution during the AddJoining process. Good visual adhesion between deposited ABS and the coated aluminum substrate was achieved (Figure 24b), resulting in strong bond formation at the interface. Moreover, no bond line could be visually detected between deposited ABS and ABS-coated aluminum (ABS coating layer of 98 ± 9 μm). This is an indication of improved intermolecular-diffusion supported by the high deposition temperature. In other words, strong bond formation between the two ABS layers was formed.

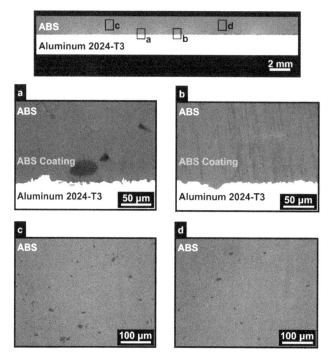

Figure 24. Microstructure for aluminum 2024-T3/ABS hybrid joints obtained by the AddJoining process: (**a**) voids in the ABS coating layer, (**b**) the interface between ABS and the aluminum, and (**c,d**) void formation in the printed ABS (PT: 280 °C, RT: 0.1 mm; DS: 60 mm/s; AC: 25 wt.%; NC: 12).

A net-tension failure mode in the ABS 3D-printed was obtained for the optimum parameter combination (Figure 25). The total printing time to produce the sample was 40 min with the optimum combinations of parameters (120 s per layer were necessary to manufacture a total of 20 layers). By observing the fracture surface, Figure 25a shows that the ABS layers were melted together for the first 16 layers with a printing time of 32 min. As the bottom layers maintained a relatively high temperature for a longer time, deposition of the new layers continued, leading to the intermolecular diffusion between the layers. This promoted ABS diffusion, where it was in agreement with the literature, where the ABS diffusion time was in the range of 390 to 870 s to allow a good intermolecular diffusion [18,34]. In contrast, the last three layers of the ABS 3D-printed were visibly distinct. These layers did not experience the maintenance at higher temperature to reach the diffusion time because the printing time reached the final part. The fracture patterns at the macroscopic level failed along the 45° bonding line [37,39]. Furthermore, the fracture surface was investigated in the microscopic level with an SEM. The fracture surface was predominantly brittle, where on each road, the crack path was driven on each road face (Figure 25b). During the loading, stress resulted in microshearing and high plastic deformation. The presence of fibrils in the pulling direction was observed, where it indicated that crazes were formed, and it developed prior to the ABS that yielded locally (Figure 25c). Moreover, the fracture surface also displayed evidence of brittle failure, with microshearing on the roads (Figure 25d).

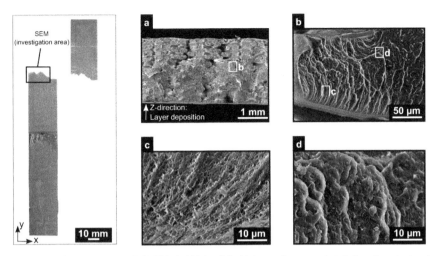

Figure 25. Aluminum 2024-T3/ABS hybrid joint failed joint under a quasi-static lap shear test and SEM images of the fracture surface (**a**) at low magnification in the cross-section with the direction of deposition along the polymer thickness, (**b**) high magnification of the road fractured, (**c**) fibrils in pulling direction, and (**d**) brittle failure (PT: 280 °C, RT: 0.1 mm; DS: 60 mm/s; AC: 25 wt.%; NC: 12).

4. Conclusions

The AddJoining feasibility was demonstrated for the material combination composed of aluminum 2024-T3 and ABS to form hybrid joints. The base material ABS, represented as ABS BM FDM, was investigated to correlate the mechanical performance with the hybrid joints.

The mechanical performance of aluminum 2024-T3/ABS hybrid joints varied from 910 ± 59 N to 1686 ± 39 N. Moreover, for ABS BM FDM, it ranged from 1142 ± 33 N to 1682 ± 63 N. This study showed that four factors were predominantly important for AddJoining hybrid joints under quasi-static loading in the following order of significance: deposition speed, ABS coating concentration, number of contours, and road thickness. For ABS BM FDM, the factors order was in a slightly different order of significance following the number of contours, deposition speed, and road thickness. Based on ANOVA, printing temperature showed no statistically significant influence on the mechanical performance considering the selected confidence level of 95% and in the selected range of variation. Based on the statistical significance in the investigated range for AddJoining hybrid joints, it can be concluded that:

1. At a higher deposition speed (60 mm/s), the road lost the heat to the consolidated neighboring road or the road below. Hence, it facilitated intermolecular diffusion where the deposited road remained softened upon the deposition of the following road. Therefore, it allowed for a better bonding between the layers and promotes a reduction in pores.

2. Higher ABS coating concentration (25 wt.%) increased the coating thickness to nearly 100 μm. Therefore, it had a smoother surface reducing local stress concentration. Moreover, it had more mass to deform, promoting a better interaction of the metal–polymer leading to plastic deformation and low shear and peel stress.

3. For the highest number of contours (22), the carrying load was decreased by the road orientation in the overlap area. The road deposition for 90° was inevitably formed in the overlap area, which caused the joint to turn weaker. For ABS BM FDM, the road deposition for 90° was in the grips during mechanical testing, which was far from the carrying loading area, and which did not directly influence the performance of the specimen.

4. Thinner road thickness (0.1 mm) resulted in considerable inter-bonding strength and compact interactions with the roads, where the low pores formation in the internal structure of the 3D-printed polymer was found.

Nevertheless, at the microscopic level, increasing printing temperature in the considered range in this work led to the promotion of a thermal fusion between the ABS layers and attenuation of the void content in the 3D-printed part.

The ULSF that was obtained with the optimized joining parameters was 1686 ± 39 N from the OFAT (condition ten; printing temperature: 280 °C; road thickness: 0.1 mm; deposition speed: 60 mm/s; ABS coating concentration: 25 wt.%; number of contours: 12), failing by net-tension failure mode with failure pattern along the 45° bonding line. This could be considered a positive output as the final failure took place in the printed base material and not at the metal–film or film–printed polymer interfaces. Finally, from the microstructure point of view, good mechanical interlocking was achieved between the coated metal substrate and printer polymer. Overall, the results of this study may be considered as a base for further understanding of joint formation in layered AddJoining hybrid structures, as well as the general joint mechanical behavior of additive manufactured metal–polymer structures.

Author Contributions: S.T.A.-F. conceived the structure of the manuscript; R.F. designed and performed most of the experiments, and analyzed all experimental data; J.F.d.S. contributed with the discussions of experimental results. All authors contributed in the preparation and review of the manuscript.

Funding: This research was funded by Conselho Nacional de Pesquisa—CNPq, Brazil (grant number: 200674/2015-3) to support the work from R. Falck. S.T. Amancio-Filho would like to acknowledge "the Austrian aviation programme TAKE OFF" and the "BMVIT-Austrian Ministry for Transport, Innovation, and Technology" for the financial support.

Conflicts of Interest: The authors declare no conflict of interest.

References

1. Goede, M.; Stehlin, M.; Rafflenbeul, L.; Kopp, G.; Beeh, E. Super Light Car—Lightweight construction thanks to a multi-material design and function integration. *Eur. Transp. Res. Rev.* **2009**, *1*, 5–10. [CrossRef]
2. Amancio-Filho, S. Friction Riveting: Development and analysis of a new joining technique for polymer-metal multi-material structures. *Weld. World* **2011**, *55*, 13–24.
3. Goushegir, S.M.; Santos, J.F.; Amancio-Filho, S.T. Influence of process parameters on mechanical performance and bonding area of AA2024/carbon-fiber-reinforced poly (phenylene sulfide) friction spot single lap joints. *Mater. Des.* **2015**, *83*, 431–442. [CrossRef]
4. Goushegir, S.M.; Santos, J.F.; Amancio-Filho, S.T. Friction Spot Joining of aluminum AA2024/carbon-fiber reinforced poly (phenylene sulfide) composite single lap joints: Microstructure and mechanical performance. *Mater. Des.* **2014**, *54*, 196–206. [CrossRef]
5. Abibe, A.B.; Sônego, M.; Santos, J.F.; Canto, L.B.; Amancio-Filho, S.T. On the feasibility of a friction-based staking joining method for polymer-metal hybrid structures. *Mater. Des.* **2016**, *92*, 632–642. [CrossRef]
6. Abibe, A.B.; Amancio-Filho, S.T.; Dos Santos, J.F.; Hage, E., Jr. Mechanical and failure behaviour of hybrid polymer-metal staked joints. *Mater. Des.* **2013**, *46*, 338–347. [CrossRef]
7. Feistauer, E.E.; Guimarães, R.P.M.; Ebel, T.; Dos Santos, J.F.; Amancio-Filho, S.T. Ultrasonic joining: A novel direct-assembly technique for metal-composite hybrid structures. *Mater. Lett.* **2016**, *170*, 1–4. [CrossRef]
8. Feistauer, E.E.; Ebel, T.; Santos, J.F.; Amancio-Filho, S.T. Ultrasonic joining of through-the-thickness reinforced Ti-4Al-6V and polyetherimide hybrid joints. In Proceedings of the ANTEC, Anaheim, CA, USA, 8–10 May 2017; pp. 1718–1724.
9. Balle, B.F.; Wagner, G.; Eifler, D. Ultrasonic metal welding of aluminium sheets to carbon fibre Reinforced thermoplastic composites. *Adv. Eng. Mater.* **2009**, *11*, 35–39. [CrossRef]
10. Balle, F.; Wagner, G.; Eifler, D. Ultrasonic spot welding of aluminum sheet/carbon fiber reinforced polymer–joints. *Materialwissenschaft und Werkstofftechnik: Entwicklung, Fertigung, Prüfung, Eigenschaften und Anwendungen Technischer Werkstoffe* **2007**, *38*, 934–938. [CrossRef]
11. Mitschang, P.; Velthuis, R.; Emrich, S.; Kopnarski, M. Induction Heated Joining of Aluminum and Carbon Fiber Reinforced. *Thermoplast. Compos. Mater.* **2008**, *22*, 17–27. [CrossRef]

12. Türk, D.; Kussmaul, R.; Zogg, M.; Klahn, C.; Spierings, A.; Ermanni, P.; Meboldt, M. Additive manufacturing with composites for integrated aircraft structures. In Proceedings of the International SAMPE Technical Conference, Long Beach, CA, USA, 23–26 May 2016; pp. 1404–1418.

13. Riss, F.; Schilp, J.; Reinhart, G. Load-dependent optimization of honeycombs for sandwich components-new possibilities by using additive layer manufacturing. *Phys. Procedia* **2014**, *56*, 327–335. [CrossRef]

14. Falck, R.; Goushegir, S.M.; dos Santos, J.F.; Amancio-Filho, S.T. AddJoining: A novel additive manufacturing approach for layered metal-polymer hybrid structures. *Mater. Lett.* **2018**. [CrossRef]

15. Jarvela, P.; Heponen, V.P.; Jarvela, P. Hot isostatic pressing of plastics. *Polym. Commun.* **1986**, *27*, 180–181.

16. *Aluminum AA2024-T3 Technical Datasheet*; Constellium: Issoire, France, 2012.

17. Boyer, H.; Gall, T. *Metals Handbook*; American Society for Metals: Metals Park, OH, USA, 1985.

18. Sun, Q.; Rizvi, G.M.; Bellehumeur, C.T.; Gu, P. Effect of processing conditions on the bonding quality of FDM polymer filaments. *Rapid Prototyp. J.* **2008**, *14*, 72–80. [CrossRef]

19. Agarwala, M.K.; Jamalabad, V.R.; Langrana, N.A.; Safari, A.; Whalen, P.J.; Danforth, S.C. Structural quality of parts processed by fused deposition. *Rapid Prototyp. J.* **1996**, *2*, 4–19. [CrossRef]

20. Stratasys ABS-ESD7—Production Grade Thermoplastic for Fortus 3D Production Systems. Available online: https://www.google.com.hk/url?sa=t&rct=j&q=&esrc=s&source=web&cd=5&cad=rja&uact=8&ved=2ahUKEwiqsJHhpYHhAhV8JaYKHVckDyYQFjAEegQIBhAC&url=https%3A%2F%2Fwww.stratasys.com%2F-%2Fmedia%2Ffiles%2Fmaterial-spec-sheets%2Fmss_fdm_absesd7_1117a.pdf&usg=AOvVaw303AzA8Xxr7XtUNjz0XsWS (accessed on 14 March 2019).

21. Uddandapu, P.K. Impact Analysis on Car Bumper by varying speeds using Materials ABS Plastic and Poly Ether Imide by Finite Element Analysis software Solid Works. *Int. J. Mod. Eng. Res.* **2013**, *3*, 391–395.

22. Froelich, D.; Maris, E.; Haoues, N.; Chemineau, L.; Renard, H.; Abraham, F.; Lassartesses, R. State of the art of plastic sorting and recycling: Feedback to vehicle design. *Miner. Eng.* **2007**, *20*, 902–912. [CrossRef]

23. Thompson, A.; Maskery, I.; Leach, R.K. X-ray computed tomography for additive manufacturing: A review. *Meas. Sci. Technol.* **2016**, *27*, 72001. [CrossRef]

24. Mendelson, R.A. A generalized melt viscosity-temperature dependence for styrene and styrene-acrylonitrile-based polymers. *Polym. Eng. Sci.* **1976**, *16*, 690–696. [CrossRef]

25. Rosenzweig, N.; Narkis, M. Sintering rheology of amorphous polymers. *Polym. Eng. Sci.* **1981**, *21*, 1167–1170. [CrossRef]

26. Davis, C.S.; Hillgartner, K.E.; Han, S.H.; Seppala, J.E. Mechanical strength of welding zones produced by polymer extrusion additive manufacturing. *Addit. Manuf.* **2017**, *16*, 162–166. [CrossRef] [PubMed]

27. Anitha, R.; Arunachalam, S.; Radhakrishnan, P. Critical parameters influencing the quality of prototypes in fused deposition modelling. *J. Mater. Process. Technol.* **2001**, *118*, 385–388. [CrossRef]

28. Sood, A.K.; Ohdar, R.K.; Mahapatra, S.S. Parametric appraisal of mechanical property of fused deposition modelling processed parts. *Mater. Des.* **2010**, *31*, 287–295. [CrossRef]

29. Wu, W.; Geng, P.; Li, G.; Zhao, D.; Zhang, H.; Zhao, J. Influence of layer thickness and raster angle on the mechanical properties of 3D-printed PEEK and a comparative mechanical study between PEEK and ABS. *Materials* **2015**, *8*, 5834–5846. [CrossRef] [PubMed]

30. Shubham, P.; Sikidar, A.; Chand, T. The Influence of Layer Thickness on Mechanical Properties of the 3D Printed ABS Polymer by Fused Deposition Modeling. *Key Eng. Mater.* **2016**, *706*, 63–67. [CrossRef]

31. Ning, F.; Cong, W.; Hu, Y.; Wang, H. Additive manufacturing of carbon fiber-reinforced plastic composites using fused deposition modeling: Effects of process parameters on tensile properties. *J. Compos. Mater.* **2016**. [CrossRef]

32. Hashemi Sanatgar, R.; Campagne, C.; Nierstrasz, V. Investigation of the adhesion properties of direct 3D printing of polymers and nanocomposites on textiles: Effect of FDM printing process parameters. *Appl. Surf. Sci.* **2017**, *403*, 551–563. [CrossRef]

33. Eiliat, H.; Urbanic, R.J. Minimizing voids for a material extrusion based process. *Rapid Prototyp. J.* **2018**, *24*, 485–500. [CrossRef]

34. Bellehumeur, C.; Li, L.; Sun, Q.; Gu, P. Modeling of Bond Formation Between Polymer Filaments in the Fused Deposition Modeling Process. *J. Manuf. Process.* **2004**, *6*, 170–178. [CrossRef]

35. Seppala, J.E.; Hoon Han, S.; Hillgartner, K.E.; Davis, C.S.; Migler, K.B. Weld formation during material extrusion additive manufacturing. *Soft Matter* **2017**. [CrossRef]

36. Objois, A.; Gilibert, Y.; Fargette, B. Theoretical and experimental analysis of the scarf joint bonded structure: Influence of the adhesive thickness on the micro-mechanical behavior. *J. Adhes.* **1999**, *70*, 13–32. [CrossRef]
37. Rodríguez, J.F.; Thomas, J.P.; Renaud, J.E. Mechanical behaviour of acrylonitrile butadiene styrene fused deposition materials modeling. *Rapid Prototyp.* **2003**, *9*, 219–230. [CrossRef]
38. Ahn, S.H.; Baek, C.; Lee, S.; Ahn, I.S. Anisotropic Tensile Failure Model of Rapid Prototyping Parts—Fused Deposition Modeling (FDM). *Int. J. Mod. Phys. B* **2003**, *17*, 1510–1516. [CrossRef]
39. Ziemian, C.; Sharma, M.; Ziemian, S. Anisotropic mechanical properties of ABS parts fabricated by fused deposition modelling. In *Mechanical Engineering*; Gokcek, M., Ed.; InTech: Rijeka, Croatia, 2012; pp. 159–180. ISBN 978-953-51-0505-3.

Correction

Correction: Falck, R. et al. Microstructure and Mechanical Performance of Additively Manufactured Aluminum 2024-T3/Acrylonitrile Butadiene Styrene Hybrid Joints by AddJoining Technique. *Materials* 2019, *12*, 864

Rielson Falck [1], Jorge F. dos Santos [1] and Sergio T. Amancio-Filho [2,*]

[1] Helmholtz-Zentrum Geesthacht, Center for Materials and Coastal Research, Institute of Materials Research, Materials Mechanics, Solid State Joining Processes, 21502 Geesthacht, Germany; rielson.falck@hzg.de (R.F.); jorge.dos.santos@hzg.de (J.F.d.S.)

[2] Institute of Materials Science, Joining and Forming, BMVIT Endowed Professorship for Aviation, Graz University of Technology—TU Graz, Kopernikusgasse 24/1, 8010 Graz, Austria

* Correspondence: sergio.amancio@tugraz.at; Tel.: +43-316-873-1610; Fax: +43-316-873-7184

Received: 13 March 2020; Accepted: 17 March 2020; Published: 23 March 2020

The authors wish to make the following correction to the paper [1]. Due to identical data in Table 6 and Table 7, replace:

Table 7. ANOVA results for ULSF for ABS BM FDM.

Factor	Unit	Level 1	Level 2	Level 3	F-Value	*p*-Value
PT	°C	230	255	280	2.15	1.34×10^{-1}
RT	mm	0.1	0.2	0.3	5.73	8.0×10^{-3}
DS	mm/s	20	40	60	32.38	1.24×10^{-6}
AC	wt.%	5	15	25	29.42	2.43×10^{-5}
NC	-	2	12	22	15.64	1.46×10^{-5}

with

Table 7. ANOVA results for ULSF for ABS BM FDM.

Factor	Unit	Level 1	Level 2	Level 3	F-Value	*p*-Value
PT	°C	230	255	280	1.28	2.97×10^{-1}
RT	mm	0.1	0.2	0.3	5.65	1.0×10^{-2}
DS	mm/s	20	40	60	14.09	1.78×10^{-6}
NC	-	2	12	22	17.19	2.32×10^{-5}

These changes have no material impact on the discussion and conclusions of the paper. The authors would like to apologize for any inconvenience caused to the readers by these changes.

Acknowledgments: Open Access Funding by the Graz University of Technology.

Conflicts of Interest: The authors declare no conflicts of interest.

Materials **2020**, *13*, 1460

Reference

1. Falck, R.; dos Santos, J.F.; Amancio-Filho, S.T. Microstructure and Mechanical Performance of Additively Manufactured Aluminum 2024-T3/Acrylonitrile Butadiene Styrene Hybrid Joints Using an AddJoining Technique. *Materials* **2019**, *12*, 864. [CrossRef] [PubMed]

Article

CFRP Thin-Ply Fibre Metal Laminates: Influences of Ply Thickness and Metal Layers on Open Hole Tension and Compression Properties

Benedikt Kötter *,†, Julian Karsten *,†, Johann Körbelin and Bodo Fiedler

Institute of Polymer and Composites, Hamburg University of Technology, Denickestraße 15, 21073 Hamburg, Germany; johann.koerbelin@tuhh.de (J.K.); fiedler@tuhh.de (B.F.)
* Correspondence: benedikt.koetter@tuhh.de (B.K.); julian.karsten@tuhh.de (J.K.)
† These authors contributed equally to this work.

Received: 23 December 2019; Accepted: 7 February 2020; Published: 18 February 2020

Abstract: Thin-ply laminates exhibit a higher degree of freedom in design and altered failure behaviour, and therefore, an increased strength for unnotched laminates in comparison to thick-ply laminates. For notched laminates, the static strength is strongly decreased; this is caused by a lack of stress relaxation through damage, which leads to a higher stress concentration and premature, brittle failure. To overcome this behaviour and to use the advantage of thin-ply laminates in areas with high stress concentrations, we have investigated thin-ply hybrid laminates with different metal volume fractions. Open hole tensile (OHT) and open hole compression (OHC) tests were performed with quasi-isotropic carbon fibre reinforced plastic (CFRP) specimens. In the area of stress concentration, $90°$ layers were locally substituted by stainless steel layers of differing volume fractions, from 12.5% to 25%. The strain field on the specimen surface was evaluated in-situ using a digital image correlation (DIC) system. The embedding of stainless steel foils in thin-ply samples increases the OHT strength up to 60.44% compared to unmodified thin-ply laminates. The density specific OHT strength is increased by 33%. Thick-ply specimens achieve an OHC strength increase up to 45.7%, which corresponds to an increase in density specific strength of 32.4%.

Keywords: stainless steel foil; stress distribution; hybrid material; non-destructive testing; digital image correlation

---

1. Introduction

Fibre reinforced composites (FRPs) are used in structural applications, such as aircraft construction, automotive manufacturing, shipbuilding and sports equipment because of their excellent weight-specific mechanical properties. Fastener-based joining techniques such as bolting or riveting are commonly used in these applications, as parts become highly maintainable and can be easily disassembled and reattached. However, for FRPs such as carbon fibre reinforced plastics (CFRPs), riveting is not a material-appropriate design, due to their low bearing strength and high notch sensitivity [1,2]. Therefore, different attempts to reduce the notch sensitivity of composites are utilised; e.g., local thickening of the laminate [3], optimised laminate layup and stacking sequence [4,5], local inserts [6], z-pinning [4,7] and hybridisation with other materials [8–10].

High-performance carbon-fibre reinforced plastics (CFRPs) are widely applied as structural materials in applications where a low density combined with high stiffness and strength is required. Due to the multi-scale nature and the different constituents, the failure in composites is complex. Matrix-cracks, delamination and fibre failure can occur, and failure at the micro-level influences the failure process at all higher levels. As a result, not only do the mechanic properties of the constituents of the composite define the strength and failure process, but the lay-up design and the layer thickness do as well [11–15]. Thin-ply laminates are characterised by a layer thickness of less than <60 µm. These layer thicknesses became available through the advancement and industrialisation of the spread-tow process as presented by Kawabe [16] and Sihn [13]. By reducing the thickness of the single layer, the number of layers can be chosen to be more load-dependent. This increases the degrees of freedom in the orientation and the quantity of the individual layers.

Thin layers suppress transverse microcracking and free edge delamination. As a result, the occurring failure modes change from complex multi-mode failure to a quasi-brittle failure, from thick- to thin-ply [13–15,17,18]. For unnotched quasi-isotropic laminates, this leads to a significant increase in tensile strength, which utilises the potential of the constituents [13,19]. The damage initiation changes with decreasing layer thickness to higher strains. Thin-ply specimens show little to no visible premature damage before ultimate failure. Under compressive loading of quasi-isotropic specimens, a similar behaviour is observed. The compressive strength increases with decreasing layer thickness. In addition to the changing failure behaviour, the material quality also plays an important role. Due to the small layer thicknesses and the spreading process, a more homogeneous fibre distribution and smaller resin-rich regions are achieved [15].

For notched laminates, the static strength is strongly decreased, because the lack of stress relaxation through damage leads to a higher stress concentration and premature, brittle failure compared to thick-ply laminates [13,15,18], which is limiting to the design space of thin-ply composites.

One possibility to change the failure mechanisms and improve the mechanical properties of notched specimens is to insert metallic layers into the laminate. Fibre metal laminates (FMLs) show improved load-bearing and a progressive failure mechanism. Fibre metal laminates are utilised to combine the favourable properties of metallic and composite behaviours. The main advantages compared to pure fibre reinforced composites are: quasi ductile failure behaviour due to the additional plasticity of the steel foils [3,20], better energy absorption under tensile loads, better structural integrity in crash tests and local electrical conductivity, which allows amongst other things for non-destructive testing (NDT) and structural health monitoring (SHM) [21].

With conventional layer thicknesses, the adhesion between metal and matrix is a major challenge. Interlaminar shear forces, caused by thermal loads from the curing process and external loads, act between composite layers and metal foils. The strength of the interface is therefore of high importance, as it influences the failure process of the laminate extensively. Due to the higher number of layers and the associated higher number of interfaces, the shear stresses are lower and the pretreatment process of the metal has less influence. In addition, a high number of layers offers freedom of design concerning hybrid composites. Various proportions of steel or positions of the steel in the laminate can be realised. An additional advantage is the use of thin and more flexible stainless steel foils. Especially in components with complex geometries and curved areas like the wings of an aircraft, adapting and shape forming of the material is necessary. Thicker steel foils would be needed to be preformed before lamination, whereas thin steel foils can be shaped during the process of laminating up to a level of deformation similar to the CFRP layers. A first study concerning the combination of thin-ply CFRP and stainless steel foils was published in 2015 by Masani et al. [22]. They investigated open hole tensile (OHT) and load-bearing properties of thin-ply fibre metal laminates with a CFRP-layer and metal foil thickness of 30 µm and a steel volume content of 25%. An increase of up to two times in bearing strength was encountered. The specific bearing strength, bearing strength in relation to the density of the specimen, is lower than that of CFRP without stainless steel foils. However, according to Studer et al. [20], it is sufficient to use local stainless steel reinforcements in regions of load introduction or high local stresses; as a result the component density would decrease. The aim of this study is to analyse a new method to improve the open hole tensile and compressive strength of thin-ply laminates by replacing 90°-CFRP-layers with stainless steel foils as patches with the same layer thickness.

2. Materials and Methods

2.1. Materials and Specimen Preparation

In this study, austenitic steel alloy inserts 1.4310 (X10CrNi18-8) from Knight Strip Metals Ltd. (Hertfordshire, UK) were used as metal reinforcement foil in CFRP. The alloy has a metastable austenitic structure due to its high chromium and nickel content, which strengthens the material during processing due to work hardening in a cold rolling process. The tensile strength is between 500 and 700 MPa, with a yield strength of 210 MPa and a Young's modulus of 200 GPa. Due to its good mechanical and durability properties, the alloy is used in aircraft construction and automotive engineering, and has been used in multiple previous studies on fibre metal laminates [8,23–27].

The steel foils were cut with a precision cutter for electronic boards, which results in no visible deformation at the edges of the foils. The samples for the tension tests of the stainless steel foils have the dimensions 250 mm × 25 mm. The nominal thicknesses of the foils are 0.03 mm and 0.15 mm. Unidirectional CFRP prepregs with fibre areal weights (FAWs) of 30 gsm, 60 gsm and 120 gsm are used. Other FAWs (150 gsm, 240 gsm) are achieved via block-scaling. The prepreg was manufactured by North Thin Ply Technology Switzerland (NTPT), using T700S carbon fibres from Toray Carbon Fibres America Inc (CMA) and ThinPreg 402 epoxy resin from NTPT. The experimentally determined mechanical properties of the prepreg system are shown in Table 1. Tensile tests were conducted in compliance to ASTM D 3039 [28] standard with a quasi-isotropic layup and specimen dimensions of 1.82 mm × 25 mm × 150 mm. Five specimens were tested per configuration. In Figure 1, microsections of the tensile specimens show the difference in thickness of the individual layers in red. In order to compare different steel foil surface pretreatments, interlaminar shear strength (ILSS) tests were carried out. For ILSS tests, an unidirectional prepreg system HexPly M21/35%/268/T800S from Hexcel Corporation, with M21 epoxy based resin and CMA's T800S carbon fibres, was used. The single-layer thickness of this prepreg system is 0.262 mm.

Table 1. Ply thickness dependent tensile properties of quasi-isotropic CFRP-laminates (ASTM D 3039) [28].

FAW	Lay-up	Tensile Strength	Young's Modulus
30 gsm	$[45/90/-45/90]_{8s}$	956.59 ± 31.81 MPa	47.88 ± 1.65 GPa
60 gsm	$[45/90/-45/90]_{4s}$	963.66 ± 18.21 MPa	50.02 ± 1.60 GPa
120 gsm	$[45/90/-45/90]_{2s}$	825.49 ± 24.56 MPa	48.13 ± 2.54 GPa
240 gsm	$[45_2/90_2/-45_2/90_2]_s$	736.86 ± 32.61 MPa	47.30 ± 1.47 GPa

The prepreg was cut using a computer numerical control (CNC) cutter Aristomat TL 1625 from ARISTO Graphic System GmbH and Co. KG. and laminated by hand. For every fourth prepreg layer, a pre-evacuation was performed to further compress the laminate and to prevent voids and air inclusions. The different laminate layups are shown in Table 2. Depending on the layer structure, some 90°-layers were replaced by stainless steel foils, which exhibit a limited contribution to the global load carrying capacity; 60 mm wide stainless steel foils were inserted as patches in the area of the centred hole of the specimens. This is shown schematically in Figure 2. The black areas represent the stainless steel foil. In the case of the hybrid laminates with a metal volume content of 12.5%, the stainless steel layers were placed on the outside, so that the benefit of the bending stiffness of the metal foils could be utilised under compressive load. For each ILSS sample, a steel foil with a layer thickness of 0.15 mm was placed in the middle of the laminate. The remaining layers are unidirectional in 0°-orientation. The Layup is listed in Table 2. The sample dimensions of the ILSS samples were 40 mm × 12 mm × 6 mm according to the ASTM D2344 standard [29].

Table 2. Laminate layups for the OHT, OHC and ILSS tests.

Test Setup	Configuration (SF: Steel Foil)	Layup	Number of Specimen
OHT/C	CFRP: 30 gsm	$[45/-45/0/90]_{16s}$	5
OHT/C	CFRP: 30 gsm; SF: 25% (0.03 mm)	$[45/-45/0/SF]_{16s}$	4
OHT/C	CFRP: 60 gsm	$[45/-45/0/90]_{8s}$	5
OHT/C	CFRP: 120 gsm	$[45/-45/0/90]_{4s}$	5
OHT/C	CFRP: 150 gsm; SF: 12.5% (0.15 mm)	$[(45/-45/SF/0)_2/(45/-45/0/90)_2]_s$	3
OHT/C	CFRP: 150 gsm; SF: 25% (0.15 mm)	$[45/-45/SF/0]_{4s}$	3
OHT/C	CFRP: 240 gsm	$[45/-45/0/90]_{2s}$	5
ILSS	CFRP: 268 gsm	$[0]_{16}$	5
ILSS	CFRP: 268 gsm; SF: 6.25% (0.15 mm)	$[(0_7/SF)/0_8]$	5

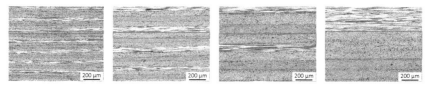

Figure 1. Microsections of the used CFRP laminates, left to right: 30, 60, 120 and 240 gsm (block-scaling 2 × 120 gsm).

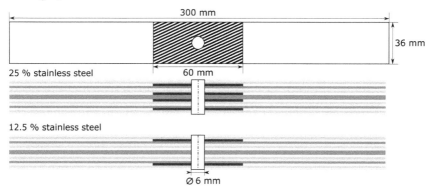

Figure 2. Schematic drawing of the sample design for OHT and OHC tests according to the standards ASTM D5766 [30] and ASTM D6484 [31].

The surfaces of stainless steel foils were pretreated to ensure sufficient adhesion between the stainless steel and the epoxy resin matrix. Six pretreatment methods which had been proven to be effective were investigated [32]. For all methods presented, the first step was to clean the stainless steel foils with acetone. Two chemical etching methods were chosen. For the first method, the samples were chemically etched by sulphuric acid (30% concentration at 60 °C for 4 min) followed by a solution of 22–28 parts by weight (PBW) of sulphuric acid and 2–3 PBW of potassium dichromate. For the second etching method, the samples were primarily prepared with hydrofluoric acid (4% concentration at 50 °C for 20 min), followed by a solution of 22–28 PBW of sulphuric acid and 2–3 PBW of potassium dichromate.

Plasma surface treatment was chosen for methods three and four. In one group, the stainless steel foils were plasma treated directly after the cleaning process with acetone, and the other group was sanded with 500 grit silicon carbide sandpaper before plasma treatment. The plasma system in use was a SmartPlasma 10 system by Plasma Technology GmbH (parameters: 300 W, 90 s, 0.3 mbar).

In addition, the sol-gel process was used. This surface pretreatment was prepared according to the procedure outlined by 3M Aerospace and Aircraft Maintenance Division with the 3M surface pretreatment AC-130-2. The surface pretreatment AC-130-2 is a water-based system and can be used in combination with different metals. According to 3M, the achieved benefits of the pretreatment are in the same range or better than conventional etching processes. An additional advantage of the system is the formation of a chemical bond between the metal and the matrix without using potentially carcinogenic and allergenic chromates. The sol-gel surface pretreatment can be easily applied to the metal by spraying, brushing or immersion, allowing for an on-site use on the aircraft. For one sample group, the surface was roughened with 500 grit silicon carbide sandpaper, which increases the metal bonding surface and removes coarse contamination. Further, the foil surface was cleaned with acetone to remove any sanding residue and grease from the surface. After this, the AC-130-2 was applied with an immersion bath at room temperature and dried for 60 min. This increases the adhesion effect due to an increased surface area and more chemical bonds between the metal surface and the epoxy resin. The second group was directly pretreated with AC-130-2 after cleaning the surface with acetone without any surface roughening. To compare the results with samples without stainless steel foil, some reference samples were prepared for the ILSS tests.

The laminates (420 mm × 300 mm) were cured in an autoclave at 120 °C and 4 bar in a nitrogen atmosphere. The cured plates were milled using an Isel Euromod 25 three axis milling machine. The specimen dimensions are determined according to the standards for OHT (ASTM D5766 [30]), OHC (ASTM D6484 [31]) and ILSS (ASTM D2344 [29]) tests. The dimensions are 300 mm × 36 mm × 3.84 mm with a central hole (diameter: 6 mm) for the OHT and OHC samples. After milling, the edges of the samples were polished and all samples dried in a vacuum furnace at 40 °C for 12 h before they are tested.

2.2. Experimental Methods

All mechanical tests were performed under constant ambient conditions (temperature 23 °C, relative humidity 50%). An universal testing machine Z2.5 by ZwickRoell GmbH and Co. KG (Ulm, Germany) was used for the tensile tests of the stainless steel foils. The foils were clamped using mechanical clamping jaws. The test speed was set to 3 mm/min. For the strain measurement, cross-head position and an optical camera measuring system from ZwickRoell were used. In order to achieve this, two high contrast markings were applied to the specimen surface and tracked by the camera system.

The ILSS tests were carried out according to ASTM D2344 [29] on a ZwickRoell Z10 universal testing machine. The support radius was 1.5 mm and the radius of the compression cylinder was 3 mm. The span length was chosen as proposed by the standard (24 mm) and the speed of testing applied was 1 mm/min. Displacement and strain measurement were recorded using the traverse path of the upper stamp, directly connected to the cross-head displacement.

Open hole tensile and compression tests were performed in accordance to ASTM D5766 [30] and ASTM D6484 [31] using a ZwickRoell Z400 universal testing machine. Mechanical wedge clamps were used for the tensile tests, whereby the forces were introduced into the specimen via shear forces. The cross-head speed was set to 2 mm/min. The displacement and strain were recorded using mechanical displacement transducers (MultiXtens from ZwickRoell), and the digital image correlation (DIC) system Aramis 4M system from GOM GmbH. A high contrast speckle pattern (consisting of white and black acrylic paint) sprayed onto the specimen surfaces allowed for computer-aided image evaluation and strain monitoring with the software GOM Correlate Professional. The camera focus was set directly at the open hole in the centre of the specimen.

For the open hole compression tests, a cross-head speed of 2 mm/min and an anti-buckling support as specified in the ASTM were used. The mechanical loads were applied via the end faces of the specimens. The displacement was determined over the cross-head traverse, since there was no possibility of using the MultiXtens due to the anti-buckling support. Furthermore, the DIC system was used, recording the sample through a small window inside the anti-buckling support.

For the micrographs, the tested specimens were embedded in epoxy resin so that the fracture surfaces were not damaged during further mechanical processing. Depending on the specimen and the fracture pattern, the specimens were sawn and embedded in resin so that they could be polished.

The subsequent polishing was done in several steps. First, the samples were ground with sandpaper in various grit sizes and then polished with diamond suspension up to a particle size of 3 μm.

3. Results and Discussion

Figure 3 shows the results of the stainless steel foil tensile tests. The yield strength is plotted over the foil layer thickness in relation to the rolling orientation of the stainless steel. RD (rolling direction) means that the main load direction is parallel to the rolling direction of the foil. Accordingly, TRD (transverse rolling direction) means that the main load direction is perpendicular to the rolling direction of the foil. A comparison of the measured yield strength reveals that a significant difference between the rolling and transverse rolling direction is apparent in the case of the thin foils. For the thick foils, no difference could be found. However, strong evidence of an increase of yield strength with decreasing foil thickness was found. The yield strength of the thin foil in the rolling direction is 27.1%, and transverse to the rolling direction it is 18.9% higher than for the thick foils. The results of the yield strength and the results of the fracture strength are shown in Table 3. No significant difference in fracture strength was found. This can be explained by the work or strain hardening of the metal foils.

Table 3. Measured mechanical properties of stainless steel (1.4310) foils.

Foil Thickness in μm	Orientation	Strength in MPa	Yield Strength in MPa
30	RD	1347.3 ± 52.7	1273.8 ± 85.8
30	TRD	1410.2 ± 30.8	1121.7 ± 27.0
150	RD	1337.8 ± 71.1	1002.2 ± 69.9
150	TRD	1371.3 ± 8.3	943.4 ± 55.0

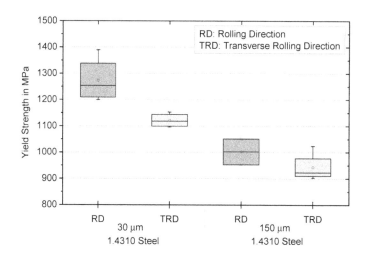

Figure 3. Yield strength regarding foil thickness and orientation during the rolling process.

It is difficult to compare the results of the specimens with stainless steel with the specimens without stainless steel, because ILSS samples with stainless steel do not have a symmetrical structure and therefore cannot be regarded as ideal specimens. The lower and upper parts of the specimen have different bending stiffness. However, the different pretreatment methods can be compared, and significant differences between the pretreatments can be seen. A comparison reveals that the interlaminar shear strength of the specimen pretreated with abrasive paper and AC-130-2 is most pronounced. Figure 4 shows the results of the ILSS tests. CFRP without stainless steel foil reaches 92.91 MPa, which is 2.91 MPa above the value specified by the manufacturer Hexcel. It is also interesting to note that the interlaminar shear strength of the stainless steel decreases as a result of plasma treatment, which is contrary to the current literature. From the results, it follows that due to the high interlaminar shear strength and the low standard deviation, the sol-gel process with the combination between abrasive paper and AC-130-2 surface treatment system from 3M was used for further open hole tensile and compressive tests.

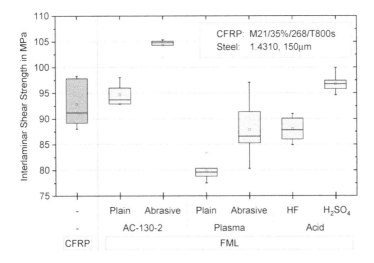

Figure 4. Interlaminar shear strengths (ILSSs) of different surface pretreatments of the stainless steel foils according to ASTM D2344 [29].

Figure 5 shows scanning electron microscope (SEM) images of the surface of pretreated stainless steel foils. It is noticeable that the etched surfaces have a finely structured surface, which in turn indicates theoretically good adhesion. Since the the sol-gel process merely forms a chemical intermediate layer (film) on the stainless steel surface and thus does not cause any geometric changes to the surface, no difference can be detected between the surfaces of the samples ground and those ground and treated with AC-130-2 using SEM.

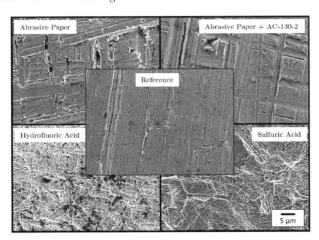

Figure 5. Scanning electron microscope images of the pretreated stainless steel surfaces.

Figure 6 illustrates the open hole tensile strengths (black, left axis) of the samples with and without stainless steel patches. The ordinate on the right side shows the specific open hole tensile strength (grey). The specific open hole tensile strength means that the open hole tensile strength of a sample is related to its density. The calculation of the density takes into account that the stainless steel foils are only used as patches, as they will be used in practical applications; see Figure 2.

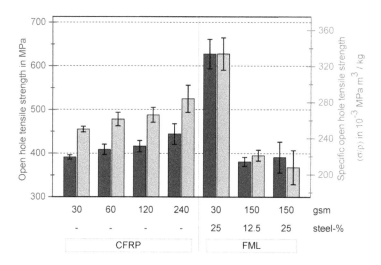

Figure 6. Open hole tensile strength and specific open hole tensile strength of CFRP samples with and without steel foils and different layer thicknesses.

From Figure 6 it is obvious that the open hole tensile strength decreases significantly with decreasing layer thickness without stainless steel foil. The open hole tensile strength of the thin-ply specimens decreases by 12% compared to the samples with the thickest layer thickness. In contrast, the tensile strength of quasi-isotropic (QI) samples without a hole increases from 736.86 MPa (thick-ply) to 956.59 MPa (thin-ply), which corresponds to an increase of 29.8%. This can be explained by the changing fracture behaviour of the specimens, as described by Sihn [13] or Amacher [15]. In the case of thicker layers, the material is damaged at the hole during loading. Interfibre fractures and delaminations occur. The different damages at the surface could be detected with the DIC system. Figure 7 shows two fracture patterns on the left side after the tensile tests, where the left specimen is a thin-ply and the right specimen a thick-ply. The right side shows DIC images taken one second before final failure. The DIC images illustrate the strain field on the surface of the samples. The strain field can be used to draw qualitative conclusions about the stress field of the samples. In the case of thick-ply samples, predamage was detected before ultimate failure. As a result of this predamage, there is a relaxation process near the hole, and the stress peak near the hole will be reduced. Stresses are deflected by the damage in the material. In contrast, for thin-ply laminates, no predamage was visible until final failure with the DIC system. The samples failed in a brittle way, perpendicular to the load direction. Other studies used an acoustic emission system [13] and showed that there is no predamage before final failure within thin-ply laminates. The result of this behaviour is reflected in the fracture patterns (left side, Figure 7). It can be seen that in the case of the thin layer specimens, no delaminations are visible, which suggests that the critical failure mechanism must be fibre breakage. Only a partial detachment of the upper layer can be seen. In contrast, in the case of specimens with thicker layer delaminations and pull-outs, a mixed failure mode can be found.

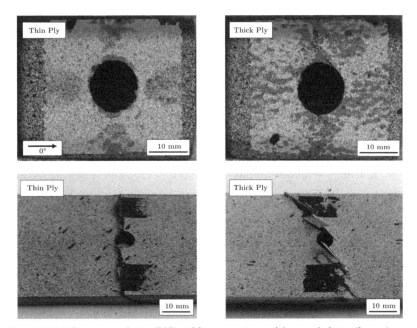

Figure 7. Digital image correlation (DIC) and fracture patterns of the open hole tensile specimens.

For comparison purposes, Figure 6 shows on the right side the specimens with stainless steel. In the case of thin-ply specimens with a stainless steel content of 25%, the strength increases by 60.44%. Hybridisation with stainless steel foils locally increases the strength of the specimen and reduces the stress within the CFRP layers. Crack propagation at the hole is suppressed. The potential of the fibres can be further exploited. Most thin layer specimens with stainless steel failed at the transition zone between the area with and without stainless steel. This is also visible in the microsections in Figure 8. The upper left and right images show a thin-ply hybrid sample after final failure.

Due to the transition from stainless steel foils to 90°-CFRP-layers, stress concentrations occur, which could be increased by local defects. The microsections in Figure 8 show a small difference in the locations of the transitions between steel foils and matrix. The positions of the foils vary on average by 0.3 mm. In addition, some waviness of the foils or deformation at the edges can increase the stress concentration at the transition zone, and resin rich areas appear in the transition zone. Another disadvantage of this design is the local stiffness discontinuity due to the discontinuous transition between metal layers and 90° CFRP layers. Nevertheless, it should be mentioned that although high stresses were present, no delaminations are visible. This shows the advantage of thin-ply hybrid materials. Due to a large number of layers and the associated interfaces, the interlaminar shear strength between the layers is lower, so that the surface pretreatment selected here was sufficient.

Figure 9 exhibits DIC images for selected loads. The upper four images show the damage process of a thin-ply sample. It can be seen that there are no large delaminations due to a shift in the upper layer. At the stress of 70% of the maximum stress, a stress peak is visible at the hole as well as stress peaks at the outer edges of the transition zone (red areas in the lower left and right corner of the image). However, these spread very slowly compared to the thick-ply specimens. The thick layer samples (lower images) show a delamination growth starting from the transition zone and the hole at 70% of the maximum stress. At 60% no delaminations are visible yet (left picture). As the load increases, the delaminations increase and move towards each other until the complete area of the sample in the area of the stainless steel shows delaminations.

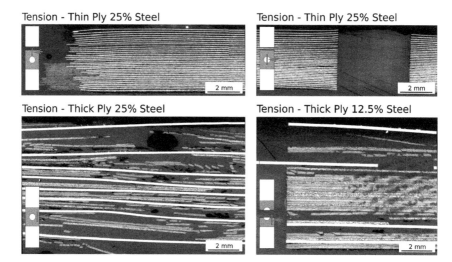

Figure 8. Microsections of the fracture surfaces of the open hole tension specimens.

In addition to the DIC images, the delaminations that occur can also be seen in the microsections in Figure 8. All delaminations are between the stainless steel foils and the matrix layers. The bonding between the stainless steel and the matrix was not sufficient. The interlaminar shear stress between steel and matrix was higher than the bonding strength between them.

However, for technical applications, the specific strength is more valuable, as it provides information on whether it is worthwhile to use such a material in the future. Even the strength of thin-ply samples in relation to the density increases by 33.14%; see Figure 6. This shows that by adding stainless steel foils as patches to make hybrid materials, an increase in strength relative to their densities can be achieved.

The results of the open hole compressive tests are shown in Figure 10. The bar chart shows that there is no difference in open hole compressive strength between the specimens without stainless steel foils. However, strength is increasing with decreasing layer thickness. The strength of the thin-ply specimens is 7.5% higher than that of the thick-ply specimens. Similar results were obtained by Yokozeki et al. [33]. In his study, the strength of the thin-ply samples increased by 9%. The increase of the strength can be explained by the changing failure behaviour and the tension. In the case of thin layer specimens, the formation and spread of delaminations are suppressed. The critical failure occurred in the formation of a kink band through the whole thickness of the specimen. This can also be seen in Figure 11. On the left side, DIC images of a thin- (left DIC image) and a thick-ply (right DIC image) sample one second before failure are shown. In the case of thin-ply samples, no previous damage could be detected before final failure, whereas delaminations and fibre breaks of the surface of the thick-ply specimens were visible. The failure of the thick-ply samples is a combination of fibre kinking and delaminations. This combination results in final failure, as shown in Figure 11.

Concerning the hybrid samples, a significant increase in strength can be observed in the case of the thick-ply samples with a steel content of 12.5%. The open hole compressive strength increased from 340 MPa to nearly 500 MPa, an improvement of 47%. The other configurations did not show any major improvements. In the case of thick-ply samples with a steel content of 25%, the OHC strength did not change, and in the case of thin-ply hybrid specimens a large variation in the results could be observed. Some samples showed an improvement in OHC strength from 333.4 MPa to 436.5 MPa, and others a decrease to 303.3 MPa. The microsections (Figure 12) show the different failure behaviours.

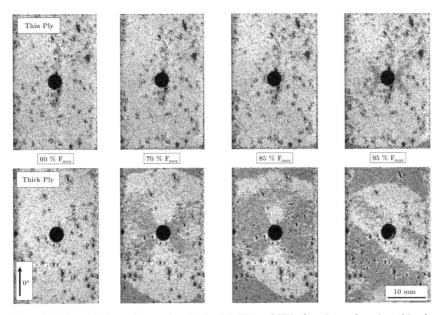

Figure 9. DIC open hole tensile samples at 60%, 70%, 85% and 95% of maximum force (top, thin-ply samples; bottom, thick-ply samples.

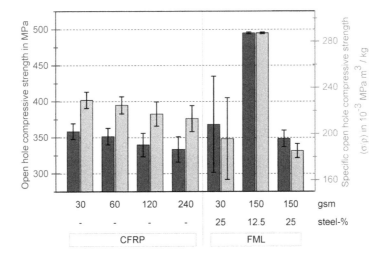

Figure 10. Open hole compressive strength and specific open hole compressive strength of CFRP samples with and without steel foils and different layer thicknesses.

In the case of thick-ply specimens with a steel content of 25%, delaminations occur between the stainless steel foil and the matrix, as is already the case under tensile load. Depending on which side the delaminations occur first, there is no symmetric bending stiffness, and the samples preferably kink to one side. This can also be seen in the fracture patterns or microsections. Due to this failure behaviour, no improvement in strength could be observed. In contrast, thick-ply specimens with a steel content of 12.5% have a 47% higher open hole compressive strength. The sample is supported by the increased bending stiffness of the hybrid composite due to the stainless steel layers and buckling is suppressed. No major delaminations can be detected within the sample such that a behaviour usual for composite materials can be seen here, whereby this is further strengthened by the outer steel layers as already mentioned.

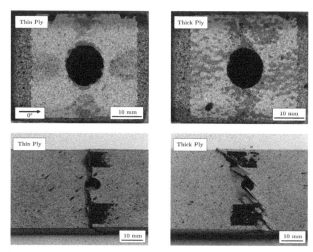

Figure 11. DIC (top) and fracture patterns (bottom) of the open hole compressive specimens without stainless steel.

The thin-ply hybrid specimens exhibit no predamage until final failure. No deformations in Z-directions (perpendicular to the sample surface) could be found via DIC. The microsection in Figure 12 displays numerous kinks in the specimen. Some kinks are local kink bands and other extend globally over several layers. The steel layers with a thickness of 30 μm have low compressive stiffness and due to small defects like waviness of the foil or voids lead to local deformations and kinks. The open hole compressive strength of the thin-ply hybrid specimens shows a large standard deviation based on this local deformations and bucklings. Specimens with a low content or number of local kinks exhibit a higher strength. Specimens with a high content or a high number of local kinks exhibit a lower strength.

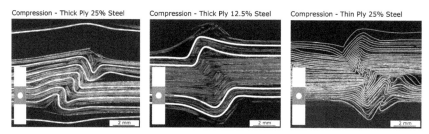

Figure 12. Microsections of the fracture surfaces of the open hole tension and compression specimens.

As in the case of the tensile results, the specific open hole strength is shown in grey in Figure 10. The specific open hole compressive strength shows that in the case of thick-ply specimens with a steel content of 25%, there is a decrease in the specific strength. In the case of the thin-ply specimens with a steel content of 25%, a increase or decrease strength can be determined depending on the number of kinks. Only in the case of thick-ply specimens with a steel content of 12.5%, an improvement in the specific strength can be detected, which can be explained by the anti-buckling support of the laminate by the outer steel layers.

4. Conclusions

This study shows that the hybridisation of thin-ply CFRP samples with stainless steel foil patches increases the open hole tensile strength by up to 60.44% compared to CFRP samples. Even if the strength is normalised to the density of the samples, the OHT strength is increased by up to 33%. Hybridisation with stainless steel foils locally increases the strength of the specimen and reduces the stress within the CFRP layers. Crack propagation at the hole is suppressed. The potential of the fibres can be further exploited. For thick-ply hybrid samples, no improvement in OHT strength could be found. The laminates failed due to the formation of delaminations between the stainless steel foils and the matrix. The compression test showed different results. The thin-ply hybrid and the thick-ply hybrid samples with a steel content of 25% exhibit no improvement in open hole compressive strength. In the case of the specimens with thin layers, many kinks could be found which led to premature failure. The hybrid samples with the thicker layers and 25% steel failed due to delaminations. The thick-ply samples with a steel content of 12.5% exhibited an improvement in open hole compressive strength up to 47%. Due to the higher local bending stiffness of the hybrid material, buckling of the sample is suppressed. In summary, the hybridisation of CFRP laminates with stainless steel foils in exchange for the 90°-CFRP-layers can improve the OHT and OHC strength. Additionally, the specific OHT and OHC strength increase, so that this hybrid material could be an opportunity to reduce the notch sensitivity of composites, especially for thin-ply composites. For further investigations, the transition zone should be modified so that a strong local stiffness discontinuity can be avoided.

Author Contributions: Conceptualisation, B.K. and J.K. (Julian Karsten); data curation, B.K. and J.K. (Julian Karsten); formal analysis, B.K., J.K. (Julian Karsten) and J.K. (Johann Körbelin); investigation, B.K., J.K. (Julian Karsten) and J.K. (Johann Körbelin); methodology, B.K., J.K. (Julian Karsten) and J.K. (Johann Körbelin); project administration, J.K. (Julian Karsten) and B.F.; resources, B.F.; supervision, B.F.; validation, B.K., J.K. (Julian Karsten), J.K. (Johann Körbelin) and B.F.; Visualization, B.K.; writing—original draft, B.K. and J.K. (Julian Karsten); writing—review and editing, J.K. (Johann Körbelin) and B.F. All authors have read and agreed to the published version of the manuscript.

Funding: This research received no external funding.

Acknowledgments: The authors acknowledge 3M Germany GmbH for supplying surface pretreatment AC-130-2, and the support for the Open Access fees by Hamburg University of Technology (TUHH) in the funding program Open Access Publishing.

Conflicts of Interest: The authors declare no conflict of interest.

Abbreviations

The following abbreviations are used in this manuscript:

MDPI	Multidisciplinary Digital Publishing Institute
OHT	open hole tension
OHC	open hole compression
CFRP	carbon fibre reinforced plastic
gsm	grams by square meters
QI	quasi-isotropic
UD	Unidirectional
FML	fibre metal laminate
NDT	non-destructive testing
SHM	structural health monitoring
NTPT	north thin ply technology
CMA	Toray Carbon Fibres America, Inc
ILSS	interlaminar shear strength
CNC	computer numerical control
ASTM	American Society for Testing and Materials
SF	steel foil
SEM	scanning electron microscope
DIC	digital image correlation

References

1. Camanho, P.P.; Matthews, F.L. Stress analysis and strength prediction of mechanically fastened joints in FRP: A review. *Compos. Part A Appl. Sci. Manuf.* **1997**, *28*, 529–547. [CrossRef]
2. Eriksson, I. On the Bearing Strength of Bolted Graphite/Epoxy Laminates. *J. Compos. Mater.* **1990**, *24*, 1246–1269. [CrossRef]
3. Fink, A.; Camanho, P.P.; Andrés, J.M.; Pfeiffer, E.; Obst, A. Hybrid CFRP/titanium bolted joints: Performance assessment and application to a spacecraft payload adaptor. *Compos. Sci. Technol.* **2010**, *70*, 305–317. [CrossRef]
4. Crosky, A.; Kelly.; Li, R.; Legrand, X.; Huong, N.; Ujjin, R. Improvement of bearing strength of laminated composites. *Compos. Struct.* **2006**, *76*, 260–271. [CrossRef]
5. Gray, P.J.; O'Higgins, R.M.; McCarthy, C.T. Effect of thickness and laminate taper on the stiffness, strength and secondary bending of single-lap, single-bolt countersunk composite joints. *Compos. Struct.* **2014**, *107*, 315–324. [CrossRef]
6. Camanho, P.P.; Tavares, C.; de Oliveira, R.; Marques, A.T.; Ferreira, A. Increasing the efficiency of composite single-shear lap joints using bonded inserts. *Compos. Part B Eng.* **2005**, *36*, 372–383. [CrossRef]
7. Li, R.; Huong, N.; Crosky, A.; Mouritz, A.P.; Kelly, D.; Chang, P. Improving bearing performance of composite bolted joints using z-pins. *Compos. Sci. Technol.* **2009**, *69*, 883–889. [CrossRef]
8. Petersen, E.; Stefaniak, D.; Hühne, C. Experimental investigation of load carrying mechanisms and failure phenomena in the transition zone of locally metal reinforced joining areas. *Compos. Struct.* **2017**, *182*, 79–90. [CrossRef]
9. Van Rooijen, R.G.J.; Sinke, J.; de Vries, T.J.; van der Zwaag, S. The Bearing Strength of Fiber Metal Laminates. *J. Compos. Mater.* **2006**, *40*, 5–19. [CrossRef]
10. Bosbach, B.; Baytekin-Gerngross, M.; Sprecher, E.; Wegner, J.; Gerngross, M.D.; Carstensen, J.; Adelung, R.; Fiedler, B. Maximizing bearing fatigue lifetime and CAI capability of fibre metal laminates by nanoscale sculptured Al plies. *Compos. Part A Appl. Sci. Manuf.* **2019**, *117*, 144–155. [CrossRef]
11. Parvizi, A.; Bailey, J.E. On multiple transverse cracking in glass fibre epoxy cross-ply laminates. *J. Mater. Sci.* **1978**, *13*, 2131–2136. [CrossRef]
12. Kim, R.Y.; Soni, S.R. Experimental and Analytical Studies On the Onset of Delamination in Laminated Composites. *J. Compos. Mater.* **1984**, *18*, 70–80. [CrossRef]
13. Sihn, S.; Kim, R.; Kawabe, K.; Tsai, S. Experimental studies of thin-ply laminated composites. *Compos. Sci. Technol.* **2007**, *67*, 996–1008. [CrossRef]
14. Wisnom, M.R.; Khan, B.; Hallett, S.R. Size effects in unnotched tensile strength of unidirectional and quasi-isotropic carbon/epoxy composites. *Compos. Struct.* **2008**, *84*, 21–28. [CrossRef]
15. Amacher, R.; Cugnoni, J.; Botsis, J.; Sorensen, L.; Smith, W.; Dransfeld, C. Thin ply composites: Experimental characterization and modeling of size-effects. *Compos. Sci. Technol.* **2014**, *101*, 121–132. [CrossRef]
16. Kawabe, K.; Tomoda, S.; Matsuo, T. Technology for spreading tow and its application to composite materials. I. A new pneumatic method for spreading carbon tow. *Sen'i Kikai Gakkaishi (J. Text. Mach. Soc. Jpn.)* **1997**, *50*, 50–57. [CrossRef]
17. Guillamet, G.; Turon, A.; Costa, J.; Renart, J.; Linde, P.; Mayugo, J.A. Damage occurrence at edges of non-crimp-fabric thin-ply laminates under off-axis uniaxial loading. *Compos. Sci. Technol.* **2014**, *98*, 44–50. [CrossRef]
18. Cugnoni, J.; Amacher, R.; Kohler, S.; Brunner, J.; Kramer, E.; Dransfeld, C.; Smith, W.; Scobbie, K.; Sorensen, L.; Botsis, J. Towards aerospace grade thin-ply composites: Effect of ply thickness, fibre, matrix and interlayer toughening on strength and damage tolerance. *Compos. Sci. Technol.* **2018**, *168*, 467–477. [CrossRef]
19. Arteiro, A.; Catalanotti, G.; Xavier, J.; Camanho, P.P. Large damage capability of non-crimp fabric thin-ply laminates. *Compos. Part A Appl. Sci. Manuf.* **2014**, *63*, 110–122. [CrossRef]
20. Studer, J.; Keller, A.; Leone, F.; Stefaniak, D.; Dransfeld, C.; Masania, K. Local reinforcement of aerospace structures using co-curing RTM of metal foil hybrid composites. *Prod. Eng.* **2018**, *12*, 195–201. [CrossRef]
21. Bosbach, B.; Ohle, C.; Fiedler, B. Structural health monitoring of fibre metal laminates under mode I and II loading. *Compos. Part A Appl. Sci. Manuf.* **2018**, *107*, 471–478. [CrossRef]

22. Masania, K.; Geissberger, R.; Stefaniak, D.; Dransfeld, C. Steel foil reinforced composites: Experimental and numerical study of strength, plasticity and ply size effects. In Proceedings of the International Conference of Composite Materials, Copenhagen, Denmark, 19–24 July 2015.

23. Stefaniak, D.; Kappel, E.; Kolesnikov, B.; Hühne, C. Improving the mechanical performance of unidirectional CFRP by metal-hybridization. In Proceedings of the ECCM15—15th European Conference on Composite Materials, Venice, Italy, 24–28 June 2012.

24. Prussak, R.; Stefaniak, D.; Hühne, C.; Sinapius, M. Residual Stresses in Intrinsic UD-CFRP-Steel-Laminates-Experimental Determination, Identification of Sources, Effects and Modification Approaches. *Mater. Sci. Forum* **2015**, *825-826*, 369–376. [CrossRef]

25. Zinn, C.; Schaper, M.; Gonzalez, J.S.; Meiners, D.; Wang, Z.; Troester, T.; Pottmeyer, F.; Weidenmann, K.A. Shear edge tests: A benchmark in investigating the influence of different surface pretreatment methods on the shear stress of intrinsically manufactured metal-CFRP hybrids. *Int. J. Automot. Compos.* **2016**, *2*, 244. [CrossRef]

26. Stefaniak, D.; Prussak, R.; Weiß, L. Specific challenges in the application of fibre-metal laminates. *Lightweight Des. Worldw.* **2017**, *10*, 20–25. [CrossRef]

27. Prussak, R.; Stefaniak, D.; Kappel, E.; Hühne, C.; Sinapius, M. Smart cure cycles for fiber metal laminates using embedded fiber Bragg grating sensors. *Compos. Struct.* **2019**, *213*, 252–260. [CrossRef]

28. ASTM D3039. *Standard Test Method for Tensile Properties of Polymer Matrix Composite Materials*; ASTM: West Conshohocken, PA, USA, 2017. [CrossRef]

29. ASTM D2344. *Test Method for Short-Beam Strength of Polymer Matrix Composite Materials and Their Laminates*; ASTM: West Conshohocken, PA, USA, 2006. [CrossRef]

30. ASTM D5766. *Test Method for Open-Hole Tensile Strength of Polymer Matrix Composite Laminates*; ASTM: West Conshohocken, PA, USA, 2002. [CrossRef]

31. ASTM D6484. *Test Method for Open-Hole Compressive Strength of Polymer Matrix Composite Laminates*; ASTM: West Conshohocken, PA, USA, 2004. [CrossRef]

32. Ebnesajjad, S. *Handbook of Adhesives and Surface Preparation: Technology, Applications and Manufacturing*; PDL Handbook Series; William Andrew/Elsevier: Amsterdam, The Netherlands, 2011.

33. Yokozeki, T.; Aoki, Y.; Ogasawara, T. Experimental characterization of strength and damage resistance properties of thin-ply carbon fiber/toughened epoxy laminates. *Compos. Struct.* **2008**, *82*, 382–389. [CrossRef]

Article

Effect of Metal Surface Topography on the Interlaminar Shear and Tensile Strength of Aluminum/Polyamide 6 Polymer-Metal-Hybrids

Erik Saborowski [1,*], Axel Dittes [1], Philipp Steinert [2], Thomas Lindner [1], Ingolf Scharf [1], Andreas Schubert [2] and Thomas Lampke [1]

[1] Materials and Surface Engineering Group, Faculty of Mechanical Engineering, Chemnitz University of Technology, D-09107 Chemnitz, Germany

[2] Micromanufacturing Technology Group, Faculty of Mechanical Engineering, Chemnitz University of Technology, D-09107 Chemnitz, Germany

* Correspondence: erik.saborowski@mb.tu-chemnitz.de

Received: 26 August 2019; Accepted: 10 September 2019; Published: 12 September 2019

Abstract: Mechanical interlocking has been proven to be an effective bonding mechanism for dissimilar material groups like polymers and metals. Therefore, this contribution assesses several surface pretreatments for the metallic adherent. Blasting, etching, combined blasting and etching, thermal spraying, and laser structuring processes are investigated with regard to the achievable interlaminar strength and the corresponding surface roughness parameters. The experiments are carried out on EN AW-6082/polyamide 6 polymer-metal-hybrids, utilizing a novel butt-bonded hollow cylinder specimen geometry for determining the shear and tensile strength. The experimental results indicate that the surface roughness slope has a major impact on the interlaminar strength. A laser-generated pin structure is found to provide the best mechanical performance as well as the highest surface slope of all investigated structuring methods.

Keywords: polymer-metal-hybrid; surface pretreatment; mechanical interlocking; roughness evaluation; interlaminar shear strength; interlaminar tensile strength

---

1. Introduction

Thermoplastic polymer-metal-hybrids (PMH) offer great potential for automotive applications due to their quick processability and high strength/stiffness-to-weight ratio. In this context, a key challenge is to develop cost and time efficient techniques for creating a well-adhering interface in-between both dissimilar materials. One promising approach is adhesion by micro-scale mechanical interlocking. During joining, the polymer itself is used as the adhesive, as it infiltrates the roughness features of the metallic surface and interlocks them.

For this purpose, various joining techniques can be applied to produce mechanically interlocked PMH. In most cases, metal and polymer are placed together under pressure, while the contact area between both adherents is heated up until the polymer starts to melt. Katayama and Kawahito [1] as well as Bergmann and Stambke [2] generated the thermal energy by a laser beam, whereas Mitschang et al. [3] used induction heating. Wagner et al. [4] as well as Steinert et al. [5] utilized ultrasonic oscillations for melting the polymer. Flock [6] as well as Haberstroh and Sickert [7] applied direct heat conduction to the metallic adherent. Another approach is the direct infiltration of the metallic surface with molten thermoplastic by injection molding. Ramani [8] as well as Kleffel and Drummer [9] achieved a considerable interlaminar tensile strength when employing this method.

Besides the influence of the selected joining process, the level of achievable adhesion is directly connected to the surface characteristics of the metallic adherent. Therefore, a roughly structured and undercut surface of the metallic partner drastically increases the bonding strength compared to an untreated surface. Grit blasting is the most widely used structuring method, since it provides satisfactory adhesion with low effort and can be easily implemented in industrial applications. Consequently, it is often used as a benchmark for other structuring processes. Pan et al. [10] conducted a parameter study with different abrasive particle sizes on magnesium/carbon fiber-reinforced polymer (Mg/CFRP) laminates, concluding that larger particles create a rougher surface with a slightly increased shear strength. Etching processes offer the possibility of structuring large surfaces within a short duration, usually reaching an interlaminar strength slightly below the blasted equivalent. Mitschang et al. [11] achieved good adhesion with acidic pickling in nitric acid (HNO_3) for an aluminum/fiber-reinforced polyamide (Al/FRPA) hybrid, whereas Nestler et al. [12] obtained the best results with alkaline pickling in a sodium hydroxide (NaOH) solution for a similar Al/FRPA hybrid. Laser structuring offers a high degree of freedom in designing the roughness features. Therefore, the highest adhesion can be obtained, although this technique is usually expensive and time consuming. Heckert and Zaeh [13] compared different laser manufactured structure sizes, wherein a kerf structure with a distance and depth of 200 μm provided the best adhesion between Al and FRPA. Steinert et al. [5] presented a self-organizing pin structure with a height of approximately 40 μm and a distance between the pins of 20 μm that reached a lap shear strength that was around 2.5 times higher than that of a blasted surface in an Al/FRPA hybrid. As an additive structuring method, thermal spraying provides an irregular, rough, and undercut surface. Utilizing a NiAl5 coating, Lindner et al. [14] reported a lap shear strength that was around 1.35 times higher than that of a blasted surface within an Al/FRPA hybrid.

As the shape of the microstructure is so important to the interface properties, proper surface characterization is mandatory for predicting the possible interlaminar strength. The most commonly used characterization method is the surface roughness measurement since it is a quick, inexpensive and widely standardized approach. Chen et al. [15] investigated the relation between various roughness parameters and the achieved shear strength of a steel/bone cement joint. Spacing (correlation length β) and amplitude parameters (arithmetical average roughness R_a) gave no accordance, whereas the root mean square slope $R\Delta q$ that considers the relation between amplitude and spacing gave a good accordance. However, no relation between the investigated roughness parameters and the achievable tensile strength was given.

Regarding the contributions of different authors, a significant shortcoming is the missing comparability of the obtained test results due to the different test methods that have been used. Saborowski et al. [16] reported that especially the very popular lap shear test massively underestimates the shear strength for single lap joints of metal and unreinforced thermoplastics. Therefore, Saborowski et al. [17] adapted a test method which was initially proposed by Mahnken and Schlimmer [18] for testing adhesives. Thereby, butt-bonded hollow cylinders were utilized for interlaminar strength testing. The determined shear strength values were found to be way more precise than the results of the lap shear test. Moreover, tensile strength testing can be accomplished with the same specimen geometry.

The aim of this contribution is to investigate the correlation of different roughness parameters with the interlaminar shear and tensile strength of EN AW-6082/polyamide 6 (PA6) hybrids. For this reason, several state-of-the-art surface structuring methods are applied and the surface roughness parameters R_z (average maximum profile height) and tanθ (surface roughness slope) are evaluated. Reliable strength values are obtained by using the butt-bonded hollow cylinder specimen geometry. Preliminary lap shear tests are performed to determine strength-optimized processing parameters for grit blasting, etching, and combined blasting and etching processes for the selected PMH. Optimized laser structuring as well as thermal spraying parameters are deduced from previous investigations conducted by Steinert et al. [5] and Saborowski et al. [17], respectively. The specimens are manufactured by heat conduction hot pressing. Finally, the fracture surfaces are characterized in terms of their morphology and topography in order to investigate the relation between interlaminar strength and load direction as well as the failure mode depending on the applied structuring method.

2. Materials and Methods

2.1. Materials

The investigated metal-thermoplastic hybrid consists of Ultramid® B3 PA6 (BASF, Ludwigshafen, Germany) and EN AW-6082 aluminum alloy. Table 1 shows the material properties. The parameters for the PA6 are given for a humid condition, which is achieved by conditioning the material according to ISO 1110 at 343 K and 62% relative humidity. The PA6 was conditioned before testing following this standard.

Table 1. Material properties.

	EN AW-6082	PA6 (humid)
Density (kg/m^3)	2.7	1.14
Elastic modulus (MPa)	70000	1800
Poisson's ratio (-)	0.34	-
Yield strength (MPa)	260	60
Ultimate strength (MPa)	310	-
Elongation to failure (%)	7	200
Melting temperature (K)	933	496
Thermal expansion coefficient (10^{-6}/K)	23.4	70
Thermal conductance (W/(m·K))	170–220	0.23
Specific heat (J/(kg·K))	898	1700

2.2. Testing Methods

2.2.1. Lap Shear Test

The lap shear specimen illustrated in Figure 1 consists of two overlapping plates of height h (indices: m = metal, p = polymer), width w and overlapping length l_o. The clamping length is given by l_c and the free length is given by l_f.

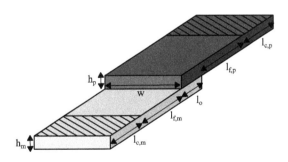

Figure 1. Lap shear specimen geometry.

The geometrical parameters can be seen in Table 2. The experiments were carried out utilizing an Allround-Line 20 kN testing machine (Zwick/Roell, Ulm, Germany) with a crosshead speed of 1 mm/min. Five specimens were tested for each surface treatment.

Table 2. Geometrical parameters of the lap shear specimens.

w (mm)	l_o (mm)	$l_{c,m}$ (mm)	$l_{f,m}$ (mm)	$l_{f,p}$ (mm)	$l_{c,p}$ (mm)	h_m (mm)	h_p (mm)
25	5	45	50	40	35	3	3

The specimen was loaded with a tensile force perpendicular to the joining zone, causing a shear stress within the interface. The lap shear strength $\tau_{l,max}$ was calculated from the fracture force F_{max} divided by the overlap area A_0.

$$\tau_{l,max} = \frac{F_{max}}{A_0} = \frac{F_{max}}{l_0 w} \tag{1}$$

2.2.2. Butt-Bonded Hollow Cylinder Test

The specimen illustrated in Figure 2 consists of two butt-bonded hollow cylinders with the outer diameter d_o and the inner diameter d_i.

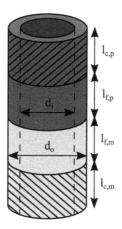

Figure 2. Hollow cylinder specimen geometry.

The specimen was tested with a PTT 250 K1 hydraulic testing machine (Carl Schenck AG, Darmstadt, Germany). ER40 - 472E collets according to ISO 15488 were utilized for clamping. A steel plug was put into the polymer cylinder to support it against squeezing when the collet was tightened. The geometrical parameters of the hollow cylinder specimens are listed in Table 3. Five specimens were tested for each load case and surface treatment.

Table 3. Geometrical parameters of butt-bonded hollow cylinder specimens.

d_i (mm)	d_o (mm)	$l_{c,m}$ (mm)	$l_{f,m}$ (mm)	$l_{c,p}$ (mm)	$l_{f,p}$ (mm)
23	28	20	20	30	30

For determining the interlaminar shear strength, the joint was loaded with a torsional moment, which caused an almost pure shear stress within the interface. The specimen was twisted until it fractured, with an angular velocity of 15°/min. The shear strength τ_{max} was calculated from the maximum torque T_{max} divided by the polar section modulus W_p.

$$\tau_{max} = \frac{T_{max}}{W_P} = \frac{16 T_{max} d_o}{\pi (d_o{}^4 - d_i{}^4)} \tag{2}$$

For identifying the tensile strength, the specimen was loaded with a tensile force, causing an almost pure normal stress within the interface. The specimen was pulled until it fractured, with a crosshead speed of 0.36 mm/min. The tensile strength σ_{max} was calculated from the maximum tensile force F_{max} divided by the overlapping area A_0.

$$\sigma_{max} = \frac{F_{max}}{A_0} = \frac{4 F_{max}}{\pi (d_o{}^2 - d_i{}^2)} \tag{3}$$

2.3. Surface Pretreatment

2.3.1. Grit Blasting

The morphology of grit blasted surfaces depends on the particle type, particle size, blasting angle, blasting distance, blasting pressure and blasting time. A corundum (Al_2O_3) particle type, a blasting distance of 100 mm and a treatment time of 10 s were utilized. Amada and Hirose [19] as well as Mohammedi et al. [20] found that a blasting angle of 75° provided the best adhesion for thermally sprayed ceramic coatings on a metallic substrate. Since these coatings also mainly adhere by mechanical interlocking, the same blasting angle was used here. Four different particle sizes (Wiwox F120 (90–125 µm), Wiwox F54 (250–355 µm), WFA F24 (600–850 µm) and WFA F16 (1000–1400 µm)) with three different pressures (1 bar, 2 bar and 3 bar) were investigated.

2.3.2. Etching

The etching processes are based on the findings of Nestler et al. [12], who identified alkaline (NaOH) and acidic (HNO_3) treatment to provide strong adhesion between EN AW-6082 and fiber-reinforced PA6. Alkaline etching was carried out with 2% NaOH solution at 343 K. Afterwards, the sheets were dipped into 50% HNO_3 solution at ambient temperature for 2 min to remove reaction products from the surface. For acidic etching, the sheets were dipped for 1 min into 3% NaOH solution at 323 K in order to remove the oxide layer from the aluminum. Afterwards, the sheets were treated with 50% HNO_3 solution. Treatment times of 1 min, 3 min, 10 min, and 20 min were investigated.

2.3.3. Grit Blasting and Alkaline Etching

According to the findings of Nestler et al. [12], corundum blasting (cb) with a F24 grit size at 2 bar creates a surface roughness approximately six times higher than alkaline etching in 2% NaOH solution at 343 K for 10 min. Combined corundum blasting and etching is motivated by forming small etching structures on the much coarser blasting structures. Thereby, the additional specific surface area and fracturing of the surface should further enhance the interlaminar strength. Three different particle sizes (Wiwox F54 and WFA F24/F16, 3 bar each) and a subsequent NaOH treatment (2%, 343 K, 5 min) were investigated.

2.3.4. Thermal Spraying

The thermal spraying process is based on the findings of Lindner et al. [14] and Saborowski et al. [17], who identified a NiAl5 coating suitable for creating good adhesion between aluminum and PA6. The resulting surface is characterized by a high roughness as well as the formation of undercuts. A strong adhesion of the coating onto the aluminum is achieved by corundum blasting. WFA F24 Al_2O_3 particles are applied with a pressure of 2 bar, an angle of 75° and a distance of 100 mm. The coating is applied by electric wire arc spraying, utilizing a VisuArc 350 spraying system (Oerlikon Metco, Pfäffikon, Switzerland). The spraying parameters are summarized in Table 4.

Table 4. Feedstock material and parameters used for the thermal spraying process.

Chemical Composition	Current (A)	Voltage (V)	Spraying Distance (mm)	Air Pressure (bar)	Feed Speed (m/s)	Row Spacing (mm)
Ni–95%/Al–5%	150	30	130	3.5	0.6	5

2.3.5. Laser Structuring

The laser processing of the cylinder specimens was carried out by a nanosecond laser system (Spectra Physics®, Santa Clara, CA, USA) with the specifications shown in Table 5.

Table 5. Parameters used for the laser structuring process.

Laser Medium	Wavelength (nm)	Pulse Duration (ns)	Max Mean Power (W)	Focus Diameter (µm)
Nd:YVO4	532	10	13	15

During laser processing, the material behavior significantly depends on the energy input into the surface. In accordance with the work of Baburaj [21], pin microstructures can be manufactured by applying a defined energy input above the material-specific threshold laser fluency. In preliminary experiments reported by Steinert et al. [5], it was found that the conditions for the generation of pin microstructures prevail in the range of a laser intensity of I ≈ 3–6 J/cm². These intensities are realized by using a defocused laser spot measuring 55 µm in diameter. The energy input leads to pin structures with an average structure height of about 40 µm and a maximum structure height of about 80 µm.

2.4. Specimen Production

The specimens were produced by heat conduction hot pressing. Beforehand, the PA6 was dried at 343 K. This avoided the formation of interfacial cavities by evaporating water during the hot pressing process. Moreover, the metallic surfaces were ultrasonically cleaned and degreased in ethanol. Figure 3 illustrates the hot pressing tool used for producing the hollow cylinder specimens.

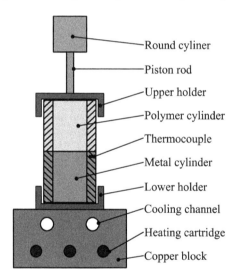

Figure 3. Hot pressing tool.

Note, that the lap shear specimens were manufactured using the same tool with adapted specimen holders. According to the optimized production parameters determined by Haberstroh and Sickert [7], a constant interfacial joining pressure of 0.2 MPa was chosen. The maximum joining temperature was set to 508 K, which is just slightly above the melting temperature of the polyamide, in order to prevent excessive melting. Subsequently, the copper block was cooled down with an air cooling system until the temperature dropped below 373 K. Figure 4 illustrates the interfacial temperature over time during the joining process.

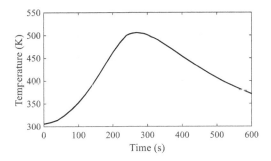

Figure 4. Interfacial temperature during the joining process (hollow cylinder specimens).

The temperature in the interface was observed by a thermocouple placed inside a drill-hole slightly below the metal surface. The complete hot pressing procedure can be summarized as follows:

(1) Application of joining pressure (0.2 MPa);
(2) Activation of heating cartridges (480 W in total) for heat generation;
(3) Deactivation of heating cartridges when joining temperature (508 K) is reached;
(4) Activation of air cooling;
(5) Cooling down to 373 K;
(6) Removal of joining pressure;
(7) Removal of joined specimen;

The joined hollow cylinder specimens are reworked by turning on the inner and outer surface in order to ensure the necessary centricity for testing.

2.5. Roughness Evaluation

The average maximum profile height R_z as well as the roughness slope $\tan\theta$ are evaluated in this contribution. Assuming scale-independent material behavior and complete penetration of the molten polymer into the structured surface, the interlaminar strength should also be independent of the scale. An alteration in the load-bearing cross-sectional area for one profile element is exactly balanced out by a corresponding alteration in the total number of profile elements. Consequently, R_z should not show a meaningful accordance with the interlaminar strength as it is only a measure for the scale, but not for the shape, for the profile elements.

On the other hand, the slope angle θ should have a direct relation to the interlaminar strength for two reasons: Firstly, a higher slope indicates the occurrence of more roughness features in relation to the roughness profile height. This leads to an enlarged specific surface and, therefore, to more possibilities for the polymer to interlock with the metallic surface. Secondly, the slope angle is directly related to micro-friction forces between metal and polymer. Figure 5 shows a shear force F_s (e.g., induced by a shear load or polymer shrinkage) pressing the polymer against the metallic roughness feature. The resulting normal force $F_n = F_s \sin\theta$ and the tangential force $F_t = F_s \cos\theta$. An increase in θ leads to an increase in F_n. Hence, the maximum friction force μF_n hindering the polymer from slipping is increased. μ denotes the friction coefficient between the polymer and metal. Additionally, F_t which forces the polymer to slip is decreased.

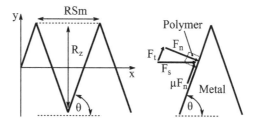

Figure 5. Roughness slope and resulting forces.

The roughness measurements were carried out according to ISO 4287, using a Hommel-Etamic® T8000 stylus profiler (JENOPTIK AG, Jena, Germany) with a 5 μm/90° stylus tip for the lap shear specimens and a 2 μm/60° stylus tip for the hollow cylinder specimens. R_z describes the average maximum profile height of the roughness features (Figure 6) within five times the sampling length l_r ($5l_r$ equals the total evaluation length l_n). Accordingly,

$$R_z = \frac{1}{5}\sum_{i=1}^{5} R_{zi}. \tag{4}$$

Assuming a simplified symmetrical wedge shape of the roughness profile, as shown in Figure 5,

$$\tan\theta = \frac{2R_z}{RSm} \text{ with } RSm = \frac{1}{m}\sum_{i=1}^{m} x_{si}, \tag{5}$$

where *RSm* denotes the average width of the roughness features x_s within one sampling length (Figure 6).

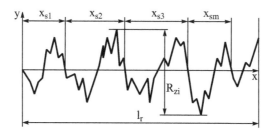

Figure 6. Schematic representation of the surface profile.

Usually, the actual roughness profile does not consist of symmetrical, repeating wedges, but of shapes very different in terms of the horizontal and vertical extent. Therefore, ISO 4287 proposes a minimum segment length of $0.01l_r$ and a minimum segment height of $0.1R_z$ for the peaks that constitute one profile element. Peaks below this threshold are treated as noise and considered a part of the preceding peak. Depending on the measured R_z value as well as the chosen sampling length and threshold values the resulting *RSm* value can vary within a certain range. Another approach is presented by NASA Tech Brief 70-10722 [22], where the recorded output signal from the surface roughness tester is used to calculate

$$\tan\theta = \frac{1}{l_n}\int_0^{l_n} \left|\frac{dy}{dx}\right| dx, \tag{6}$$

where y is the profile height signal as a function of distance x within the evaluation length l_n. This approach yields the exact same value of $\tan\theta$ when applied to the simplified profile shape shown in Figure 5. Applied to an actual roughness profile, a clear value is received, being independent from arbitrarily chosen threshold values like those of the $2R_z/RSm$ approach. Consequently, Equation (6) was chosen for roughness slope evaluation within this study.

3. Results and Discussion

3.1. Lap Shear Specimens

Figure 7a illustrates the results for the corundum blasted surfaces obtained by the lap shear tests. Despite considerable differences in the pressure, particle size and achieved roughness, the results only vary in a range of 9.98–12.17 MPa. The corresponding surface parameters for the highest strength values achieved with each particle size are shown in Table 6.

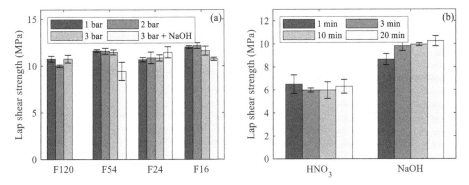

Figure 7. Lap shear test results for (**a**) blasting and combined treatment and (**b**) etching treatment.

Table 6. Highest test results and roughness parameters (5 μm tip) for blasting treatment.

Treatment	$\tau_{l,max}$ (MPa)	R_z (μm)	$\tan\theta$
F120, 3 bar	10.76	26	0.325
F54, 1 bar	11.62	32	0.364
F24, 2 bar	10.87	81	0.459
F16, 2 bar	12.17	111	0.503

Despite a drastic difference in the average maximum profile height, the lap shear strength as well as the slope values are relatively close together. Except for the F24 treated surfaces, the lap shear strength increases with an increasing particle size. However, a clear correlation between the blasting pressure and strength is not observed. A higher pressure increases R_z as well as $\tan\theta$ but also forces the embedding of corundum particles into the aluminum surface. Embedded particles may come loose when a load is applied to the interface. However, they are also considered roughness features when performing the surface roughness evaluation. Hence, the interlaminar strength in relation to $\tan\theta$ decreases.

Figure 7b shows the lap shear strength for the etched surfaces. For the alkaline etching with NaOH, the strength (8.65–10.26 MPa), R_z and $\tan\theta$ increase with the treatment time. For the acidic etching with HNO_3, no noticeable structuring effect could be observed, and the obtainable lap shear strength is thus quite low and almost equal for all investigated treatment times.

The results for the combined blasting and etching treatment are shown in Figure 7a. The change in strength as well as in roughness values is shown in Table 7.

Table 7. Change in test results and roughness parameters (blasting (3 bar) → combined blasting (3 bar) and etching (5 min, NaOH) treatment, 5 μm tip).

Treatment	$\tau_{l,max}$ (MPa)	R_z (μm)	tanθ
F54	11.47 → 9.44	45 → 43	0.397 → 0.365
F24	10.87 → 11.46	91 → 87	0.478 → 0.467
F16	11.63 → 10.75	142 → 131	0.542 → 0.531

The additional etching leads to a considerable decrease in the lap shear strength for F54 blasted aluminum, whereas for F24 and F16, the difference is rather small. Since the difference in the maximum profile height between F54 blasted and NaOH etched aluminum is not as pronounced as for larger particle sizes, the etching causes a leveling of smaller roughness features rather than an additional structuring effect. For the F16 particle size, an additional structuring effect is more obvious, as shown in the cross-sections in Figure 8b. The small roughness features created by the etching treatment (Figure 8d) are clearly pronounced on the much larger roughness features created by the blasting treatment (Figure 8a). However, a leveling of sharp edges, as well as a loss of undercuts, are observed, leading to a decrease in the micro-clamping area. For the F16 particle size, the additional etching led to a slight decrease in the lap shear strength, whereas a slight increase is noted for the F24 particle size. Therefore, no final statement can be made on whether additional etching is beneficial to the interlaminar strength.

Figure 8. Cross-sections for (**a**) blasting (F16, 3 bar) (**b**) combined blasting (F16, 3 bar) and etching (5 min NaOH) (**c**) acidic etching (20 min HNO₃) and (**d**) alkaline etching (20 min, NaOH) treatment applied to EN AW-6082 sheets.

It is noteworthy that a completely untreated aluminum surface was not able to create adhesion to PA6. The specimens delaminated in the climate chamber. Therefore, no results can be provided.

In Figure 9a, the lap shear strength data for the different treatment conditions is related to the determined R_z value. For all of the tested treatment techniques, a clear correlation of R_z and the lap shear strength is not observed and both values are rather randomly distributed. Only the surfaces that show a low R_z value show a correspondingly low lap shear strength (HNO₃ treatment 1–20 min/NaOH treatment 1 min). In Figure 9b, the lap shear strength is related to the tanθ value. In contrast to R_z, an acceptable correlation between the lap shear strength and tanθ is observed. However, the measured data still shows considerable scattering. Possible influencing factors are as follows:

- Omission of undercuts when recording the roughness profile;
- Embedding of corundum particles;
- Scale-dependent material behavior.

- Poon et al. [23] reported an underestimation of vertical roughness parameters and the loss of submicron details due to the stylus tip size of the surface roughness tester. Therefore, more detail in relation to the structure's size is lost for surfaces with smaller R_z, leading to a stronger underestimation of $\tan\theta$.
- Fluctuations due to the used test method, differences in meltdown in the overlapping area and in the overlapping length due to the tolerances of the sheets, and misalignment between the sheets due to play in the specimen holders have a negative influence on the overall specimen quality.

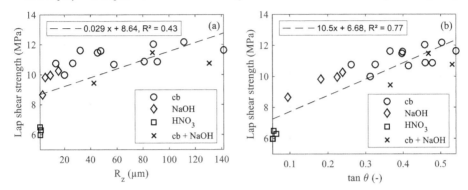

Figure 9. Lap shear strength (**a**) over R_z and (**b**) over $\tan\theta$, both with a 5 μm tip diameter.

For the hollow cylinder tests, differences in geometry can be almost excluded by turning the specimens to uniform diameters. Additionally, the surface roughness measurements will be carried out with a 2 μm stylus tip size instead of a 5 μm size for increasing the precision of the deduced roughness parameters.

3.2. Hollow Cylinder Specimens

Figure 10 shows the interlaminar shear and tensile strength obtained from the hollow cylinder tests. The laser-generated pin structure created the best adhesion by far, followed by the NiAl5 thermal spray coating and the F16 blasted surface. The lowest strength values were achieved with the combined F16 blasting and NaOH etching treatment.

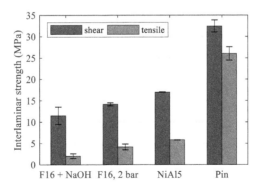

Figure 10. Interlaminar strength of hollow cylinder specimens.

The ratio τ_{max}/σ_{max} decreases homogeneously when increasing the overall strength. When looking at the corresponding roughness values in Table 8, it is obvious that R_z does not allow a prediction of the possible interlaminar strength. In example, the pin structure provides the highest interlaminar strength by far, but shows the lowest R_z value.

Table 8. Interlaminar strength and roughness parameters (2 µm tip) of hollow cylinder specimens.

Treatment	τ_{max} (MPa)	σ_{max} (MPa)	τ_{max}/σ_{max}	R_z (µm)	tanθ
F16 + NaOH	11.49	2.02	5.69	124	0.557
F16, 2 bar	14.15	4.16	3.40	131	0.590
NiAl5	17.00	5.81	2.93	80	0.616
Pin	32.46	26.04	1.25	46	0.778

However, tanθ shows much better accordance, as illustrated by Figure 11. The interlaminar shear and tensile strength increase homogeneously with tanθ, showing a huge gap between the NiAl5 coating and pin structure.

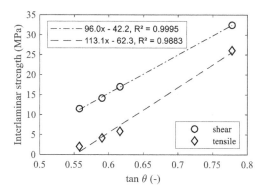

Figure 11. Shear and tensile strength over tanθ (2 µm tip diameter).

It is noteworthy that the actual tanθ of the pin structure is obviously much higher than the measured value. Assuming an average structure height of 40 µm and an average structure width of 20 µm, as shown in Figure 12d, the resulting tanθ according to Equation (5) would be approximately 4. Since the measuring line does not hit every peak and Equation (6) is applied to the resulting profile, the actual tanθ should be a bit lower, but still much higher than the measured 0.778. When comparing the measured roughness profile shown in Figure 13b with the cross-section in Figure 12d, the loss of detail due to the missing penetration of the stylus tip can clearly be seen. However, when comparing the measured profile of the F16 blasted structure in Figure 13a with the corresponding cross-section in Figure 12a, the loss of detail is far less pronounced.

When comparing the morphology of the corundum blasted surfaces in Figure 12a,b and Figure 14a,b, respectively, the indentations created by the additional etching treatment are clearly pronounced. On the other hand, there is an obvious loss of undercuts and all sharp submicron features. In particular, the loss of undercuts may cause the drastic decrease of 51% in σ_{max}, whereas τ_{max} only decreased by 19%. The NiAl5 coating illustrated in Figures 12c and 14c, respectively, shows a high amount of small splats that function as undercut features. Hence, the achieved interlaminar strength is higher than that obtained from corundum blasting treatment only. The laser treatment illustrated in Figures 12d and 14d, respectively, causes the formation of steep, pin-like structural elements arranged in a high spatial density. Undercuts are provided by molten together or crooked pins as well as submicron roughness features of the almost perpendicular pins. In consequence, a high interlaminar strength for both the tensile and the shear load is achieved.

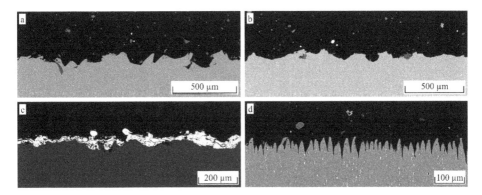

Figure 12. Representative cross-sectional images (SEM) of hollow cylinder specimens, scale normalized to image width/R_z = 1/15 (**a**) F16, 2 bar (**b**) F16, 3 bar + 5 min NaOH (**c**) NiAl5 coating and (**d**) pin structure.

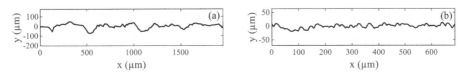

Figure 13. Roughness profiles (2 µm tip), equal axis scaling (**a**) F16, 2 bar and (**b**) pin structure.

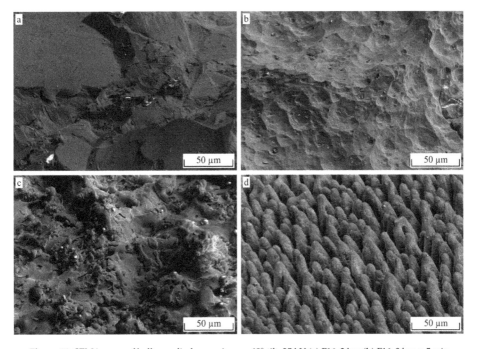

Figure 14. SEM images of hollow cylinder specimens, 60° tilt, 25 kV (**a**) F16, 2 bar (**b**) F16, 3 bar + 5 min NaOH (**c**) NiAl5 coating and (**d**) pin structure.

The fractured surfaces of the tensile as well as the shear-loaded hollow cylinder specimens are depicted in Figure 15. Dark areas indicate the residing polymer, since the images were taken using the back-scattering detector (BSD). For all the tested joints and surface pretreatment conditions, polymer residues are present at the metallic adherent. However, almost no polymer residues are present at the fractured surfaces of the blasted and subsequently etched specimens (a, e). Additionally, a higher number of coarse residues are found at the shear-loaded, just-blasted specimen (b), whereas nearly no residues are observed for the corresponding tensile load case (f). In contrast, a high number of comparably small residues are located at the fractured surface of the shear-loaded thermal spray coating (c) and likewise, significantly less residues of a once again reduced size are found for the tensile load case (g).

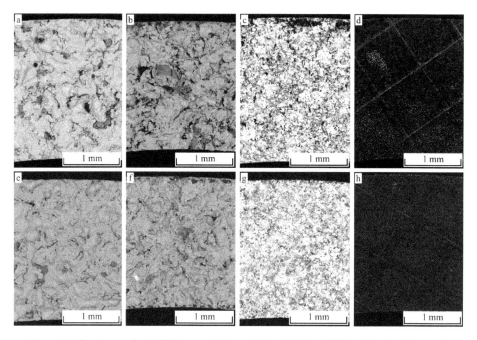

Figure 15. Fracture analysis (SEM-images back-scattering detector (BSD) contrast) of the tested hollow cylinder specimens. Shear- (**a–d**) and tensile- (**e–h**) loaded specimens are depicted for the differently structured surfaces: (**a,e**) F16, 3 bar + 5 min NaOH, (**b,f**) F16, 2 bar (**c,g**) NiAl5 coating and (**d,h**) pin structure.

Generally, an increasing content of polymer residues is observed along with an increasing joint strength and fragmentation of the treated surfaces, respectively (Figure 15a–c,e–g). Further, the difference in the number of residues in-between the shear and tensile load case is explained by the orientation of the roughness features that predominantly provide undercuts against shear rather than tensile loads.

For the tested laser pin structure, the BSD images for both load cases show that an outstandingly high amount of residing polymer is located in-between the structure. Figure 16 provides a detailed view of these fractured surfaces. For the shear (a, b) and the tensile (c, d) load case, failure takes places in the polymeric adherent. However, different types of failure, like failure above the pins oriented parallel to the surface (a) as well as clearly plastically deformed polymeric residues (b–d) can be found.

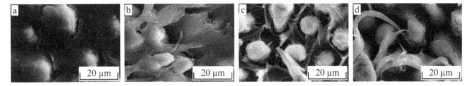

Figure 16. SEM images of the fractured surface of the pin-structured hollow cylinder specimens (**a**,**b**) shear load and (**c**,**d**) tensile load.

4. Conclusions

Based on the experimental results and analyzes performed in the present work, the following conclusions can be drawn:

- Corundum blasting creates considerable adhesion between PA6 and EN AW-6082, even with a smaller grit size and low pressure. There is no evidence that a higher blasting pressure leads to better adhesion.
- A combination of corundum blasting and alkaline etching treatment decreases the adhesion compared to corundum blasting only due to the loss of undercuts and submicron roughness features.
- A thermally-sprayed NiAl5 coating creates better adhesion than corundum blasting.
- A self-organized, laser-generated pin structure creates the highest adhesion by far due to its high spatial density of roughness features.
- The torsion and tension test using butt-bonded hollow cylinders allows for a more meaningful determination of interlaminar strength values than the lap shear test. Additionally, all load directions can be tested with one specimen geometry.
- The interlaminar strength in the shear as well as tensile direction is strongly related to the surface roughness slope $\tan\theta$.
- Roughness evaluation with a stylus profiler leads to an underestimation of $\tan\theta$ due to the missing penetration of tight roughness profile valleys as well as the loss of submicron details. This effect increases with an increasing structure density and decreasing structure size. A stylus tip size as small as possible should be used.
- There is no meaningful relation between the average maximum profile height R_z and the interlaminar strength for structure sizes within the investigated range (1.26 μm $< R_z <$ 142 μm).
- The fracture analysis of the hollow cylinder specimens reveals that the interlaminar strength is strongly related to the number of polymer residues in the surface structure. A higher interlaminar strength leads to more residues. Shear testing leads to more residues than tensile testing.

Author Contributions: Conceptualization, E.S.; data curation, E.S.; investigation, E.S., A.D., P.S., and T.L. (Thomas Lindner); methodology, E.S., P.S., and T.L. (Thomas Lindner); project administration, T.L. (Thomas Lampke); software, E.S.; Supervision, T.L. (Thomas Lindner), I.S., A.S., and T.L. (Thomas Lampke); validation, E.S.; visualization, E.S.; writing—original draft, E.S., A.D., and P.S.; writing—review and editing, E.S., A.D., P.S., T.L. (Thomas Lindner), and T.L. (Thomas Lampke).

Funding: This study was supported by the Federal Cluster of Excellence EXC 1075 "MERGE Technologies for Multifunctional Lightweight Structures". The publication costs were funded by the German Research Foundation/DFG-392676956 and the Technische Universität Chemnitz as part of the funding programme Open Access Publishing.

Acknowledgments: The support by Christoph Wollschläger, Torsten Rabes, Michael Zychski, Paul Clauß, Christian Loos, and Steffen Clauß (all from the Institute of Materials Science and Engineering) is gratefully acknowledged.

Conflicts of Interest: The authors declare no conflicts of interest.

References

1. Katayama, S.; Kawahito, Y. Laser direct joining of metal and plastic. *Scr. Mater.* **2008**, *59*, 1247–1250. [CrossRef]

2. Bergmann, J.P.; Stambke, M. Potential of Laser-manufactured Polymer-metal hybrid Joints. *Phys. Procedia* **2012**, *39*, 84–91. [CrossRef]

3. Mitschang, P.; Velthuis, R.; Didi, M. Induction Spot Welding of Metal/CFRPC Hybrid Joints. *Adv. Eng. Mater.* **2013**, *15*, 804–813. [CrossRef]

4. Wagner, G.; Balle, F.; Eifler, D. Ultrasonic Welding of Aluminum Alloys to Fiber Reinforced Polymers. *Adv. Eng. Mater.* **2013**, *15*, 792–803. [CrossRef]

5. Steinert, P.; Dittes, A.; Schimmelpfennig, R.; Scharf, I.; Lampke, T.; Schubert, A. Design of high strength polymer metal interfaces by laser microstructured surfaces. *IOP Conf. Ser. Mater. Sci. Eng.* **2018**, *373*, 012015. [CrossRef]

6. Flock, D. *Heat Conduction Bonding of Plastic-Metal Hybrid Parts*; RWTH Aachen: Aachen, Germany, 2011; pp. 81–86.

7. Haberstroh, E.; Sickert, M. Thermal Direct Joining of Hybrid Plastic Metal Components. *Kmutnb Int. J. Appl. Sci. Technol.* **2014**, *7*, 29–34. [CrossRef]

8. Ramani, K.; Moriarty, B. Thermoplastic bonding to metals via injection molding for macro-composite manufacture. *Polym. Eng. Sci.* **1998**, *38*, 870–877. [CrossRef]

9. Kleffel, T.; Drummer, D. Investigating the suitability of roughness parameters to assess the bond strength of polymer-metal hybrid structures with mechanical adhesion. *Compos. Part B Eng.* **2017**, *117*, 20–25. [CrossRef]

10. Pan, Y.; Wu, G.; Huang, Z.; Li, M.; Ji, S.; Zhang, Z. Effect of surface roughness on interlaminar peel and shear strength of CFRP/Mg laminates. *Int. J. Adhes. Adhes.* **2017**, *79*, 1–7. [CrossRef]

11. Mitschang, P.; Velthuis, R.; Emrich, S.; Kopnarski, M. Induction Heated Joining of Aluminum and Carbon Fiber Reinforced Nylon 66. *J. Compos. Mater.* **2009**, *22*, 767–801. [CrossRef]

12. Nestler, D.; Arnold, S.; Jung, H.; Wielage, B.; Kroll, L. Untersuchung geeigneter Oberflächenbehandlungsverfahren der Metallkomponente thermoplastbasierter hybrider Laminate. In *Schriftenreihe Werkstoffe und werkstofftechnische Anwendungen, Proceeding of the 17th Werkstofftechnisches Kolloquium*; Technische Universität Chemnitz: Chemnitz, Germany, November 2014; pp. 208–216.

13. Heckert, A.; Zaeh, M.F. Laser surface pre-treatment of aluminum for hybrid joints with glass fiber reinforced thermoplastics. *J. Laser Appl.* **2015**, *27*, S29005. [CrossRef]

14. Lindner, T.; Saborowski, E.; Scholze, M.; Zillmann, B.; Lampke, T. Thermal Spray Coatings as an Adhesion Promoter in Metal/FRP Joints. *Metals* **2018**, *8*, 769. [CrossRef]

15. Chen, C.Q.L.; Scott, W.; Barker, T.M. Effect of metal surface topography on mechanical bonding at simulated total hip stem–cement interfaces. *J. Biomed. Mater. Res.* **1999**, *48*, 440–446. [CrossRef]

16. Saborowski, E.; Scholze, M.; Lindner, T.; Lampke, T. A numerical and experimental comparison of test methods for the shear strength in hybrid metal/thermoplastic-compounds. *IOP Conf. Ser. Mater. Sci. Eng.* **2017**, *181*, 12031. [CrossRef]

17. Saborowski, E.; Kießling, R.; Dittes, A.; Paczkowski, G.; Ihlemann, J.; Lampke, T. Determination of the strength of polymer-metal interfaces under mixed mode loading using butt-bonded hollow cylinders. *Int. J. Adhes. Adhes.* **2019**, *89*, 30–39. [CrossRef]

18. Mahnken, R.; Schlimmer, M. Simulation of strength difference in elasto-plasticity for adhesive materials. *Int. J. Numer. Methods Eng.* **2005**, *63*, 1461–1477. [CrossRef]

19. Amada, S.; Hirose, T. Influence of grit blasting pre-treatment on the adhesion strength of plasma sprayed coatings: fractal analysis of roughness. *Surf. Coat. Technol.* **1998**, *102*, 132–137. [CrossRef]

20. Mohammadi, Z.; Ziaei-Moayyed, A.A.; Mesgar, A.S.M. Grit blasting of Ti–6Al–4V alloy. *J. Mater. Process. Technol.* **2007**, *194*, 15–23. [CrossRef]

21. Baburaj, E.; Starikov, D.; Evans, J.; Shafeev, G.; Bensaoula, A.; Shafeev, G. Enhancement of adhesive joint strength by laser surface modification. *Int. J. Adhes. Adhes.* **2007**, *27*, 268–276. [CrossRef]

22. Cassidy, J.F.; Donner, H.C. Measurement of Surface Roughness Slope. *NASA Tech Brief.* **1970**, *70*, 10722.

23. Poon, C.Y.; Bhushan, B. Comparison of surface roughness measurements by stylus profiler, AFM and non-contact optical profiler. *Wear* **1995**, *190*, 76–88. [CrossRef]

 *materials*

Article

Process-Related Changes in Polyetherimide Joined by Friction-Based Injection Clinching Joining (F-ICJ)

André B. Abibe [1], Marilia Sönego [2], Leonardo B. Canto [2], Jorge F. dos Santos [1] and Sergio T. Amancio-Filho [3,*]

[1] Helmholtz-Zentrum Geesthacht, Centre for Materials and Coastal Research, Institute of Materials Research, Materials Mechanics, Solid State Joining Process, 21502 Geesthacht, Germany; andre.abibe@gmail.com (A.B.A.); jorge.dos.santos@hzg.de (J.F.d.S.)
[2] Graduate Program in Materials Science and Engineering (PPGCEM), Federal University of São Carlos (UFSCar), São Carlos 13.565-905, SP, Brazil; mrl.sonego@gmail.com (M.S.); leonardo@ufscar.br (L.B.C.)
[3] Graz University of Technology, Institute of Materials Science, Joining and Forming, BMVIT Endowed Professorship for Aviation, 8010 Graz, Austria
* Correspondence: sergio.amancio@tugraz.at; Tel.: +43-316-8731610

Received: 2 December 2019; Accepted: 21 February 2020; Published: 25 February 2020

Abstract: This work presents a comprehensive study on the effects of the Friction-based Injection Clinching Joining (F-ICJ) process on the microstructure and local properties of the stake head. The manuscript evaluates the consequences on the quasi-static mechanical performance of hybrid joints of amorphous polyetherimide (PEI) with aluminium AA6082. Through an overlay of microhardness map on a cross-polarized transmitted-light optical microscopy (CP-TLOM) image, two lower-strength microstructural zones in the PEI stake head were observed: a plastically-deformed zone (PDZ) and a thermo-mechanically-affected zone (PTMAZ). When compared to the base material, PDZ and PTMAZ have a reduction of 12%–16% and 8%–12%, respectively, in local mechanical properties. The reduced local strength was associated with distinct volumes of loosely packed PEI chains with unsteady chain conformation and thus larger free volume in the affected regions. The mechanical strength reduction is reversible through physical aging by thermal annealing the joints, which additionally shows that process-induced thermomechanical degradation of PEI by chain scission, as evidenced by size exclusion chromatography (SEC) analysis, does not appear to affect local mechanical strength. An evaluation of typical loading regimes of staked joints in lap shear (average ultimate force of 1419 ± 43 N) and cross tensile (average ultimate force of 430 ± 44 N) testing indicates that the process-induced changes of PEI do not compromise the global mechanical performance of such a structure. These findings provide a better understanding of the relationships between processing, microstructure, and properties for further F-ICJ process optimization.

Keywords: staking; hybrid structures; microstructural change; amorphous polymer; joining

---

1. Introduction

Lightweight design has been established as one of the most successful strategies for the reduction of emissions in transport industry. By applying the right material in the right place, it is possible to obtain a multi-material structure with optimized weight and strength. This approach has driven research on several new joining methods which are potentially able to assemble these advanced polymer-metal hybrid structures.

Several staking processes have been developed in recent years. Threaded Hole Friction Spot Welding (THFSW), based on filling of the pre-threaded metallic hole by melting and re-solidifying polymer, was used to join AA5052 aluminum to short-carbon-fiber-reinforced polypropylene (PP-SCF) composite [1]. The increase of the polymeric melted surface was due to higher rotational speeds, and therefore, the growth of loading bearing area resulted in higher strength and fracture energy of the joints. Another technique, named friction filling staking joining (FFSJ), was used to join aluminum and polypropylene sheets by filling a metallic hole with polymer to create a local stake [2]. The joining mechanism of FFSJ involves the mechanical interlocking of the formed stake and the partial adhesion of polymer-metal and polymer-polymer interfaces. FFSJ lap shear joints achieved maximum tensile shear strength of 13 MPa, which is comparable to state-of-art staking performance. Hahn and Finkeldey [3] used ultrasonic riveting and hot-air-sticking to join fiber-reinforced thermoplastics to steel. They proved that hot-air-sticking preserved the fibers better than ultrasonic riveting, resulting in a load-bearing performance 50%–90% higher.

However, the application of new technologies in demanding industries such as aircraft and automotive requires a deep comprehension of several aspects of the joints. Manufacturing processes often causes alterations to the microstructure of materials, which in turn affects the final properties and performance of the joint. Therefore, not only the mechanical performance and damage tolerance are important investigation subjects, but also the effects of the process on local material properties. This understanding is essential for clarifying the influence of the process on joint properties to target joint efficiency.

Although much of the research in this topic has been performed with metallic materials, there is interest on the behavior of polymer and polymer composites affected by various joining processes. Simões and Rodrigues [4] used transmitted-light optical microscopy (TLOM) on thin samples of polymethymethacrylate (PMMA) friction-stir-welded (FSW) joints to identify its microstructural zones. TLOM with crossed polarizers (CP-TLOM) has been used to analyze residual stresses through photoelasticity in joints with transparent polymers. With CP-TLOM, Kiss and Czigány [5] observed a heat-affected zone (HAZ) defined by molecular orientation and residual stresses in FSW joints of poly-ethylene-terephtalate-glycol (PETG). In a similar manner, Krishnan et al. [6] analyzed the flow-induced residual fields in polycarbonate (PC) welded by ultrasonic, hot plate, and vibration welding. These examples are not only useful for the prediction of the joint's behavior in service, but also to improve process development of new technologies.

The effect of these microstructural changes on local properties of the joined materials can be further investigated by indentation testing (microhardness) [2] and physical–chemical analyses. Indentation testing has been proven as a powerful method to identify structural changes in polymers [7]. The measured strength can be related to internal packing of polymeric chains (i.e., free volume) [8,9], whereas features of the indentations indicate inelastic and elastic contributions of deformation [7,10,11]. A number of analytical methods such as differential scanning calorimetry (DSC) [12,13], thermogravimetry (TGA) [14], and size exclusion chromatography (SEC) [15,16] have been used to identify physical–chemical changes in microstructural zones of joined materials. These combined analyses provide useful insights of the relationships between process control, microstructural changes, and local properties within the joint area.

This work describes the process-related changes observed in an amorphous engineering thermoplastic (polyetherimide; PEI) when joined to a metal (aluminum AA6082) by a friction-based staking process (F-ICJ [17]). The nature of the process-related changes is investigated by microstructural analyses, local mechanical properties, and physical–chemical properties of the polymer stake head. It is showed that PEI joined by F-ICJ presents a plastically deformed zone (PDZ) and a thermo-mechanically-affected zone (PTMAZ) of lower mechanical strength due to more loosely packed chains that increases the free volume in these regions. Although polymeric thermomechanical degradation takes place at some processing conditions, it does not seem to affect the mechanical properties of the joints as the local mechanical properties could be enhanced by annealing.

2. Friction-Based Injection Clinching Joining (F-ICJ)

Friction-based Injection Clinching Joining (F-ICJ) has been recently explored as an alternative advanced staking process for new lightweight structures by Abibe et al. [17–19]. Typical staked structures use joints in the most common configurations of rosette, dome, or hollow stakes (Figure 1a) [20]. They provide a reliable process for simply attaching dissimilar materials. The strength of these joints comes from the large stake head, which can be a limitation in exterior or lightweight applications.

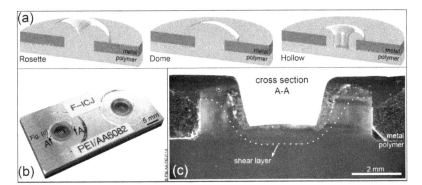

Figure 1. (**a**) Conventional stake designs for metal-polymer structures; (**b**) surface view of an F-ICJ structure; (**c**) cross-sectional view of an F-ICJ stake. Adapted from [19].

F-ICJ polymer stake heads are flush to the surface of the metal part (Figure 1b). A thermomechanical process induces polymer flow within a shear layer to form the stake. The mechanical strength of an F-ICJ joint comes from anchoring of the stake in cavities inside of the through hole, made possible by the material flow in the shear layer (Figure 1c). This feature allows F-ICJ stakes to be smaller, lighter, and more aesthetically flexible than standard staking processes [17].

The basic process steps for the F-ICJ welding technique are shown in Figure 2. The thermoplastic and other joining components are pre-assembled (preferably on a backing plate) and aligned with the moving axis of the non-consumable tool (Figure 2a). After this positioning step, the rotating tool moves towards the thermoplastic stud (Figure 2b). The contact between the rotating tool and the stud generates frictional heat at their interface, gradually softening or melting the polymer, and allowing the tool to penetrate further into the stud (Figure 2c). The friction heats and deforms the thermoplastic stud, causing softening (or melting) and flow. Next, tool rotation stops and axial pressure acts further upon the molten polymer, pushing it into the cavities and shaping the final stake geometry (Figure 2d). The tool remains in this position until the thermoplastic is cooled (Figure 2e). The tool retreats and the F-ICJ joint is created.

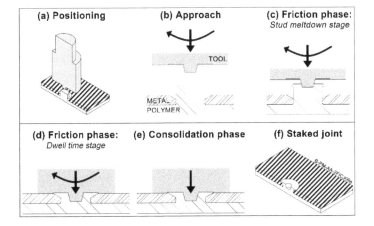

Figure 2. (**a–f**) Steps of the Friction-based Injection Clinching Joining (F-ICJ) process. Adapted from [18].

The fundamentals of the F-ICJ process have been described in [18,19]. Joints are formed by providing frictional heat to a polymeric stud, which flows within a shear layer around the tool to create a stake. The stake is cooled down under pressure, avoiding large dimensional recovery. A stop-action procedure with monitoring of polymer temperature and process-related signals provide insight in the joint formation mechanisms. Material flow within the shear layer is fundamental for efficient filling of the cavities by the molten polymer, while also eliminating volumetric flaws. The preliminary investigation on the mechanical behavior identified the main failure mechanisms of joints in lap-shear and cross-tensile configurations. The benchmark study showed that F-ICJ is comparable to state-of-the-art ultrasonic staking in terms of mechanical properties, but needs improvement in cycle time.

3. Materials and Methods

Polymer parts with a stud were machined from 6.35 mm thick extruded polyetherimide plates (PEI, grade Duratron U1000 PEI, Quadrant Plastics, Lenzburg, Switzerland), as showed schematically in Figure 3a. The stud base has a radius of 0.3 mm to decrease stress concentration in this region. Through holes with a chamfer cavity were machined in 2 mm thick aluminum 6082-T6 plates (AA6082, Aalco Metals Ltd, Halesowen, UK), which fit the stud of the PEI part (Figure 3b). Although other specimen manufacturing methods can result in better final properties [21–23], conventional machining is still the most common technique adopted, which were selected here to simulate real conditions. A non-consumable tool of stainless steel 316L depicted in Figure 2c was used for the F-ICJ process.

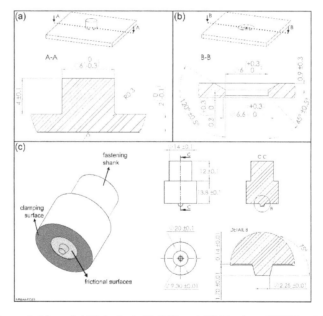

Figure 3. Base materials used. (**a**) Polyetherimide (PEI) part. (**b**) Aluminum 6082-T6 part; (**c**) F-ICJ tool made of stainless steel 316L.

The pre-assembled parts were joined by F-ICJ using an automated gantry system (model RNA, H.Loitz-Robotik, Hamburg, Germany) equipped with a high-speed friction welding machine (model RSM410, Harms + Wende, Hamburg, Germany). The system operates with rotational speeds ranging from 6000 to 21,000 rpm and axial forces of up to 24 kN. A torque sensor (model 9049, Kistler, Winterthur, Switzerland) was used to obtain the materials' torque response. The unified system allows signal monitoring from rotational speed, axial force, spindle displacement, and torque. The specimens were cleaned with pressurized air (PEI) and acetone (AA6082) prior to joining. They were clamped in a standard sample holder to avoid slippage during joining.

Microstructural analysis of PEI was carried out with a Leica DM IRM optical microscope (Leica Microsystems, Wetzlar, Germany). Reflected light optical microscopy (RLOM) and transmitted light optical microscopy (TLOM) were used for general microstructural and material flow observation. Samples were prepared by cutting the specimens 1 mm from their center and embedding them in low-temperature epoxy resin. Embedded samples were ground and polished for RLOM analyses according to the standard materiallographic procedure. For TLOM analyses, thin sections of 1 mm thickness were cut from embedded samples and subsequently had both sides polished.

Qualitative evaluation of residual stresses in the PEI part after joining was performed using transmitted optical microscopy with crossed polarizers (CP-TLOM) on 1 mm thick section samples. The light source was a standard microscope filament lamp producing a continuous white light spectrum. The observed image produces a colored fringe pattern, in which each isochromatic corresponds to a local stress level caused by F-ICJ. A grayscale image of this pattern can qualitatively indicate the stress levels. In this study, the zero-order fringes were identified in color images as the non-stressed regions, then the grayscale images were used to interpret the local stresses and its dependence on the F-ICJ process parameters. Typical colored and grayscale fringe patterns and zero-order fringe identification of the PEI base material are showed in Figure 4.

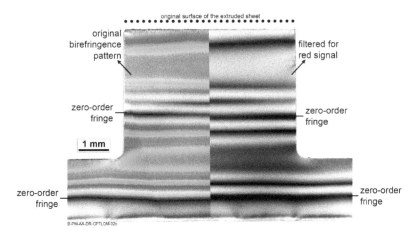

Figure 4. Transmitted-light optical microscopy with crossed polarizers (CP-TLOM) of the PEI base material. Left-hand image is the original output; right-hand image is filtered for red signal only. Adapted from [19].

Local mechanical properties of PEI were measured on embedded and polished cross sections of joints. Zwick ZHV (Zwick Roell, Ulm, Germany) equipment was used with an indentation load of 0.495 N over 15 s, and distance between indentations of 200 μm. The testing procedures are based on the ASTM E384 [24].

Changes in molecular weight distribution (MWD) of PEI were evaluated by size exclusion chromatography (SEC) with a HT-GPC equipment (Viscotek, Berkshire, UK) using HT-806 M columns coupled to a refractive index detector. Samples of PEI were removed with a scalpel from the PTMAZ of each specimen, and dissolved in trichlorobenzene (TCB) in a heated bath at 150 °C for 10 min at concentration of 2 mg L^{-1}. The analyses were performed using 200 μL of PEI/TCB solution at 150 °C and flow rate of 1 mL min^{-1}. The calibration curve was built using monodisperse polystyrene standards with molecular weights between 845 and 1,900,000 g mol^{-1}.

The energy input provided by each set of F-ICJ process parameters was calculated to establish a correlation with physical–chemical changes in the PEI. Mechanical work is commonly used to estimate energy input in friction welding processes [25,26]. Equation (1)) calculates mechanical work as the energy input E_{work} for the F-ICJ process. The frictional contribution E_f can be described by the product of the average angular velocity $\bar{\omega}$ and the integral of the torque M over the frictional time FT. The deformational contribution E_d is calculated by the product of the frictional force FF and the integral of the tool displacement rate v over FT.

$$E_{work} = E_f + E_d = \bar{\omega} \int_{t_0}^{FT} M \, dt + FF \int_{t_0}^{FT} v \, dt = M_{total}\bar{\omega} + FF \, \Delta x \; [J] \tag{1}$$

Both constants FF and $\bar{\omega}$ are calculated from the experimental curves. The tool displacement Δx is the result of the integral of the tool displacement rate v over time. Within the parameter sets used in this work, the deformational component $FF \, \Delta x$ contributed with a maximum of 10 J to energy input, amounting to less than 1% of total energy input. For simplification, only the rotational component $M_{total}\bar{\omega}$ was used in this work. The total torque M_{total} is experimentally obtained from the torque curves of the friction phase (stud meltdown and dwell time stages).

4. Results and Discussion

4.1. Overview of the Microstructure of the Polymeric Stud

A typical F-ICJ joint results from the effect of heating and deformation imposed by rotational and axial movement of the tool in contact with the polymeric stud. Its microstructure is highly influenced by heat input, which in turn depends on the tool geometry and process parameters. The cross-section of such a PEI-aluminum F-ICJ joint is shown in Figure 5, with details of its microstructural zones and joint features. This joint was produced with the set of parameters shown in Table 1.

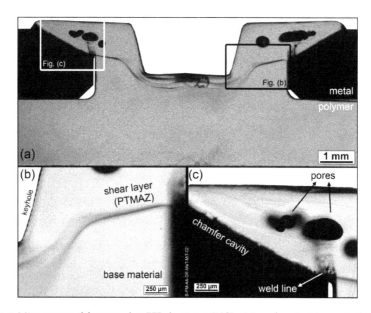

Figure 5. Microstructural features of an PEI-aluminum F-ICJ joint produced with a conical-pin tool and chamfer cavities. (**a**) Overview of joint cross-section; (**b**) polymer-polymer interface. (**c**) pores and remnant weld lines in the polymer thermo-mechanically-affected zone (PTMAZ; TLOM images). For processing conditions see Table 1. Adapted from [19].

Table 1. Parameters set used for Friction-based Injection Clinching Joining (F-ICJ) joint production. E_{work}= 1415 ± 7 J.

Phase	Duration [ms]	Rotational Speed [rpm]	Axial Force [N]
Stud meltdown	765	7472	2551
Dwell time	1812	7018	2551
Consolidation	5000	0	5363

The use of transmitted-light optical microscopy (TLOM) through a thin section of an F-ICJ joint makes it possible to observe the microstructural features and discontinuities in the polymer. A dark line across the diameter of the stake shaft delineates a polymer-polymer interface (Figure 5b). The volume above this interface interacted with the frictional surfaces of the conical-pin tool, and was heated and deformed by its rotation and axial force. This interface is the border of the shear layer displayed in Figure 1c. This is a polymer thermo-mechanically-affected zone (PTMAZ), which is characterized by material flow and the presence of volumetric discontinuities such as pores and remnant weld lines (Figure 5c).

To better visualize the microstructural zones and understand their local properties, further characterization methods were performed. The right-hand side of Figure 6 presents a micrograph of the joint from Figure 5 by transmitted-light optical microscopy with crossed polarizers (CP-TLOM) that displays birefringence patterns. To complement the analysis and help to understand possible changes in the local mechanical properties of the polymer, a microhardness map of the joint produced with the same joining condition is overlaid on the left-hand side of Figure 6. The coupled analysis reveals three microstructural zones with different local mechanical properties: a polymer thermo-mechanically-affected zone (PTMAZ), a plastically deformed zone (PDZ), and unaffected base material (BM). At this resolution of the microhardness map (200 µm between indentations), no sharp transition zone between the PTMAZ and the BM can be identified that would otherwise characterize an extensive polymer heat-affected zone (PHAZ).

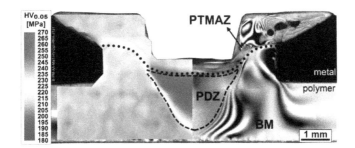

Figure 6. Overlay of a microhardness map (left) on a CP-TLOM micrograph of the PEI-aluminum F-ICJ joint from Figure 5. Dotted lines are the boundaries of the polymer thermo-mechanically-affected zone (PTMAZ); dashed lines are the boundaries of the plastically deformed zone (PDZ). Base material (BM) was labeled for the unaffected PEI region. For processing conditions see Table 1. Adapted from [19].

4.2. Microstructural Zones and Interfaces at the Polymeric Stud

4.2.1. Plastically Deformed Zone (PDZ) and Base Material (BM)

Beneath the shear layer boundary of the PTMAZ (dotted line in Figure 6), two zones can be identified. The highest-strength volume BM has base material properties and is not affected by the process. The lowest-strength PDZ (boundaries marked by a dashed line in Figure 6) is directly below the conical pin's line of action, and has 12%–16% less local strength compared to the base material. This region displays no signals of material flow as seen in the PTMAZ, indicating that the temperature of this volume is not significantly altered by the rotating action of the tool, so that this volume remains in a glassy state during processing. A well-formed PDZ is only observed for F-ICJ processing conditions where the axial joining force is notably high (above 2400 N) [19], creating stresses above the yielding point of the solid polymer; therefore it follows that the PDZ is plastically deformed by compression.

PEI undergoes strain softening under compression in the 7%–13% strain range [27], as shown schematically in Figure 7a. Strain softening in polymer glasses is related to the difference in conditions (energy or stresses) required to initiate yielding and to propagate it [28]. In the case of the polymer in the PDZ, its mechanical history owing to F-ICJ can be schematically represented by the solid stress-strain curve in Figure 7b. The polymer in the PDZ is stressed up to a point in the strain softening region, and after removal of load a residual plastic strain $\varepsilon_{plastic}$ is present. When reloading a previously yielded amorphous polymer during the microhardness test (dotted curve in Figure 7b), a new lower yielding stress is reached (σ_{y-PDZ}), because the necessary conditions for initiation of yielding were previously achieved (σ_{y-BM}). A peak of yielding stress is usually still present, due to a certain level of physical aging (hardening as a result of the reduction of free volume at temperatures close to but below the glass-transition (T_g)) during cooling or at room temperature. Plastic deformation by yielding is described as conformational changes of the chains, leading to increased free volume in amorphous polymers [28–31], which is detected as reduced hardness in indentation testing [8,9].

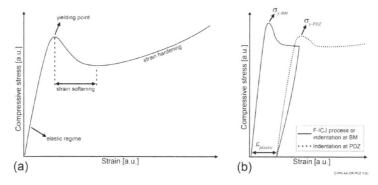

Figure 7. (**a**) Behavior of PEI under uniaxial compression (based on [27,32]). (**b**) Yielding of PEI up to strain softening (solid curve), and reloading the yielded PEI during microhardness (dotted curve). Adapted from [19].

Identification of the shape and limits of the PDZ can be additionally supported by the birefringence pattern with crossed polarizers. Birefringence patterns are associated with the residual stresses in a material through the stress-optic law (Equation (2) [33]).

$$\sigma_{res} = (\sigma_1 - \sigma_2) = (n_1 - n_2)\, C_{opt} = \frac{\delta}{y} C_{opt}\ [MPa] \tag{2}$$

where σ_{res} is the residual stress, $(\sigma_1 - \sigma_2)$ is the difference in normal stresses in the specimen, $(n_1 - n_2)$ is the birefringence, C_{opt} is the stress-optical coefficient of the material, δ is the retardation of light in the specimen, and y is the specimen thickness. Photoelasticity [34] can be used to quantify stresses in birefringence patterns by defining these parameters. However, a quantitative measurement of residual stresses through the photoelastic effect requires adequate equipment and complex analyses [35,36], which were not within the scope of this work. Such analyses can be performed more commonly using a color image and obtaining the intensity of the red–green–blue signals, or by using a Michel–Levy chart. These methods assist in the definition of the number of fringes in a certain region, which are a measurement of the retardation δ [37]. In this work a grayscale image filtered from the red signal was used to qualitatively estimate the number of fringes in a given region of the polymer joint.

An increasing number of fringes (larger retardation δ) can be associated with an increasing level of residual stresses (see Equation (2)) [33].

Figure 8a is one half of the cross-section previously presented in Figure 6; the transition region between the PDZ and BM zones is highlighted with a black rectangle. This highlighted region is shown in greater detail in Figure 8b. In this image, a first-order fringe is on the right-hand side, and increasing orders of isochromatic fringes can be observed towards the PDZ on the left of the figure. The brighter, well-defined fringes in the base material region are low-order fringes, indicating lower stresses, while the lighter shades in the PDZ are high-order fringes, associated with high residual stresses [35,38]. The high-order fringes correspond to higher retardation (δ) values, which indicate higher residual stresses, as described in Equation (2). Therefore, yielding in the PDZ creates a highly-stressed volume, whereas away from the PDZ and into the BM the fringe orders are of the same level as observed in the as-received material (Figure 4) where no significant residual stresses are present.

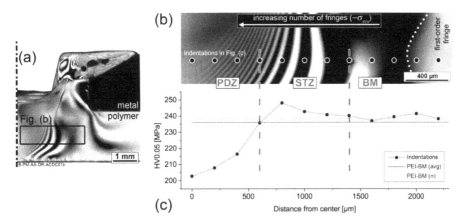

Figure 8. (**a**) Half of a cross-sectional view of a PEI-aluminum F-ICJ joint featuring a PDZ. (**b**) Birefringence of the PDZ-BM transition highlighted in (**a**), with number of fringes ($-\sigma_{res}$) increasing in the PDZ direction (CP-TLOM). (**c**) Indentation profile highlighted in (**b**), showing the formation of a strengthened transition zone (STZ) between the PDZ and BM. The gray horizontal lines in (**c**) correspond to the PEI base material's hardness. For processing conditions see Table 1. Adapted from [19].

It can be also observed in Figure 8c that local mechanical strength—represented by microhardness values—is decreased at the PDZ. The black dots in Figure 8b represent the position of the indentations of the profile shown in Figure 8c, covering the transition between PDZ and BM. The horizontal gray lines in Figure 8c indicate the as-received hardness of PEI and its standard deviation, and the black disks are the indentation measurements of the profile. It is possible to see that a strengthened transition zone (STZ) was detected between the BM and PDZ. It is known that compressive stresses increase hardness values [10,11], whereas plastic deformation decrease them [7,8]. Therefore, there are two competing effects taking place in the STZ. The combined analysis demonstrates that in the PDZ and STZ significant compressive residual stresses ($-\sigma_{res}$) are present, but in the PDZ the effect of free volume increasing because of yielding dominates and hardness is lower, whereas in the STZ no yielding is present and the $-\sigma_{res}$ increases hardness. In the BM, none of these effects play a role and the hardness values are in the range of the as-received material.

4.2.2. Polymer Thermo-Mechanically-Affected Zone (PTMAZ)

Following the polymer–polymer interface line in Figure 5b, the volume previously described as the PTMAZ presents 8%–12% lower strength (as shown in the hardness map of Figure 6) than the base material. The PTMAZ corresponds to the shear layer described in Figure 1c. This is a polymer volume that is affected by frictional heat and shear stresses, and changes in local properties are related to the thermomechanical processing and its subsequent thermal history in service. Unlike the PDZ, no effects of yielding below T_g are seen, because this volume is above the T_g of polymer during processing. Competing phenomena may act in this volume to change its microhardness: topological changes affecting internal order, and molecular weight changes [7]. Conformational chain changes that alter entanglement density occur from quenching (increasing free volume) or physical aging (reducing free volume). Lower hardness in this case indicates larger free volume [8,9,39]. Reduction of molecular weight by chain scission tends to reduce microhardness, because a larger fraction of chains with low molecular weight represent more chain ends and degradation products [40]. By contrast, thermally-induced crosslinking increases local strength as a result of a rigid network with lower free volume [7]. A combination of entanglement density and molecular weight reduction is probably associated with microhardness reduction in the PTMAZ.

Chain entanglement density in PEI at the stake head of F-ICJ joints is related to the available energy for chain diffusion at the end of the friction phase. During the friction phase, the PTMAZ reaches temperatures (up to 385 °C) far above the T_g of PEI (215 °C), and it cools down rapidly ($\approx$35 °C·s^{-1}) during consolidation [19]. At the end of the consolidation phase the polymer is well below T_g in a glassy state [33]; this does not allow the chains to achieve a densely packed conformation, and therefore reduces the local strength compared to the as-received polymer [9,32]. This indicates that the cooling regime in the PTMAZ is probably faster than for the manufacturing process of the as-received material. The extruded thick PEI sheets either use slow cooling after exiting the die, or are annealed after extrusion to achieve a relaxed chain conformation [41]. Either way the industrial process allows the polymer chains to achieve a more packed chain conformation than the as-joined PTMAZ. The local mechanical properties of PTMAZ are also lower than its base material due to physical–chemical effects in FFSJ joints [2].

4.3. Physical–Chemical Changes in the Microstructural Zones of F-ICJ Joints

To investigate if a certain level of degradation is present, physical–chemical properties related to chain length were studied. The hypothesis of PEI degradation caused by F-ICJ stated in the previous sections is proven in Figure 9 with measurements of molecular weight distribution (MWD) through SEC. The MWD for the base material is shown along with the MWD from the PTMAZ of joints with different levels of energy input E_{work}. A trend of lowering the average molecular weight (M_n and M_w) and increasing of the polydispersity (M_w/M_n) towards higher energy input levels can be observed. This trend is an indication that the temperature and shear rate imposed by the F-ICJ process are high enough to cause thermomechanical degradation of PEI through chain scission [42]. Previous work by Sônego [42] showed that breakage of the imide and ether bonds cause multiple non-random chain scission, resulting in a considerable increase in the fraction of low-molecular-weight chains.

In the previous discussion, it has been shown that microstructural changes in PEI joined by F-ICJ decrease local strength in the PTMAZ and PDZ (Figure 6) and created residual stress gradients around the PDZ (Figure 8). To verify the assumption of increased free volume in the PDZ, and whether changes to the molecular weight also affect the local strength in the PTMAZ, a replicate of the high-energy-input joint from Figure 9 was subsequently annealed for 24 h at 200 °C (Tg—15 °C). The time and temperature of annealing were based on the maximized physical aging of PEI as reported by Belana et al. [43]. Annealing of amorphous polymers promotes accelerated physical aging. Through this annealing procedure the majority of free-volume effects on mechanical strength is removed [29,39], therefore making the effects of lower molecular weight on PEI joined by F-ICJ visible.

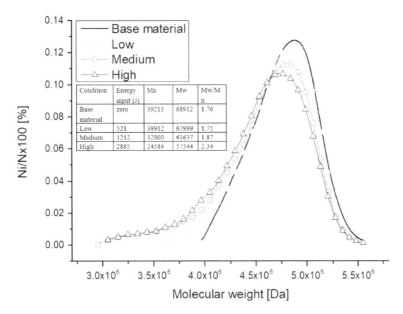

Figure 9. Molecular weight distribution curves of base material and PEI from F-ICJ joints at three levels of energy input: low (E_{work} = 521 J), medium (E_{work} = 1212 J), and high (E_{work} = 2885 J) energy inputs. Adapted from [42].

A cross-section of the joint showing the indentation positions prior to and after thermal aging are showed in Figure 10a. Five vertical profiles were executed before aging (black lines); and after aging five further profiles (blue lines) were indented between the previous ones. Local mechanical strength distribution is showed for the as-joined joint in Figure 10b and for the aged joint in Figure 10c.

The microhardness distribution for the as-joined PEI shows clear boundaries for the typical low-strength PTMAZ and PDZ of an F-ICJ joint. After annealing no microstructural zones can be distinguished. A region of lower strength is observed below the keyhole, corresponding to non-process-related cracks which develop during annealing (Figure 10d). Average measured microhardness was 235.0 ± 6.2 MPa across the annealed joint. The homogeneity of local mechanical properties over the joint indicates that any differences between the base material and PTMAZ or PDZ in the as-joined specimen were due to an unsteady chain conformation with increased free volume. Although thermomechanical degradation was present at the PTMAZ of this joint (high energy input, Figure 9), no noticeable difference in local strength can be measured after accelerated physical aging. Therefore, thermal annealing after F-ICJ process can enhance the local mechanical properties of joints, similar to ball-burnishing in the friction stir welding process [44,45].

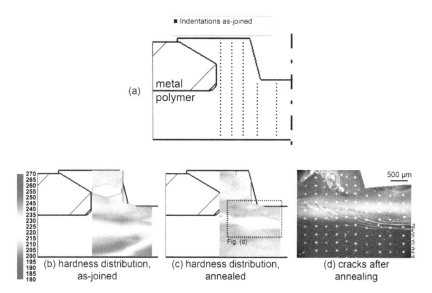

Figure 10. (a) Indentation positions for the annealing study; microhardness distribution maps from (b) as-joined and (c) annealed high-energy-input F-ICJ joint (E_{work} = 2339 J). (d) Cracks in the polymer after annealing.

4.4. Effect of the PTMAZ on the Joint Mechanical Behavior

It is of interest to correlate significant microstructural changes in a joint with the expected mechanical behavior of the structure in service. The mechanical behavior of staked joints is commonly tested through lap-shear and cross-tensile configurations. These tests simulate typical stresses in rivet-like assemblies.

Lap shear tests are carried out in overlap specimens as depicted in Figure 11a. The lap shear joints had an average ultimate force of 1419 ± 43 N. In a metal-polymer configuration, the metallic part transfers the load to the stake shaft, practically shearing it from the polymer base plate. The distinct stiffness of the materials creates a secondary bending moment during this test, which generates the forces acting as drawn in Figure 11b. The secondary bending forces the rotation of the stake head as represented by the torque M. As a result, from M and F, the metal plate transfers load to the polymer in the form of F_M and F_F. These forces, along with the reaction forces of the polymer part F_{N1} and F_{N2}, create the stress field showed in Figure 11b, as seen by FEM simulation of F-ICJ PEI/AA6082-T6 joints. Compressive stresses are present on the stake shaft, while high-magnitude tensile stresses arise on the stake base. Lower-magnitude tensile stresses are present on the stake head at the opposite side, as a result from the secondary bending effect. The high tensile stresses on the stake base lead to a failure of the base plate as showed in Figure 11c. A detailed description of the failure mode was described in [19]. Summarizing, the load is supported at the marked regions both by the stake head (red circle) and the stake base (blue circle). The stake head contributes to diminish the secondary bending effect. As the secondary bending intensifies, the stake head stops supporting the load, and a main crack at the stake base grows rapidly leading to a catastrophic failure.

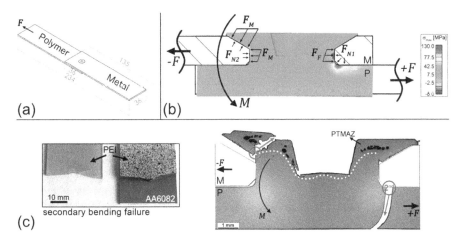

Figure 11. (**a**) Specimen and forces configuration for lap shear tests. (**b**) Stress concentration regions in an F-ICJ joint during lap shear tests. (**c**) Typical failure mode of F-ICJ lap shear specimens.

A correlation can be established with the as-joined microstructure of an F-ICJ joint. At the stake base, where the final crack grows, there were no microstructural changes due to the joining process. This region's resistance to failure can mainly be improved by geometrical design. On the other hand, the stake head region is the PTMAZ, with lower local mechanical strength. The stake head crack grows through this volume, and the crack growth is influenced by its properties and features. For instance, extreme levels of thermal–mechanical degradation may reduce PTMAZ strength to a point where the crack growth is facilitated. The presence of pores (Figure 5c) allows for a shorter crack growth path, accelerating the failure. Therefore, optimizing the microstructure and properties of the PTMAZ can increase the reliability of staked structures by halting the initial failure mechanisms.

Cross-tensile tests use an overlap specimen as shown schematically in Figure 12a. The joints had an average ultimate force of 430 ± 44 N in this test configuration. The metal plate is fixed, while the polymer plate is pulled away. This induces a tensile stress on the stake. Figure 12b shows the stress concentrations through FEM for a PEI-aluminum joint during cross tensile testing. Pulling down the polymeric plate creates a bending moment on the plate, which results in tensile stresses at the stake base. No significant stresses were observed at the stake head itself, showing that the PTMAZ is not bearing loads in such a configuration. Such a stress distribution leads most frequently to a failure by base-plate bending, where cracks nucleate at the stake base and grow rapidly towards the base plate's lower surface (Figure 12c). The stake head is not damaged in such a failure mode. Differently from fastener staking [46], THFSW [1], and FFSJ [2] joints, the joining mechanism of F-ICJ does not depend on polymer-metal adhesion, as it relies mostly on the mechanical interlocking of the components.

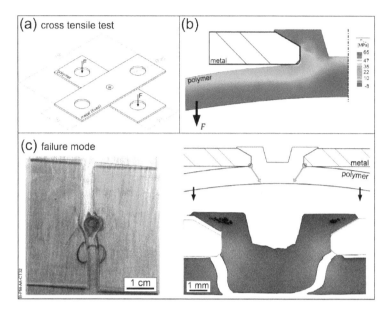

Figure 12. (**a**) Specimen and test configuration for cross tensile testing. (**b**) Stress concentration regions in an F-ICJ joint during cross tensile testing. (**c**) Main failure mode of F-ICJ cross tensile specimens.

Typically, the lower strength and degradation of the PTMAZ will not influence the reliability of assemblies suffering loads as from cross tensile test. The base plate bending failure is a function of the base material's properties and mechanical design of the polymeric part. However, in some cases foreign particles in the PTMAZ have been shown to nucleate cracks at the stake head during cross tensile tests [19]. The growth of these cracks is facilitated by the presence of pores, whose relative volume in the stake head increases with increasing energy input [19]. Therefore, it is generally advantageous to optimize the process using reduced energy input and a clean production. As shown in Figures 10 and 11, the main crack in F-ICJ joints propagates through the polymeric base plate. Such behavior was also found in FFSJ joints [2]. Although the stud base was machined with a radius of 0.3 mm to avoid stress concentration, other geometries may have a better effect on the joint failure mode and should be investigated in the future.

5. Conclusions

- The joining of polyetherimide (PEI) amorphous engineering thermoplastic to aluminum alloy through the new F-ICJ staking joining process was presented. A comprehensive study on the effects of processing on the microstructure and local properties was carried out through light optical microscopy, microhardness testing, and size exclusion chromatography techniques.
- An analysis through qualitative transmitted-light optical microscopy combined with quantitative microhardness testing allowed to identify and clearly delimitate two microstructural zones in the stake head of PEI: a thermo-mechanically-affected zone (PTMAZ) and a plastically-deformed zone (PDZ).
- The PTMAZ, a polymer layer below the keyhole that was molten and sheared by the action the stirring tool at temperatures up to 385 °C well above the T_g of PEI (215 °C), and quickly cooled ($\approx$35 °C s^{-1}) afterwards, presented an 8%–12% reduction in the microhardness values compared to the base material (BM), as well as a few volumetric defects. This zone was characterized by a distinct birefringence pattern, as revealed by cross-polarized transmitted-light optical microscopy (CP-TLOM) analysis, resulting from thermomechanically-induced residual stresses.

Furthermore, thermomechanical degradation of PEI by chain scission was identified through size exclusion chromatography (SEC) analysis.

- The PDZ, a polymer volume beneath the PTMAZ boundary that underwent strain softening as a consequence of developed compressive stresses resulting from F-ICJ, showed a 12%–16% reduction in the microhardness values and a different birefringence pattern. The boundary between the PDZ and the base material (BM) was characterized by the difference in the number of fringes presented in the CP-TLOM image.

- A post-joining annealing treatment eliminated residual stresses in the PTMAZ and PDZ, as a consequence of physical ageing of PEI. This helped to identify the nature of the above-mentioned microstructural local changes as distinct volumes of loosely packed PEI chains with unsteady chain conformation and thus larger free volume, which in turn reduced microhardness values. Although thermomechanical degradation of PEI on the staked head was evidenced by SEC, it seems not to contribute to the reduction in joint global mechanical strength.

- The consequences of the microstructural changes and thermal degradation of PEI on the global mechanical properties of staked joints were evaluated in terms of typical mechanical loading in lap shear (average ultimate force of 1419 ± 43 N) and cross tensile (average ultimate force of 430 ± 44 N) testing. Neither of the loading situations rely largely on the PDZ and PTMAZ, therefore the process-induced local strength reduction and PEI degradation by chain scission in the stake head do not compromise global mechanical properties of staked PEI-aluminum joints.

These findings extend the understanding of the relationships between processing, microstructure, and properties, as well as provide the basis for further F-ICJ process optimization.

Author Contributions: A.B.A. and M.S. designed and performed the experiments and analyzed all collected data; L.B.C. and J.F.d.S. contributed with discussions on the experimental results; S.T.A.-F. determined the structure of the manuscript; all authors contributed to the preparation and revision of the manuscript. All authors have read and agreed to the published version of the manuscript.

Funding: This research was funded by the Helmholtz Association, Germany (Grant No. VH-NG-626), FAPESP (Brazil; grant number 2013/26293-4), CNPq (Brazil; process number 304169/2014-5), and the Austrian aviation program TAKE OFF, and BMVIT-Austrian Ministry for Transport, Innovation and Technology. This study was financed in part by the Coordenação de Aperfeiçoamento de Pessoal de Nível Superior—Brasil (CAPES)—Finance Code 001.

Acknowledgments: The authors would like to thank Eduardo Tschoepke for the FEM analyses.

Conflicts of Interest: The authors declare no conflict of interest.

References

1. Karami Pabandi, H.; Movahedi, M.; Kokabi, A.H. A new refill friction spot welding process for aluminum/polymer composite hybrid structures. *Compos. Struct.* **2017**, *174*, 59–69. [CrossRef]
2. Huang, Y.; Meng, X.; Xie, Y.; Li, J.; Wan, L. New technique of friction-based filling stacking joining for metal and polymer. *Compos. Part B Eng.* **2019**, *163*, 217–223. [CrossRef]
3. Hahn, O.; Finkeldey, C. Ultrasonic Riveting and Hot-Air-Sticking of Fiber-Reinforced Thermoplastics. *J. Thermoplast. Compos. Mater.* **2003**, *16*, 521–528. [CrossRef]
4. Simões, F.; Rodrigues, D.M. Material flow and thermo-mechanical conditions during Friction Stir Welding of polymers: Literature review, experimental results and empirical analysis. *Mater. Des.* **2014**, *59*, 344–351. [CrossRef]
5. Kiss, Z.; Czigány, T. Effect of welding parameters on the heat affected zone and the mechanical properties of friction stir welded poly(ethylene-terephthalate-glycol). *J. Appl. Polym. Sci.* **2012**, *125*, 2231–2238. [CrossRef]
6. Krishnan, C.; Toussant, D.; Benatar, A. Comparison of weld morphology of polycarbonate and polypropylene for hot plate, vibration and ultrasonic welding. In *SPE ANTEC 2004*; Proceedings of the Technical Conference & Exhibition (ANTEC 2004); Society of Plastics Engineers: Chicago, IL, USA, 2004; Volume 1, pp. 1241–1245.
7. BaltáCalleja, F.J.; Fakirov, S. *Microhardness of Polymers*; Cambridge University Press: New York, NY, USA, 2007; ISBN 0-521-064218-3.

8. Flores, A.; Ania, F.; Baltá-Calleja, F.J. From the glassy state to ordered polymer structures: A microhardness study. *Polymer (Guildf)*. **2009**, *50*, 729–746. [CrossRef]
9. Rueda, D.R.; Gutiérrez, M.C.G.; Calleja, F.J.B.; Piccarolo, S. Order in the amorphous state of poly(ethylene terephthalate) as revealed by microhardness: Creep behavior and physical aging. *Int. J. Polym. Mater. Polym. Biomater.* **2002**, *51*, 897–908. [CrossRef]
10. Chen, X.; Yan, J.; Karlsson, A.M. On the determination of residual stress and mechanical properties by indentation. *Mater. Sci. Eng. A* **2006**, *416*, 139–149. [CrossRef]
11. Xiao, L.; Ye, D.; Chen, C. A further study on representative models for calculating the residual stress based on the instrumented indentation technique. *Comput. Mater. Sci.* **2014**, *82*, 476–482. [CrossRef]
12. Hahn, O.; Finkeldey, C. *Warmluftnieten von Langglasfaserverstärkten Thermoplasten mit Beschichteten Metallischen Werkstoffen*; Shaker Verlag: Aachen, Germany, 2004; Volume 63, ISBN 3-8322-3332-6.
13. Ghosh, S.; Reddy, R. Ultrasonic sealing of polyester and spectra fabrics using thermo plastic properties. *J. Appl. Polym. Sci.* **2009**, *113*, 1082–1089. [CrossRef]
14. Tan, X.; Zhang, J.; Shan, J.; Yang, S.; Ren, J. Characteristics and formation mechanism of porosities in CFRP during laser joining of CFRP and steel. *Compos. Part B Eng.* **2015**, *70*, 35–43. [CrossRef]
15. Amancio-Filho, S.T.; Roeder, J.; Nunes, S.P.; dos Santos, J.F.; Beckmann, F. Thermal degradation of polyetherimide joined by friction riveting (FricRiveting). Part I: Influence of rotation speed. *Polym. Degrad. Stab.* **2008**, *93*, 1529–1538. [CrossRef]
16. Sônego, M.; Abibe, A.B.; Santos, J.F.; Canto, L.B.; Amancio-Filho, S.T. Chemical Changes in Polyetherimide (PEI) Joined by Friction-based Injection Clinching Joining (F-ICJ) Technique. In Proceedings of the Regional Conference Graz 2015—Polymer Processing Society PPS: Conference paper, AIP Conference Proceedings, Graz, Austria, 21–25 September 2015; 2016; Volume 1779. Article number 070007. [CrossRef]
17. Abibe, A.B.; Amancio-Filho, S.T.; Sônego, M.; dos Santos, J.F. A Method for Joining a Plastic Workpiece to a Further Workpiece. European Patent EP 2 990 178 B1, 26 December 2018.
18. Abibe, A.B.; Sônego, M.; dos Santos, J.F.; Canto, L.B.; Amancio-Filho, S.T. On the feasibility of a friction-based staking joining method for polymer-metal hybrid structures. *Mater. Des.* **2016**, *92*, 632–642. [CrossRef]
19. Abibe, A.B. Friction-Based Injection Clinching Joining (F-ICJ): A New Joining Method for Hybrid Lightweight Structures. Ph.D. Thesis, Technische Universität, Hamburg, Germany, December 2015.
20. Rotheiser, J. *Joining of Plastics: Handbook for Designers and Engineers*; Carl Hanser Verlag: Munich, Germany, 1999; ISBN 1-56990-253-4.
21. Krahmer, D.M.; Polvorosa, R.; López de Lacalle, L.N.; Alonso-Pinillos, U.; Abate, G.; Riu, F. Alternatives for Specimen Manufacturing in Tensile Testing of Steel Plates. *Exp. Tech.* **2016**, *40*, 1555–1565. [CrossRef]
22. Silva, C.M.A.; Rosa, P.A.R.; Martins, P.A.F. Innovative Testing Machines and Methodologies for the Mechanical Characterization of Materials. *Exp. Tech.* **2016**, *40*, 569–581. [CrossRef]
23. Dixit, U.S.; Joshi, S.N.; Davim, J.P. Incorporation of material behavior in modeling of metal forming and machining processes: A review. *Mater. Des.* **2011**, *32*, 3655–3670. [CrossRef]
24. ASTM International. *Standard Test Method for Knoop and Vickers Hardness of Materials 2010*; ASTM International: West Conshohocken, PA, USA, 2010; ASTM E384-10e1.
25. Sawai, T.; Ogawa, K.; Yamaguchi, H.; Ochi, H.; Yamamoto, Y.; Suga, Y. Evaluation of joint strength of friction welded carbon steel by heat input. *Weld. Int.* **2002**, *16*, 432–441. [CrossRef]
26. Su, P.; Gerlich, A.; North, T.H.; Bendzsak, G.J. Energy utilisation and generation during friction stir spot welding. *Sci. Technol. Weld. Join.* **2006**, *11*, 163–169. [CrossRef]
27. Zuanetti, B. Characterization of Polyetherimide under Static, Dynamic, and Multiple Impact Conditions. Bachelor's Thesis, University of Central Florida, Orlando, FL, USA, 2013.
28. Brown, N.; Ward, I.M. Load drop at the upper yield point of a polymer. *J. Polym. Sci. Part A-2 Polym. Phys.* **1968**, *6*, 607–620. [CrossRef]
29. Struik, L.C.E. Physical Aging: Influence on the Deformation Behavior of Amorphous Polymers. In *Failure of Plastics*; Brostow, W., Corneliussen, R.D., Eds.; Carl Hanser Verlag: Munich, Germany, 1986; pp. 209–234. ISBN 3-446-14199-5.
30. Arruda, E.M.; Boyce, M.C. Evolution of plastic anisotropy in amorphous polymers during finite straining. *Int. J. Plast.* **1993**, *9*, 697–720. [CrossRef]
31. Stachurski, Z.H.H. Deformation mechanisms and yield strength in amorphous polymers. *Prog. Polym. Sci.* **1997**, *22*, 407–474. [CrossRef]

32. Brown, N. Yield Behaviour of Polymers. In *Failure of Plastics*; Brostow, W., Corneliussen, P., Eds.; Carl Hanser Verlag: Munich, Germany, 1986; pp. 98–118. ISBN 3-446-14199-5.

33. Strobl, G. *The Physics of Polymers*, 3rd ed.; Springer: Berlin, Germany, 2007; ISBN 978-3-540-25278-8.

34. Ajovalasit, A.; Petrucci, G.; Scafidi, M. Review of RGB photoelasticity. *Opt. Lasers Eng.* **2015**, *68*, 58–73. [CrossRef]

35. Redner, A.S.; Hoffman, B.R. Measuring residual stress in transparent plastics. In *Medical Plastics: Degradation Resistance & Failure Analysis*; Strainoptic Technologies: North Wales, PA, USA, 1998; pp. 45–50.

36. Scafidi, M.; Pitarresi, G.; Toscano, A.; Petrucci, G.; Alessi, S.; Ajovalasit, A. Review of photoelastic image analysis applied to structural birefringent materials: glass and polymers. *Opt. Eng.* **2015**, *54*, 81206. [CrossRef]

37. Ajovalasit, A.; Barone, S.; Petrucci, G. A review of automated methods for the collection and analysis of photoelastic data. *J. Strain Anal. Eng. Des.* **1998**, *33*, 75–91. [CrossRef]

38. Ajovalasit, A.; Petrucci, G.; Scafidi, M. RGB Photoelasticity: Review and Improvements. *Strain* **2010**, *46*, 137–147. [CrossRef]

39. Hutchinson, J.M. Physical aging of polymers. *Prog. Polym. Sci.* **1995**, *20*, 703–760. [CrossRef]

40. BaltáCalleja, F.J.; Flores, A.; Michler, G.H. Microindentation studies at the near surface of glassy polymers: Influence of molecular weight. *J. Appl. Polym. Sci.* **2004**, *93*, 1951–1956. [CrossRef]

41. Elias, H.-G. *An Introduction to Plastics*, 2nd ed.; Wiley-VCH: Weinheim, Germany, 2003; ISBN 3-527-29602-6.

42. Sônego, M.; Abibe, A.B.; Canevarolo, S.V.; Bettini, S.H.P.; dos Santos, J.F.; Canto, L.B.; Amancio-Filho, S.T. Thermomechanical Degradation of Polyetherimide (PEI) by Friction-Based Joining and the Effects on Quasi-Static Mechanical Strength of Hybrid Joints. *Int. Polym. Process.* **2019**, *34*, 100–110. [CrossRef]

43. Belana, J.; Cañadas, J.C.; Diego, J.A.; Mudarra, M.; Díaz, R.; Friederichs, S.; Jaimes, C.; Sanchis, M.J. Physical ageing studies in polyetherimide ULTEM 1000. *Polym. Int.* **1998**, *46*, 29–32. [CrossRef]

44. Rodríguez, A.; Calleja, A.; López de Lacalle, L.N.; Pereira, O.; González, H.; Urbikain, G.; Laye, J. Burnishing of FSWAluminum Al-Cu-Li components. *Metals* **2019**, *9*, 260. [CrossRef]

45. Sánchez Egea, A.J.; Rodríguez, A.; Celentano, D.; Calleja, A.; López de Lacalle, L.N. Joining metrics enhancement when combining FSW and ball-burnishing in a 2050 aluminium alloy. *Surf. Coatings Technol.* **2019**, *367*, 327–335. [CrossRef]

46. Salmon, S.; Swank, M.; Janaki Ram, G.D.; Stucker, B.E.; Palmer, J.A. Effectiveness of epoxy staking of fasteners in aerospace applications. *Assem. Autom.* **2009**, *29*, 341–347. [CrossRef]

Article

Fundamentals of Force-Controlled Friction Riveting: Part I—Joint Formation and Heat Development

Gonçalo Pina Cipriano [1,2], Lucian A. Blaga [3], Jorge F. dos Santos [3], Pedro Vilaça [2] and Sergio T. Amancio-Filho [1,*]

[1] Graz University of Technology, Institute of Materials Science, Joining and Forming, BMVIT Endowed Professorship for Aviation, 8010 Graz, Austria; goncalo.pinacipriano@tugraz.at

[2] Department of Mechanical Engineering, School of Engineering, Aalto University, FI-00076 Espoo, Finland; pedro.vilaca@aalto.fi

[3] Helmholtz-Zentrum Geesthacht, Center for Materials and Coastal Research, Institute of Materials Research, Materials Mechanics, Solid State Joining Processes, 21502 Geesthacht, Germany; lucian.blaga@hzg.de (L.A.B.); jorge.dos.santos@hzg.de (J.F.d.S.)

* Correspondence: sergio.amancio@tugraz.at; Tel.: +43-316-8731610

Received: 24 October 2018; Accepted: 13 November 2018; Published: 15 November 2018

Abstract: This work presents a systematic study on the correlations between process parameters and rivet plastic deformation, produced by force-controlled friction riveting. The 5 mm diameter AA2024 rivets were joined to 13 mm, nominal thickness, polyetherimide plates. A wide range of joint formations was obtained, reflecting the variation in total energy input (24–208 J) and process temperature (319–501 °C). The influence of the process parameters on joint formation was determined, using a central composite design and response surface methodology. Friction time displayed the highest contribution on both rivet penetration (61.9%) and anchoring depth (34.7%), and friction force on the maximum width of the deformed rivet tip (46.5%). Quadratic effects and two-way interactions were significant on rivet anchoring depth (29.8 and 20.8%, respectively). Bell-shaped rivet plastic deformation—high mechanical interlocking—results from moderate energy inputs (~100 J). These geometries are characterized by: rivet penetration depth of 7 to 9 mm; maximum width of the deformed rivet tip of 9 to 12 mm; and anchoring depth higher than 6 mm. This knowledge allows the production of optimized friction-riveted connections and a deeper understanding of the joining mechanisms, further discussed in Part II of this work.

Keywords: friction; riveting; hybrid structures; joining; response surface

---

1. Introduction

Nowadays, growing economic pressure and environmental concerns are pushing several industries to integrate alternative lightweight materials into their products [1]. As an example, for the transport industry, the usage of such materials constitutes an effective solution for reducing fuel consumption-associated costs and greenhouse gas emissions. This need for innovative designs must tackle several obstacles, such as joining different classes of materials without compromising the benefits from their individual usage.

The most commonly used methods to perform connections between dissimilar materials are mechanical fastening and adhesive bonding [2]. The latter consists on intermolecular forces created between the materials. Although it does not alter the mechanical properties of the materials, it has several drawbacks, for example the need for extensive surface preparation and long curing cycles. This type of connection is prone to degradation caused by environmental factors, such as moisture absorption and temperature [3]. Concerning the state-of-the-art of mechanical fastening, some limitations are related to the need for additional components, such as bolts and rivets, and to the pre-features necessary to accommodate them. These pre-features can constitute stress concentration points, affecting fatigue properties and corrosion resistance [2,4].

Welding can be also used for thermoplastic materials. A polymeric weld is generated from the localized melting of the material and/or the application of mechanical work [5,6]. The same cannot be said for thermosets, which do not soften due to their high-density cross-linked structure, degrading at high temperatures. These and other limitations associated with the aforementioned conventional processes, have led to the development of several alternative joining techniques.

The present work focuses on one alternative joining technique, friction riveting (FricRiveting). The FricRiveting process was developed and patented by Helmholtz-Zentrum Geesthacht [7]. It was devised as a design solution to perform similar and dissimilar polymer and hybrid metal-polymer/composite overlapping joints. Since early studies by Amancio-Filho et al. [8], works have been carried out on assessing the influence of the process parameters on joint formation. By applying a design of experiments (DoE), Altmeyer et al. [9] demonstrated the feasibility of joining short carbon-fiber-reinforced polyether-ether-ketone (PEEK) with titanium grade 3. In their work, a geometric correlation was established to quantify the rivet tip deformation. This correlation was defined as a ratio between the amount by which the diameter increased at the tip of the rivet and its original dimension. Although this ratio gave an indication regarding mechanical performance of the joint produced, it did not take into consideration the shape of the deformed tip of the metallic rivet. Rodrigues et al. [10], also investigated joint formation on AA2024-T351 and polycarbonate joints, by determining a volumetric ratio for the deformed rivet tip and its correlation with joint tensile strength. This coefficient, earlier defined by Blaga et al. [11], establishes a simplified ratio between the volume of the plastically deformed rivet and the volume of polymer offering mechanical resistance to a rivet-pull-out action. Borba et al. [12] have investigated microstructural changes in the thermo-mechanically affected zone of the rivet, in Ti-6Al-4V/GFRP friction-riveted metallic-insert joints. The authors concluded that the process parameters influenced the local mechanical properties of the rivet, where microstructural changes were observed, with the occurrence of β to α phase transformation. In a recent work, Proença et al. [13] have demonstrated the feasibility of force-controlled friction riveting for short-fiber reinforced polyamide 6 and AA6056. By using a simple one-factor-at-a-time design of experiment (OFAT), the authors have investigated the individual influence of rotational speed, friction force, forging force, forging time, and rivet displacement (or displacement at friction), on the joint quasi-static mechanical performance for four different process conditions. Nonetheless, up to this point, there was no systematic investigation on the physics of the force-controlled friction riveting process. A deeper understanding of heat generation, joint energy efficiency, joint formation and mechanical performance is necessary.

In this work, AA2024-T351 rivets and polyetherimide (PEI) metallic-insert joints were used to evaluate force-controlled friction riveting. These materials were selected due to both their mechanical properties and their frequent application in the aircraft industry. The current manuscript presents the first part of this extensive work, where the correlations between the process parameters and their influence on joint formation and energy development were investigated using a response surface methodology. A deep process understanding, over a wide range of rivet plastic deformation levels, is necessary to better control the joining mechanisms involved, and by doing so, the resulting joint strength. Considering a lean approach to the design of components and structures, it is of great importance that tailor-made joints can be produced. To accomplish this goal, it is necessary to establish models capable of yielding joining process parameters beforehand. Hence, based on statistical analysis of designed experiments, analytical models for the joint formation will be established. These models are meant to generate optimized process parameters capable of resulting in predetermined rivet deformations, which can yield a desired joint tensile strength, hence fulfilling the structural design specifications. The research methods implemented will enable an assessment of how the mechanical energy is used during the processing of the materials and influences the formation of the joint.

The hybrid joints produced and investigated in the present work were further analyzed and tested in the second part of the study (Part II). This second and final part of the work—published as a separate manuscript—focuses on the influence the joining process parameters have on joint mechanical performance and process energy efficiency, contributing to a deep and complete insight on the fundamentals of the force-controlled friction riveting process.

2. Force-Controlled Friction Riveting

FricRiveting is a friction-based spot-joining alternative technology. This process can be performed using several set-up configurations [14] and be controlled by time [15], force [13], position, or by their combination through multiple-phases. A metallic rivet can be used with a plain featureless surface or can be profiled (e.g., threaded [8]). Figure 1 schematically represents the process basic configuration (devised for the manufacture of metallic-insert joints), when joining a non-profiled rivet to a single polymeric plate. The process is divided into three distinct stages: friction; forging and consolidation [8,11,15]. Initially, the rotating rivet is pressed against the polymeric plate. This generates heat by friction, promoting a local increase in temperature, which softens or melts the polymer (i.e., temperature above the glass transition temperature range for amorphous polymers, or the melting point for semi-crystalline polymers). The rivet is then inserted into the polymeric component while rotating. Due to the low thermal conductivity of the polymer, the heat generated is accumulated in the vicinity of the rivet tip. When sufficiently high temperatures are achieved, the tip is plasticized and starts to deform. The rotation is then reduced to a full stop. At this point, although plastic deformation has been achieved, a forging phase may also be applied before consolidation, with the axial downward force being increased, in order to further plastically deform the rivet, if desired. Finally, the tip of the rivet assumes either an anchor or bell-shaped axisymmetric geometry, consolidating under constant pressure. The process parameters are: rotational speed (RS); friction time (FT); friction force (FF); forging time (FoT); and forging force (FoF). These will be discussed in the following sections, but were fully addressed in previous publications [8–10].

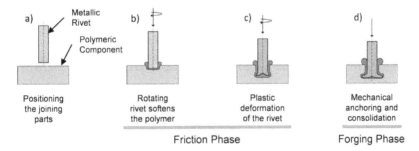

Figure 1. Schematics of the FricRiveting process using its basic configuration (metallic-insert joint geometry): (**a**) pre-joining configuration; (**b**) initial softened/molten polymer layer is formed; (**c**) plastic deformation starts; and (**d**) final deformation is achieved.

For the present work, the process was carried out using a force-controlled and time-limited approach: the axial force being applied to the rivet is monitored and kept constant during the process, being the distinct phases limited by pre-defined time intervals. In this case, the insertion of the rivet into the polymeric plate is a process response, resulting from the evolution of the material conditions.

3. Materials and Methods

3.1. Base Materials

The materials used were AA2024-T351 (rivets) and Polyetherimide (PEI). The latter is a high-performance thermoplastic developed by Wirth et al. [16]. PEI is characterized by high mechanical strength, dimensional stability and flexural modulus. It also has good flame resistance, good chemical stability and an elevated softening point, with a glass transition temperature (T_g) close to 215 °C [17,18]. By meeting specific flame resistance and low smoke evolution requirements, this material is used for both automotive and aircraft interior applications [19]. The PEI specimens were obtained from 13 mm nominal thickness extruded plates (Quadrant Engineering Plastic Products, Lenzburg, Switzerland). Specimens were cut into 70 mm × 70 mm format, for non-destructive X-ray analysis.

The metallic rivets used for this work were made of extruded AA2024-T351, with a length of 60 mm and a diameter of 5 mm. This is a solution heat-treated and cold-worked aluminum alloy naturally aged to a substantially stable temper condition (T3). The chemical composition of this alloy is presented in Table 1. The alloy is characterized by medium-to-high tensile strength (450 MPa) and it is widely used for aircraft primary structures, on fuselage and mechanical connections. Further details on the mechanical and physical properties of this alloy were addressed in the second part of this work.

Table 1. Typical nominal chemical composition of AA2024-T351 [20].

Element	Al	Cr	Cu	Fe	Mg	Mn	Si	Ti	Zn
Weight (wt%)	90.7–94.7	≤0.10	3.8–4.9	≤0.50	1.2–1.8	0.3–0.9	≤0.50	≤0.15	≤0.25

3.2. Joining Procedure

The joints performed for this study were produced using a FricRiveting lab-scale joining equipment (RNA, H. Loitz-Robotik, Hamburg, Germany). The equipment has a maximum rotational speed of 21,000 rpm and 24 kN of axial force. The force and torque measurements recorded by the sensors are used for controlling the process and provide an estimation of the mechanical energy input. For the present work, the friction time (FT) parameter varied from 1.4 up to 2.2 s and the forging time (FoT) from 0.5 up to 2.5 s. The rotational speed (RS) ranged from 17,000 up to 21,000 rpm, while the forces from 1500 up to 3500 N for friction (FF) and from 3300 up to 5700 N for forging (FoF). These parameter ranges were intentionally set so to promote a diversified range of resulting joint formation geometries and energy inputs.

3.3. Non-Destructive Joint Analysis

The joint formation of the specimens produced for mechanical testing, was evaluated by X-ray tomography. This analysis allowed the overall rivet projected geometry to be assessed, providing same-joint results for both joint formation and global mechanical performance (the latter discussed in Part II). Figure 2 exemplifies the tomographic measurements (Seifert Isovolt 320/13, Russia) performed in accordance with DIN EN ISO 17636-1, with a tube current of 5.4 mA and an 80 kV voltage. The focal spot was 1.5 mm × 1.5 mm at an 800 mm focus-to-film distance. The dimensions evaluated were: rivet penetration depth (H); maximum width of the deformed rivet tip (W); the height of the deformed rivet tip (B); and the depth until maximum width, or anchoring depth (Dp). The latter is introduced in the present work, as an improvement to the current approach on estimating rivet anchoring performance. This dimension depends on both radial deformation and penetration of the rivet tip into the polymer. The new joint formation assessment arose from the need to characterize the wide range of rivet plastically deformed geometries obtained, with the process variant and parameters being used. These measurements also serve as a basis to establish correlations with the mechanical performance in Part II.

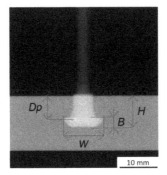

Figure 2. Example of X-ray tomography measurements for the joint formation analysis.

3.4. Energy Input

In friction-based joining processes, the heat generated can be estimated by considering the mechanical energy input applied, both for processes involving metallic materials [21] and thermoplastics [22]. For the current work, the following equation was used to estimate this energy input [23,24],

$$E_M = E_f + E_d = \int M.\omega.dt + \int F.\vartheta.dt \ (J),$$ (1)

where the first term is related to the frictional energy (E_f) resulting from applied torque (M) and rotational speed (ω). The second term estimates the deformational energy (E_d), resulting from the axial force (F) and the deformation rate (ϑ). The estimation of these energies, allows a correlation between the energy used and the resulting joint formation. With this data, it is possible to assess parameter combinations that result in more energy-efficient joints (i.e., joints resulting in more favorable plastically deformed rivet tip and yielding better mechanical properties, with less energy consumption). The torque was integrated over time (i.e., the area under the frictional torque curve), which when multiplied by the constant rotational speed gave the frictional component of the energy. The deformational energy was determined by multiplying the force being applied by the displacement over the whole process duration.

3.5. Temperature Measurement

The process temperature was measured by infrared thermometry on the expelled polymeric flash material. A thermographic camera (High-End Camera Series ImageIR, Infratech GmbH, Dresden, Germany) was used with a calibration set for temperatures ranging from 150 up to 700 °C. The distance between the measuring area and the center of the lens was 60 cm, at an incidence angle of approximately 18°. Figure 3 shows a frame from the flash material temperature measurement during the process as an example.

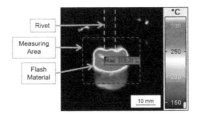

Figure 3. Example of infrared tomography measurements for the expelled flash material.

3.6. Design of Experiments and Statistical Analysis

The parameter sets used to perform the joints for this work were established via a second order design of experiments. The aim was to define parameter sets that would fit a response surface to the experimental output studied [25,26]. The statistical input factors, joining parameters, were: FF; FT; RS; FoF; and FoT. The evaluated process responses for joint formation—i.e., the plastic deformation underwent by the rivet tip—were: H; W; and Dp.

The test matrix was generated by a central composite design (CCD), which integrates a factorial design, and both a set of center and one of axial points. For the factorial part, a fractional factorial design of five parameters with two levels (2^{5-1}) was chosen. The value of α—the distance between the axial and the center points—was chosen as to give properties of rotatability and orthogonality to the design [26,27].

Response surface models, based on second order polynomial functions, were determined for the investigated responses. The statistical significance of all the linear, quadratic and two-way interaction model terms was evaluated at each iteration step by a stepwise backward elimination procedure. The least significant term was removed before the subsequent step and the model was revaluated. A polynomial regression equation was determined for each response, with an updated predictive capability when compared to the original full-quadratic model. Explanatory and predictability capabilities of the statistical models obtained were also evaluated. The response surfaces generated, for the statistically significant process parameter interactions, allow a deeper understanding into the effects these have on the studied response.

The parameter combinations set by the chosen DoE are shown in Table 2 in non-randomized order. The parameter window provides an understanding of the energy range necessary to achieve certain levels of deformation on the rivet tip and the resulting mechanical properties of the joints.

Table 2. Process parameter sets used for this study.

Condition	Process Parameters					Condition	Process Parameters				
	RS (rpm)	FT (s)	FoT (s)	FF (N)	FoF (N)		RS (rpm)	FT (s)	FoT (s)	FF (N)	FoF (N)
1	18,000	1.6	1	2000	5100	19	19,000	1.8	1.5	2500	4500
2	20,000	1.6	1	2000	3900	20	19,000	1.8	1.5	2500	4500
3	18,000	2	1	2000	3900	21	19,000	1.8	1.5	2500	4500
4	20,000	2	1	2000	5100	22	19,000	1.8	1.5	2500	4500
5	18,000	1.6	2	2000	3900	23	19,000	1.8	1.5	2500	4500
6	20,000	1.6	2	2000	5100	24	19,000	1.8	1.5	2500	4500
7	18,000	2	2	2000	5100	25	19,000	1.8	1.5	2500	4500
8	20,000	2	2	2000	3900	26	19,000	1.8	1.5	2500	4500
9	18,000	1.6	1	3000	3900	27	17,000	1.8	1.5	2500	4500
10	20,000	1.6	1	3000	5100	28	21,000	1.8	1.5	2500	4500
11	18,000	2	1	3000	5100	29	19,000	1.4	1.5	2500	4500
12	20,000	2	1	3000	3900	30	19,000	2.2	1.5	2500	4500
13	18,000	1.6	2	3000	5100	31	19,000	1.8	0.5	2500	4500
14	20,000	1.6	2	3000	3900	32	19,000	1.8	2.5	2500	4500
15	18,000	2	2	3000	3900	33	19,000	1.8	1.5	1500	4500
16	20,000	2	2	3000	5100	34	19,000	1.8	1.5	3500	4500
17	19,000	1.8	1.5	2500	4500	35	19,000	1.8	1.5	2500	3300
18	19,000	1.8	1.5	2500	4500	36	19,000	1.8	1.5	2500	5700

4. Results and Discussion

4.1. Joint Formation

The process-related plastic deformation, endured by the metallic rivet, was analyzed by non-destructive X-ray tomography, as described in Section 3.3. Table 3 shows the results of the measurements performed to assess the overall geometry of the plastically deformed rivet tip.

Table 3. Geometry variations in the plastically deformed rivet tip.

Condition	Joint Formation Measurements				Condition	Joint Formation Measurements			
	H (mm)	Dp (mm)	B (mm)	W (mm)		H (mm)	Dp (mm)	B (mm)	W (mm)
1	4.7	3.7	2.8	6.2	19	6.8	6.1	2.6	9.3
2	6.8	5.0	3.8	7.3	20	6.9	6.1	3.2	9.2
3	6.8	6.4	2.8	7.4	21	6.5	6.0	3.0	7.8
4	7.5	7.0	4.7	9.3	22	6.6	6.0	3.5	8.6
5	4.9	4.4	2.3	6.2	23	6.6	6.0	2.7	7.3
6	5.5	5.0	3.2	7.0	24	6.8	6.0	3.2	9.1
7	6.9	6.4	4.4	7.8	25	6.6	5.8	3.8	9.2
8	7.5	7.1	3.2	8.4	26	6.9	6.3	3.3	9.0
9	6.2	5.7	2.5	8.2	27	5.9	5.1	3.0	7.7
10	6.6	5.3	3.7	10.0	28	7.5	6.0	3.6	9.9
11	7.6	5.7	3.8	10.0	29	4.9	4.2	2.4	6.7
12	8.4	5.4	4.2	11.3	30	8.7	6.0	3.3	11.5
13	5.7	5.0	3.0	9.2	31	6.7	5.8	3.0	8.4
14	6.7	5.5	2.9	9.6	32	6.9	6.0	3.4	9.3
15	7.5	5.4	3.1	9.9	33	5.3	4.1	3.0	6.5
16	8.7	6.1	4.7	11.9	34	7.3	4.0	5.4	10.6
17	6.4	5.6	3.1	7.5	35	7.0	6.3	2.6	8.3
18	6.6	5.7	3.4	9.5	36	6.9	5.9	4.2	9.8

The parameter matrix yielded a wide range of rivet tip geometrical variations, as was intended. Figure 4 clearly presents the variation of the rivet dimensions.

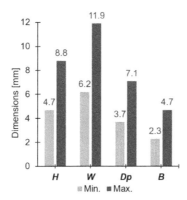

Figure 4. Maximum and minimum values of the rivet dimensions within the joint formation evaluation.

The penetration achieved by the rivet (H) varied 46.6% of its maximum. The smallest width of the deformed tip (W) was 6.2 mm, 52.1% of the maximum and a 24% increase from the original rivet diameter of 5 mm. The anchoring depth (Dp) varied 47.9% of its maximum value. Finally, the height of the deformed rivet (B) range was approximately equal to the minimum value. The sensitivity of the process to the joining parameter sets is considerably high, hence the selected joining parameter window was adequately chosen for a large variation of results. A similar trend was observed by Amancio et al. [14], for the same combination of materials, but for a time-controlled process variant.

4.2. Mechanical Energy Input

The mechanical energy applied to the materials was estimated using Equation (3). The individual energy contributions, frictional (E_f), deformational (E_d), and the resulting total energy input values (E_M) are shown in Table 4.

Table 4. Energy input determined for the investigated set of joining conditions.

Condition	Energy Input			Condition	Energy Input			Condition	Energy Input		
	E_f (J)	E_d (J)	E_M (J)		E_f (J)	E_d (J)	E_M (J)		E_f (J)	E_d (J)	E_M (J)
1	10	14	24	13	45	33	78	25	36	32	68
2	26	20	46	14	55	31	86	26	40	31	71
3	33	20	53	15	82	39	120	27	28	23	51
4	39	38	77	16	122	86	208	28	46	37	83
5	14	14	29	17	39	25	63	29	17	19	36
6	16	20	36	18	42	34	76	30	84	52	136
7	35	30	65	19	42	32	74	31	36	28	64
8	41	16	57	20	42	31	73	32	40	32	73
9	36	24	60	21	29	27	56	33	21	17	38
10	40	43	83	22	30	28	59	34	88	72	159
11	63	43	106	23	24	23	47	35	34	24	59
12	90	66	155	24	37	30	67	36	42	44	86

The range of parameters used for this work also yielded a large variation of energy contributions. In terms of total magnitude, the lowest value of the energy input was observed for Condition 1 (E_M = 24 J), and the highest with Condition 16, (E_M = 208 J). In Condition 1 (joint formation shown in Figure 5a), except for the forging force (FoF = 5100 N), the remaining joining parameters were at the second lowest level of their respective ranges (RS = 18,000 rpm; FT = 1.6 s; FF = 2000 N; and FoT = 1 s). Given the resulting joint formation, it was clear that the energy was not sufficient to promote significant plastic deformation of the rivet tip. Rodrigues et al. [10] observed similar results for friction riveting of policarbonate (PC) and AA2024-T351, reporting that lower RS, FT and FF (addressed as friction pressure in their work) lead also to lower process temperatures and a lower plastic deformation of the rivet tip. Condition 16 (joint formation shown in Figure 5b) was produced with a higher energy input, associated with higher joining parameters: 11% more rotational speed (RS = 20,000 rpm); 25% friction time (FT = 2 s); and 50% friction force (FF = 3000 N), than Condition 1. This is also in agreement with Rodrigues et al. [10], who observed an increase in H and W with these joining process parameters. In Condition 16, a rupture of part of the rivet tip outer edge was then separated from the main rivet body, remaining close to the surface of the polymer (indicated by arrows in Figure 5b). This type of defect was reported as a result of an unsteady rivet plastic deformation related to local oscillations in polymer viscosity due to excessive heat generation [14].

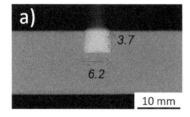 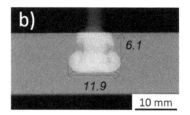

Figure 5. X-ray tomography of: (a) Condition 1 with lowest energy input, E_M = 24 J (RS = 18,000 rpm; FT = 1.6 s; FoT = 1 s; FF = 2000 N; FoF = 5100 N); and (b), Condition 16 with highest energy input, E_M = 208 J (RS = 20,000 rpm; FT = 2 s; FoT = 2 s; FF = 3000 N; FoF = 5100 N).

Besides the total amount of energy applied during the process, the balance between the individual energy contributions was also found to be determinant to the joint formation. When analyzing Conditions 14 and 36, both having the same total energy input of 86 J, the influence from the energy balance on rivet deformation can be established. Figure 6 demonstrates the balance between the frictional (E_f) and deformational (E_d) contributions to the total energy input on these two conditions.

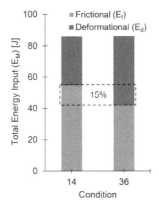

Figure 6. Energy input comparison between Conditions 14 and 36 with total energy input of 86 J.

The 15% of the total energy input that in Condition 14 originates from a frictional contribution, in Condition 36 the same 15% generated by deformational energy. This shift in the predominant source of energy promoted a considerable change in the resulting joint formations. Referring to the data presented in the previous section (Table 3), the measurements performed on these joints revealed higher dimensions for the deformed rivet tip of Condition 36. The highest difference in magnitude occurred for the B measurement, encircled in Figure 7, where Condition 36 had an increase of over 30% from the value measured for Condition 14.

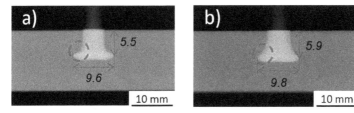

Figure 7. X-ray tomography of: (**a**), Condition 14 (RS = 20,000 rpm; FT = 1.6 s; FoT = 2 s; FF = 3000 N; FoF = 3900 N); and (**b**), Condition 36 (RS = 19,000 rpm; FT = 1.8 s; FoT = 1.5 s; FF = 2500 N; FoF = 5700 N).

The dashed-circle in Figure 7b, highlights a smoother, more gradual transition, from the original diameter to the maximum width of the deformed rivet tip. This can be considered a direct result from the difference in magnitude of the forging forces involved. The joint produced with Condition 14 was produced with a FoF of 3900 N, while the joint from Condition 36 with 5700 N. Apparently, this difference promoted higher compression in the rivet for the latter condition, which, by encountering sufficient resistance from the solid polymer in front, resulted in a larger volume of metallic material being forced to expand its diameter, at a point closer to the polymer exterior surface.

The results indicate the importance of the energy balance on the deformation of the rivet. This was found to be another important factor, which, independently from the global energy, can greatly influence the plastically-deformed rivet geometry. As was reported in [11] and as will be shown in Part II, the shape of the deformed rivet tip plays an important role in dictating joint tensile mechanical performance. Therefore, one of the energy contributions may be preferable to the other, or even a balance might be desirable. An immediate example of this will be further discussed in the next section, where, E_f is decisive to maximize Dp.

4.3. Influence of the Process Parameters on Joint Formation

The process responses H, W and Dp were statistically investigated based on a response surface design, CCD, as described in Section 3.5. Statistical models will be further discussed for each response separately.

4.3.1. Influence on the Rivet Penetration Depth, H

The reduced statistical model for H was obtained following the procedure described in Section 3.5. Using analysis of variance, the terms considered significant for this study were those with a *p*-value inferior to 0.05 [25,26]. The RS, FT and FF were the most significant parameters, with *p*-values of zero. FoF and FoT had values of 0.041 and 0.435, respectively. Although FoT had a high *p*-value, for the FT*FoT and FoT*FoF interactions this value was 0.026 and 0.014, respectively. Therefore, it was kept in the reduced model on a principle of hierarchy. Likewise, the interaction FT*FoF was considered significant with $p = 0.001$. The relative contributions of the process factors to the H model are shown in Figure 8. The largest individual contributions to H come from FT (61.9%), RS (15.0%) and FF (15.6%). This is in accordance with the work reported by Amancio-Filho and dos Santos [28], where these joining parameters directly influence heat generation in the viscous polymer layer, allowing for a larger rivet penetration. Moreover, Equation 1 shows that the longer the joining time the higher will be the energy generated, explaining the largest contribution of FT. Finally, the two-way interactions and quadratic terms, although statistically significant, display only a small combined contribution (4.2%) to this response. Both FoF and FoT individual contributions were found to be marginal, inferior to the model total error.

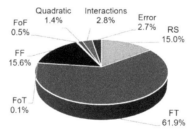

Figure 8. Contributions of the model factors to the response H.

Equation (2) presents the reduced model regression equation in CCD matrix coded values for H:

$$H = 6.7264 + 0.4375RS + 0.8875FT - 0.0292FoT + 0.4458FF - 0.0792FoF - 0.0865FF * FF \\ +0.0760FoF * FoF + 0.1062FT * FoT + 0.1687FT * FoF + 0.1188FoT * FoF \tag{2}$$

A comparison between the predicted and the observed values of H is established in Figure 9, along with additional validation experiments. The dotted line follows a 1:1 correlation between the axes. The solid grey lines enclose the upper and lower prediction limits, within which the model can predict a single response observation [29].

The adjusted R-sq—the explanatory power of the model—was 96.3%, the standard error (S) 0.18 mm, and the predicted R-sq 93.8%. Apart from one point (predicted value of 6.4 mm/actual value of 6.8), all observations lie within the prediction limit interval. From the validation runs, for the conditions closer to the extreme H values, the experimentally obtained values are higher than the predicted ones. This may be related to a limitation in model prediction power when near the extremities of the joining parameter ranges. However, these validation points might be influenced by a usual 10% uncertainty associated with variability in polymer rheological properties such as molecular weight distribution (MWD) between different grades and batches. Considering that average molecular weight and MWD affect molten viscosity [30], polymerization-related variations in temperature, time and reactor type may be enough to alter polymer base material rheological behavior [31,32] during FricRiveting.

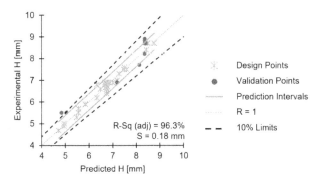

Figure 9. Validation diagrams for the reduced model of H.

The influence process parameters have on rivet penetration depth, H, is shown in Figure 10, by the main effects plots.

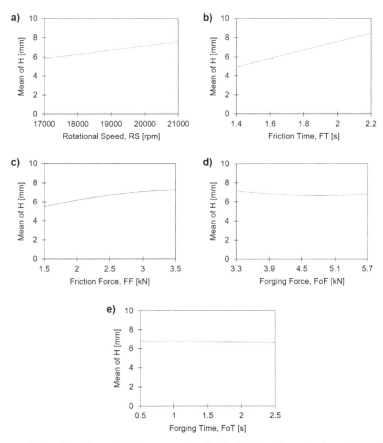

Figure 10. Main effects plots of the rivet penetration depth, H, with: (**a**) rotational speed; (**b**) friction time; (**c**) friction force; (**d**) forging force; and (**e**) forging time.

For the parameter ranges being studied, H increases with the individual values of RS and FT (Figure 10a,b). These display a relatively linear correlation with H, also reported by Altmeyer et al. [9] for Ti alloy/short-fiber reinforced polyether ether ketone joints. In the cases of FF (Figure 10c) and FoF (Figure 10d), a slight curvature can be observed, whereby for the former, this effect is more prominent, suggesting a higher order influence. The curvature of FF can be explained by taking into account that the increase of this parameter leads to an increase of E_M. One may assume, that a larger FF will promote a non-linear decrease in the polymer viscosity. This effect can be coupled on one hand with the increase in process temperature with E_M (Figure 11a), and on the other hand, with the thixotropic behavior of PEI [33]. Larger FF values will increase the shear rate, consequently promoting a decrease in polymer viscosity. A similar explanation can be extended to RS and FT, as these joining parameters also generate higher energy input (Equation (1)). This relative tendency can be seen in Figure 11b, with the correlation between H and E_M. Therefore, the higher the RS, FT and FF the larger will be the volume of softened polymer ahead of the rivet, offering less resistance to rivet insertion. This behavior is in agreement with previous works [8,9]. Finally, the FoT curve (Figure 10e) shows relatively no influence on the magnitude of H.

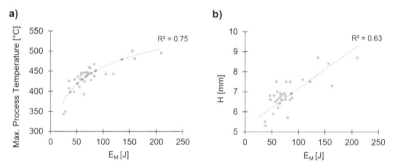

Figure 11. Total energy input, E_M, correlations with: (**a**) maximum process temperature; and (**b**) rivet penetration depth, H.

Figure 12 shows the corresponding response surface and contour plots, supporting the analysis of statistically significant two-way interactions (FT*FoT, FT*FoF and FoF*FoT) considered in the model.

When analyzing the FT*FoT interaction for FoT >1.5 s (Figure 12a,b), both minimum and maximum values of H (i.e., H < 5 and H > 8.5 mm) are achieved by respectively applying minimum and maximum values of FT. The rivet penetration increases linearly with the increase of FT as discussed in Figure 10. The FT*FoF interaction surface plot (Figure 12c) shows a pronounced curvature. Although the same tendency of H increasing with the FT is observed, there is a considerable gradient at the lower half of the FoF parameter range (3300 N ≤ FoF ≤ 4500 N). Contrary to what could be expected, an increase in FoF for the lower values of FT (1.4 s ≤ FT ≤ 1.6 s), leads to a decrease of H for this parameter range (Figure 12c,d). A possible explanation could be that (Figure 10b) at lower FT the amount of molten polymer ahead of the rivet will be smaller, as less energy is being applied to the system. For FoF, the observed influence over the range is considered small, as it was seen for the respective main effect plot (Figure 10d). Figure 12e and f show that the FoT*FoF interaction is the one producing the smallest variation in magnitude for H, across this parameter range. This trend is in agreement with the results in Figure 10e, where FoT has no relative influence in H. Therefore, one may conclude that FoT is not contributing significantly to H in the selected joining parameter range. Finally, one may derive from the surface plots that FT is the parameter with the greater influence on the two-way interactions.

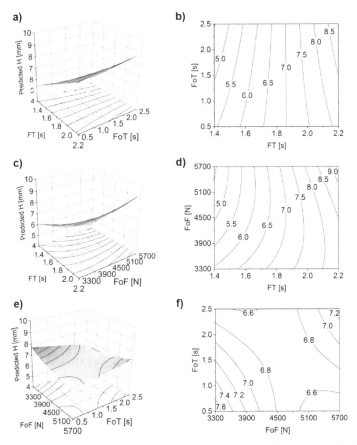

Figure 12. Two-way parameter interactions with rivet penetration depth (H) as response. Surface and contour plots for: (**a,b**) friction time (FT) and forging time (FoT); (**c,d**) FT and forging force (FoF); and (**e,f**) FoT and FoF.

4.3.2. Influence on the Maximum Width of the Deformed Rivet Tip, W

The initial factors with p-values > 0.05, were all eliminated by the stepwise backward elimination methodology. The RS, FT, FF (p-value of zero) and FoF (p-value of 0.032) were found to be significant for W. Figure 13 shows the individual contributions of the model factors to W.

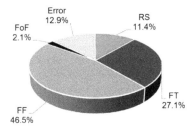

Figure 13. Contributions of the model factors to the response W.

The largest contribution for W is generated by FF (46.5%). This can be explained by the fact that this process parameter promotes higher energy input and rivet deformation, hence the increase in W.

The FT (27.1%) and RS (11.5%) also have relevant contribution on this response. These observations are in accordance with [9,10].

The regression equation for this model is:

$$W = 8.7472 + 0.596RS + 0.912FT + 1.196FF + 0.254FoF \qquad (3)$$

Figure 14 shows the validation plot for the W model, where experimental values are plotted along with model predicted values.

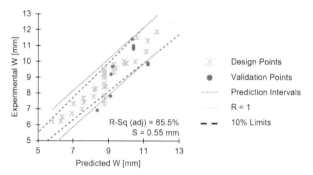

Figure 14. Validation diagrams for the reduced model of W.

The adjusted R-sq of the model is 85.5%, the standard error, S, is 0.55 mm and the predicted R-sq 84.4%. With the exception of two outliers outside the prediction intervals (experimental W values of 7.3 and 7.5 mm), the W model has a good explanatory power (i.e., large R-sq [25]).

The validation points for W, display good correlation between the experimental and the predicted values (i.e., large predicted R-sq), although some of the former fall on or just below the prediction interval. This may be correlated with the 10% uncertainty limits related to intrinsic batch-associated properties deviation. No interactions were found to be statistically significant, hence, they were not considered for the reduced model. Therefore, response surface graphs for two-way interactions were not investigated.

Figure 15 presents the main effects plots for the statistically significant joining parameters, influencing the maximum deformed width of the rivet tip (W).

For the joining parameters RS (Figure 15a), FT (Figure 15b) and FF (Figure 15c), a linear correlation with W was found, whereby the higher these joining parameters, the larger will be the W values. FoF shows a minor curvature (Figure 15d) with what can be considered a very small variation of W (8.6 to 9.3 mm) given the studied force range. Taking into account that FoF has a rather irrelevant influence on H (refer to Figure 10d), this is an indication that the forging phase may exert only a minor influence on the formation of the rivet anchoring zone for the investigated joining parameter ranges. This has been previously suggested by Proença et al. [13] for force-controlled FricRiveting. They observed that for joints produced with lower energy inputs, a larger FoF would lead to a larger W, while for high energy input conditions, such as in the current study, FoF had lesser influence. The authors explained this phenomenon through the higher process temperatures measured for higher energy input conditions, which increase rivet tip plasticizing. They assumed that this was a result of rivet plastic deformation taking place during the heating phase. This is an indication that a forging phase with FoF higher than FF is not necessarily needed to deform the rivet tip, if it is possible to achieve enough heat generation through the appropriate selection of RS, FT and FF.

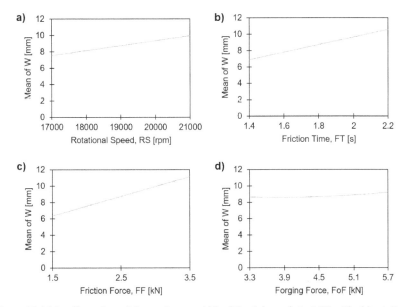

Figure 15. Main effects plots of the maximum width of the deformed rivet, W, with: (**a**) rotational speed; (**b**) friction time; (**c**) friction force; and (**d**) forging force.

The linear proportionality between RS, FF, FT, and W can be better understood by addressing the correlation of these parameters with the mechanical energy input (Equation (1)). The graph in Figure 16 demonstrates the tendency of W to increase with the mechanical energy input. Past studies [8] on this material combination, have shown that the higher the energy input the higher will be the heat generation. This could also be seen in the present study, as proven by the correlation between the process temperature and energy input (Figure 11a). Therefore, the level of plasticizing of the rivet tip will also increase, leading to larger radial plastic deformation and higher W.

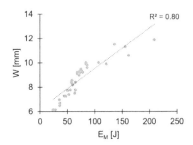

Figure 16. Correlation between maximum width of the deformed rivet tip (W), and the total mechanical energy input (E_M).

4.3.3. Influence on the Anchoring Depth, Dp

The anchoring depth is being introduced in this work as a tool to better correlate the shape of the deformed rivet tip with the joint mechanical performance. The Dp will be used in Part II of this work to allow a more accurate assessment on the volume of material, above the deformed rivet tip, offering resistance to mechanical solicitation. As previously mentioned in the introduction, a correlation between this volume and the resistance to pullout forces has been established in literature.

A reduced statistical model with only significant terms was generated with RS, FT, FF*FF and FT*FF (*p*-value of 0.000). The model also included the quadric terms FT*FT (*p*-value of 0.004) and FoF*FoF (*p*-value of 0.047), as well as two-way interaction terms (the *p*-values were 0.019 for RS*FF and 0.028 for FT*FoF). Even though the *p*-values for the first order terms of FF (*p*-value of 0.410) and FoF (*p*-value of 0.264) are outside the interval of confidence (95%) set for the analysis of variance (ANOVA), they were considered in the reduced model due to hierarchy, as they are part of the two-way interactions.

Figure 17 shows the relative contributions of the model factors to Dp.

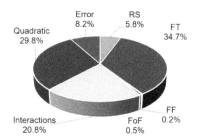

Figure 17. Contributions of the model factors to the response Dp.

Similar to the case of H, the contribution of FT to Dp is the largest. Nonetheless, in contrast to H, the contributions from the quadratic terms and two-way interactions are the second (29.8%) and third (20.8%) largest ones, respectively. As previously mentioned in Section 3.3, Dp is a measure that depends both on the penetration of the rivet and on the amount of plastic deformation that its tip undergoes. Thus, the mechanisms in play are more complex than for the previous responses. This will be discussed further in this section.

The model regression equation for Dp is:

$$Dp = 5.9243 + 0.2292RS + 0.5625FT - 0.0458FF - 0.0625FoF - 0.1510FT*FT - 0.4135FF*FF$$
$$+0.0990FoF*FoF - 0.1688RS*FF - 0.4812FT*FF + 0.1563FT*FoF, \tag{4}$$

The experimental Dp values measured are shown comparatively to the model predictions, in Figure 18.

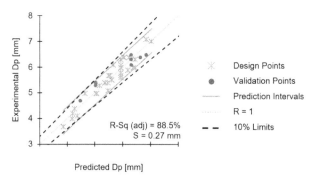

Figure 18. Validation diagrams for the reduced model of Dp.

The model has an adjusted R-sq of 88.5%, the predicted R-sq is 77% and a standard error, S, of 0.27 mm. The graph shows that all the design points fall within the model prediction interval, considered a good correlation with the experimental data. For Dp, all the validation runs performed fall within the prediction intervals. Therefore, the model can be used to explain the correlations with the joining parameters and predict Dp.

The main effects plots showing the influence of the process parameters on Dp are shown in Figure 19.

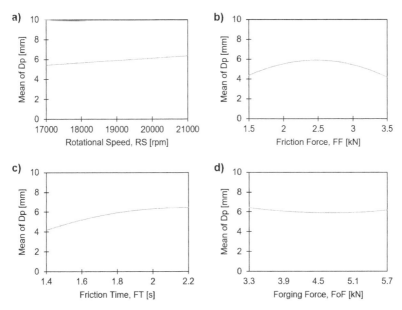

Figure 19. Main effects plots of the anchoring depth, Dp, with: (**a**) rotational speed; (**b**) friction time; (**c**) friction force; and (**d**) forging force.

As can be seen, only RS (Figure 19a) displays a linear correlation, in this case increasing, with Dp. FF (Figure 19b), FT (Figure 19c) and FoF (Figure 19b) plots indicate an influence from higher-order terms, as there is no linear correlation in these cases. In the case of FF, data shows a relative symmetry over the parameter range, having a maximum Dp of 6 mm close to the median values of friction force. At both minimum and maximum FF, Dp decreases to values close to 4 mm. This behavior may be explained by the rivet deformation regime during the process. A higher level of FF leads to a higher amount of plastic deformation at the rivet tip, as reported for W (Figure 15c). The more plasticized the metallic material being pressed, the more pronounced is the anchor-shape geometric effect of the rivet tip. Figure 20 demonstrates the effect of increasing FF from minimum (1500 N) until maximum (3500 N) values with the remnant process parameters kept constant. As Dp is the depth measured until the widest rivet tip deformation, this point occurs closer to the original upper surface of the polymer, as the plastic deformation of the rivet tip excessively increases. Given that the anchor-like deformed tip begins to curve upon itself, e.g., Figure 20c, in contrast to a bell-shape deformation seen in Figure 20b.

For the FoF, we observed similar behavior that observed for H (Figure 12d) and W (Figure 15d).

The two-way interactions between parameters, for Dp, are illustrated in Figure 21.

The behavior observed from the main effects plot of FF (Figure 19b), seems to be amplified by the RS*FF interaction. Figure 21a,b suggest that when FF is set close to its maximum, the increase in RS will result in smaller Dp values. This can be related, as mentioned in Section 4.3.1, to resultant high-energy input. The higher the combined RS*FF, the larger the plastic deformation of the rivet tip, resulting in an increase of W. Besides the widening of the rivet tip, changes in shape will also take place, as addressed in Figure 20, creating long curved upon themselves anchor-like arms in the rivet tip (Figure 20c). The overall minimum Dp that is found at lower levels of FF and RS (i.e., at very low energy inputs), is associated with a very small penetration of the rivet. In these cases, no considerable deformation (i.e., lower W values, Figure 5a) is expected.

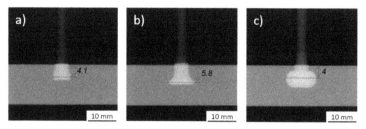

Figure 20. Friction force direct effect on Dp: (**a**) Condition 33 (RS = 19,000 rpm; FT = 1.8 s; FoT = 1.5 s; FF = 1500 N; FoF = 4500 N); (**b**) Condition 25 (RS = 19,000 rpm; FT = 1.8 s; FoT = 1.5 s; FF = 2500 N; FoF = 4500 N); and (**c**) Condition 34 (RS = 19,000 rpm; FT = 1.8 s; FoT = 1.5 s; FF = 3500 N; FoF = 4500 N).

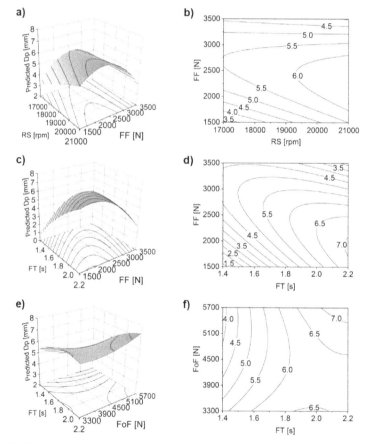

Figure 21. Two-way parameter interactions with anchoring depth, Dp. Surface and contour plots for: (**a**) rotational speed (RS) and (**b**) friction force (FF); (**c**) friction time (FT) and (**d**) friction force (FF); and forging time (FoT), (**e**), and forging force (FoF) (**f**).

The FT*FF surface and contour plots (Figure 21c,d) display the widest range of predicted Dp values, where FT appears to have a greater influence on Dp than FF. Also, an increase of FT should be coupled with a decrease in FF to maximize Dp. Similarly, as has already been discussed for Figure 20, increasing FF at high levels of energy input, contributes to an effect of over-deformation, seen by the sharp decrease of Dp at highest levels of FF and FT.

In the case of FT*FoF (Figure 21e,f), up to a certain level of FT (around 1.8 s) the increase of FoF towards maximum values becomes counterproductive for the increase of Dp. High FoF is only positive for Dp when FT is also close to maximum. This apparently complex behavior may be explained by two phenomena. Values of FoF around 4500 N seem to be enough to cause the rivet to further penetrate the polymer (Figure 12c,d) but not enough to promote an over-deformation, seen at higher values with the decrease of Dp (Figure 20c). At both maximum levels of FT and FoF, the Dp also achieves maximum values. This is due to the fact, that the gain in the rivet penetration outweighs the negative effect of over-deformation.

4.3.4. Summary of the Findings

A correlation between the joint mechanical performance and the volume of polymeric material above the deformed rivet tip has been established in previous studies [8]. To complement the existing knowledge, a fine control of the process-resulting rivet plastic deformation was now established.

The interaction plots in Figure 21 for Dp, suggest that FF must be chosen carefully, as it is the parameter which promotes the greatest variations in the two-way interactions. These interactions emphasize the importance of the energy input balance on the joint formation (Section 4.2), and geometry of the deformed rivet tip (Figure 5b). Moreover, it is clear that a simple variation of the global energy is not sufficient to tailor Dp (Figure 20). In order to prevent the occurrence of rivet over-deformation, premature increase of W, and the resulting decrease of Dp (e.g., Figure 20c), the frictional contribution to the energy input must be controlled. The effect the FF increase had on energy input, from 68 J (Condition 25, Figure 20b) to 159 J (Condition 34, Figure 20c), resulted in a plastically deformed anchor-shaped rivet tip for the latter, in contrast to the bell-shape rivet tip for the former.

As verified in the main effects plots (Figures 10, 15 and 19) and the investigated two-way interaction surfaces (Figures 12 and 21), for the three responses—H, W and Dp—the FoF and FoT parameters themselves either did not promote significant variation among these responses, or their contributions were very small. Therefore, these two joining parameters may be kept constant for process optimization purposes. Furthermore, the RS was found to have a positive linearly increasing effect on all three responses (Figures 10, 15 and 19). In this way, RS should be maximized to promote optimized joint formation, i.e., bell-shape rivet tip. This rivet shape results in improved joint mechanical performance, as will be discussed in Part II.

To illustrate the dependence of investigated H, W and Dp geometric responses on FF and FT (compiled into Figure 22), FoF and FoT were set in their mid-range values (FoF = 4500 N; FoT = 1.5 s) and RS to its maximum value (RS = 21,000 rpm).

This graph can provide the user with a process overview, allowing for a tailored selection of the process parameters according to the requirements and constraints of a specific application. For instance, to maximize the polymeric resistive volume of material above the rivet tip—a requirement for improved joint mechanical performance—it is not enough to only increase H and W, using upper-range values of both FT ($2 \leq$ FT ≤ 2.2 s) and FF ($3000 \leq$ FF ≤ 3500 N). This would sharply decrease Dp (i.e., from over 6 mm to below 3 mm at maximum values of FT and FF), resulting in an over-deformed rivet tip (Figure 5b), an undesired feature. Hence, the use of process parameters which yield such over-deformation may be considered as energetically inefficient. As will be addressed in more detail in Paper II, having Dp values close to those of H maximizes the resistive polymer volume above the rivet tip. This desired feature could be achieved with the process parameter window where the following conditions in the contour plot of Figure 22 intercept: Dp higher than 6 mm; H between 7 and 9 mm; and W between 9 and 12 mm. Part II will focus on comprehensive discussions regarding the correlation between the resultant rivet tip geometry and joint mechanical performance.

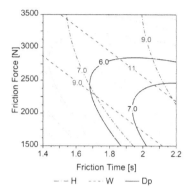

Figure 22. Influence of most relevant joining parameters FF and FT on joint formation (H, W and Dp). Values in millimeters. Regions of interest delimited by colored lines. RS is set at 21,000 rpm, FoT at 1.5 s and FoF at 4500 N.

5. Conclusions

Joint formation mechanisms of the force-controlled friction riveting process variant were systematically investigated, for the first time, in this work. A wide range of parameters was set using a central composite design of experiments. The statistical significances and influences of the process parameters on the resulting joint were determined using statistical analysis of variance and response surface methodology. The investigated joining parameter matrix yielded great variation of the measured rivet geometric responses characterizing the plastic deformation of the AA2024-T351 rivet tip inside the PEI plates. The energy input ranged between 24 and 208 J. Higher energy led to lower anchoring depth, reflecting excessive rivet plastic deformation. Process temperature also varied considerably across the parameter range (319–501 °C), resulting from the energy input. The frictional energy contribution proved decisive to the control of the overall rivet plastic deformation and process temperature, with moderate energy input levels (~100 J) preferable, avoiding excessive rivet deformation, which promotes decreasing joint mechanical performance.

The plastic deformation at the rivet tip was measured by rivet penetration depth, H (4.7–8.8 mm), maximum width of the deformed rivet tip, W (6.2–11.9 mm), and anchoring depth, Dp (3.7–7.1 mm). These responses were found to be influenced by the process parameters in different ways, with the magnitude and nature of such influence varying considerably. Rivet penetration depth was largely dependent on friction time (i.e., 61.9% of the total statistical contribution). For the maximum width of the deformed rivet tip, friction force and friction time contributed the most, with 46.5% and 27.1%, respectively. This response demonstrated a relatively linear increase in magnitude with increasing energy input. The anchoring depth displayed the most complex behavior of all three measurements. It was considerably influenced by quadratic (29.8%) and two-way interaction terms (20.8%). Similarly, in the case of rivet penetration depth, the anchoring depth also had its greater contribution deriving from friction time (34.7%).

The friction force parameter was found to have great influence on the geometry and final shape of the rivet tip. To avoid counterproductive over-deformation, both friction force and friction time should be set in a manner which does not promote excessive energy input. This excess of energy results in an undesirably low anchoring depth, reducing the resistive polymer volume above the rivet tip, responsible for offering resistance to a pull-out mechanical solicitation applied to the joint. The knowledge obtained with this work, on geometrical characterization and predictive models for joint formation, could allow for a tailor-made approach in the production of force-controlled friction-riveted joints.

The second and final part of this work will be published as a separate manuscript in this journal (Part II), focusing on the mechanical performance and energy efficiency of friction-riveted joints, based on the knowledge on joint formation and energy input gained in the present Part I.

Author Contributions: G.P.C. designed and performed the experiments and analyzed all collected data; L.A.B., P.V. and J.F.d.S. contributed with discussions on the experimental results; S.T.A.-F. determined the structure of the manuscript; all authors contributed to the preparation and revision of the manuscript.

Funding: The authors would like to acknowledge the financial support provided by the Helmholtz Association, Germany (Grant No. VH-NG-626), the Austrian aviation program TAKE OFF, and BMVIT-Austrian Ministry for Transport, Innovation and Technology.

Conflicts of Interest: The authors declare no conflict of interest.

References

1. Timmis, A.J.; Hodzic, A.; Koh, L.; Bonner, M.; Soutis, C.; Schäfer, A.W.; Dray, L. Environmental impact assessment of aviation emission reduction through the implementation of composite materials. *Int. J. Life Cycle Assess.* **2015**, *20*, 233–243. [CrossRef]
2. Amancio-Filho, S.T.; Dos Santos, J.F. Joining of polymers and polymer-metal hybrid structures: Recent developments and trends. *Polym. Eng. Sci.* **2009**, *49*, 1461–1476. [CrossRef]
3. Baldan, A. Adhesively-bonded joints and repairs in metallic alloys, polymers and composite materials: Adhesives, adhesion theories and surface pretreatment. *J. Mater. Sci.* **2004**, *39*, 1–49. [CrossRef]
4. Budynas, R.; Nisbett, K. *Shigley's Mechanical Engineering Design*; McGraw-Hill: New York, NY, USA, 2011; ISBN 978-007-352-928-8.
5. Ghassemieh, E. Materials in automotive application, state of the art and prospects. *New Trends Dev. Automot. Ind.* **2011**, *20*, 365–394. [CrossRef]
6. Mallick, P. *Materials, Design and Manufacturing for Lightweight Vehicles*; Woodhead Publishing: Cambridge, UK, 2010; ISBN 978-184-569-463-0.
7. Amancio-Filho, S.T.; Beyer, M.; dos Santos, J.F. Method of Connecting a Metallic Bolt to a Plastic Workpiece. U.S. Patent 7,575,149, 18 August 2009.
8. Amancio-Filho, S.T.; Dos Santos, J.F. Influence of processing parameters on microstructure and properties of a polyetherimide joined by fricriveting: Investigation of rotational speed. In Proceedings of the Annual Technical Conference—ANTEC, Chicago, IL, USA, 22–24 June 2009.
9. Altmeyer, J.; dos Santos, J.F.; Amancio-Filho, S.T. Effect of the friction riveting process parameters on the joint formation and performance of Ti alloy/short-fibre reinforced polyether ether ketone joints. *Mater. Des.* **2014**, *60*, 164–176. [CrossRef]
10. Rodrigues, C.F.; Blaga, L.A.; dos Santos, J.F.; Canto, L.B.; Hage, E.; Amancio-Filho, S.T. FricRiveting of aluminum 2024-T351 and polycarbonate: Temperature evolution, microstructure and mechanical performance. *J. Mater. Process. Technol.* **2014**, *214*, 2029–2039. [CrossRef]
11. Blaga, L.; Bancilă, R.; dos Santos, J.F.; Amancio-Filho, S.T. Friction Riveting of glass–fibre-reinforced polyetherimide composite and titanium grade 2 hybrid joints. *Mater. Des.* **2013**, *50*, 825–829. [CrossRef]
12. Borba, N.; Afonso, C.; Blaga, L.; dos Santos, J.; Canto, L.; Amancio-Filho, S. On the Process-Related Rivet Microstructural Evolution, Material Flow and Mechanical Properties of Ti-6Al-4V/GFRP Friction-Riveted Joints. *Materials* **2017**, *10*, 184. [CrossRef] [PubMed]
13. Proenca, B.C.; Blaga, L.A.; Dos Santos, J.F.; Canto, L.B.; Amancio-Filho, S.T. Force controlled friction riveting of glass fiber reinforced polyamide 6 and aluminum alloy 6056 hybrid joints. In Proceedings of the Annual Technical Conference—ANTEC, Orlando, FL, USA, 23–25 March 2015.
14. Amancio-Filho, S.T. Friction Riveting: Development and Analysis of a New Joining Technique for Polymer-Metal Multi-Materials Structures. Ph.D. Thesis, Technische Universität Hamburg-Harburg, Hamburg, Germany, 1 July 2007.
15. Amancio-Filho, S.T.; dos Santos, J.F. Henry Granjon Prize Competition 2009 Winner Category A: "Joining and Fabrication Technology" Friction Riveting: Development and Analysis of a New Joining Technique for Polymer-Metal Multi-Material Structures. *Weld. World* **2011**, *55*, 13–24. [CrossRef]
16. Wirth, J.G. Discovery and Development of Polyetherimides. In *High Performance Polymers: Their Origin and Development*; Springer: Dordrecht, The Netherlands, 1986; pp. 195–205.

17. Johnson, R.O.; Burlhis, H.S. Polyetherimide: A new high-performance thermoplastic resin. *J. Polym. Sci. Polym. Symp.* **2007**, *70*, 129–143. [CrossRef]

18. Fukuhara, M. Temperature dependency of elastic moduli and internal dilational and shear frictions of polyetherimide. *J. Appl. Polym. Sci.* **2003**, *90*, 759–764. [CrossRef]

19. Thomas, S.; Visakh, P.M. *Handbook of Engineering and Specialty Thermoplastics*; Scrivener Publishing LLC: Salem, MA, USA, 2012; Volume 4, ISBN 978-111-822-906-4.

20. Davis, J.R. *ASM Specialty Handbook: Aluminum and Aluminum Alloys*; ASM International: Almere, The Netherlands, 1993; ISBN 978-087-170-496-2.

21. Ma, T.J.; Li, W.; Yang, S.Y. Impact toughness and fracture analysis of linear friction welded Ti-6Al-4V alloy joints. *Mater. Des.* **2009**, *30*, 2128–2132. [CrossRef]

22. Crawford, R.J.; Tam, Y. Friction welding of plastics. *J. Mater. Sci.* **1981**, *16*, 3275–3282. [CrossRef]

23. Stokes, V.K. Analysis of the friction (spin)-welding process for thermoplastics. *J. Mater. Sci.* **1988**, *23*, 2772–2785. [CrossRef]

24. Abibe, A.B.; Dos Santos, J.F.; Amancio-Filho, S.T. Friction Staking: A novel staking joining method for hybrid structures. In Proceedings of the Annual Technical Conference—ANTEC, Las Vegas, NV, USA, 28–30 April 2014.

25. Montgomery, D.C. *Design and Analysis of Experiments*; John Wiley and Sons: New York, NY, USA, 2001.

26. Myers, R.H.; Montgomery, D.C.; Anderson-Cook, C.M. *Response Surface Methodology: Process and Product Optimization Using Designed Experiments*, 3rd ed.; John Wiley & Sons: New York, NY, USA, 1995.

27. Khuri, A.I.; Mukhopadhyay, S. Response surface methodology. *Wiley Interdiscip. Rev. Comput. Stat.* **2010**, *2*, 128–149. [CrossRef]

28. Amancio-Filho, S.T.; Dos Santos, J.F. Preliminary analytical modeling of heat input in friction riveting. In Proceedings of the Annual Technical Conference—ANTEC, Indianapolis, IN, USA, 23–25 May 2016.

29. Montgomery, D.C.; Runger, G.C. *Applied Statistics and Probability for Engineers*, 3rd ed.; John Wiley & Sons: New York, NY, USA, 2003; ISBN 978-047-120-454-1.

30. Dealy, J.M.; Wissbrun, K.F. *Melt Rheology and Its Role in Plastics Processing: Theory and Applications*; Chapman & Hall: London, UK, 1990; ISBN 978-041-273-910-1.

31. Hamielec, A.E.; Hodgins, J.W.; Tebbens, K. Polymer reactors and molecular weight distribution: Part II. Free radical polymerization in a batch reactor. *AIChE J.* **1967**, *13*, 1087–1091. [CrossRef]

32. Sacks, M.E.; Lee, S.-I.; Biesenberger, J.A. Effect of temperature variations on molecular weight distributions: Batch, chain addition polymerizations. *Chem. Eng. Sci.* **1973**, *28*, 241–257. [CrossRef]

33. Johnson, R.O.; Teutsch, E.O. Thermoplastic aromatic polyimide composites. *Polym. Compos.* **1983**, *4*, 162–166. [CrossRef]

Article

Fundamentals of Force-Controlled Friction Riveting: Part II—Joint Global Mechanical Performance and Energy Efficiency

Gonçalo Pina Cipriano [1,2], Lucian A. Blaga [3], Jorge F. dos Santos [3], Pedro Vilaça [2] and Sergio T. Amancio-Filho [1,*]

[1]   Institute of Materials Science, Joining and Forming, BMVIT Endowed Professorship for Aviation, Graz University of Technology, 8010 Graz, Austria; goncalo.pinacipriano@tugraz.at

[2]   Department of Mechanical Engineering, School of Engineering, Aalto University, 02150 Espoo, Finland; pedro.vilaca@aalto.fi

[3]   Helmholtz-Zentrum Geesthacht, Centre for Materials and Coastal Research, Institute of Materials Research, Materials Mechanics, Solid State Joining Process, 21502 Geesthacht, Germany; lucian.blaga@hzg.de (L.A.B.); jorge.dos.santos@hzg.de (J.F.d.S.)

*   Correspondence: sergio.amancio@tugraz.at; Tel.: +43-316-8731610

Received: 24 October 2018; Accepted: 3 December 2018; Published: 7 December 2018

Abstract: The present work investigates the correlation between energy efficiency and global mechanical performance of hybrid aluminum alloy AA2024 (polyetherimide joints), produced by force-controlled friction riveting. The combinations of parameters followed a central composite design of experiments. Joint formation was correlated with mechanical performance via a volumetric ratio (0.28–0.66 a.u.), with a proposed improvement yielding higher accuracy. Global mechanical performance and ultimate tensile force varied considerably across the range of parameters (1096–9668 N). An energy efficiency threshold was established at 90 J, until which, energy input displayed good linear correlations with volumetric ratio and mechanical performance (R-sq of 0.87 and 0.86, respectively). Additional energy did not significantly contribute toward increasing mechanical performance. Friction parameters (i.e., force and time) displayed the most significant contributions to mechanical performance (32.0% and 21.4%, respectively), given their effects on heat development. For the investigated ranges, forging parameters did not have a significant contribution. A correlation between friction parameters was established to maximize mechanical response while minimizing energy usage. The knowledge from Parts I and II of this investigation allows the production of friction riveted connections in an energy efficient manner and control optimization approach, introduced for the first time in friction riveting.

Keywords: friction; riveting; hybrid structures; joining; response surface

---

1. Introduction

A current concern in industry is the compromise between the benefits of using lightweight materials and how to integrate these into larger multi-material designs. The wider the range of possible joining technologies to perform hybrid connections, the less compromising or restricted the usage of these materials might be. The more traditional and well-established methods to perform connections between different material classes are mechanical fastening [1] and adhesive bonding [2].

Given existing limitations related to the use of more conventional methods to perform connections (referred to in Part I of this work [3] and in References [2,4,5]) and the need to further push the boundaries on new design solutions and methodologies, several alternative joining technologies have been recently developed. Studies into how some of these hybrid joining technologies would perform under mechanical loading can be found in the literature. Abibe et al. [4] investigated the mechanical behavior of hybrid staked joints, performed using aluminum alloy AA2024-T351 and a 30% short-glass-fiber-reinforced polyamide 6,6. In their investigation, the failure of single-lap joints resulted from the bearing of the deformed polymeric stake against the inner wall of the pre-drilled feature on the metallic component, leading to both net tension and rivet pullout failure modes. Goushegir et al. [5] studied the mechanical performance of single lap joints produced by friction spot joining of AA2024 and carbon-fiber-reinforced poly(phenylene sulfide). Their work assessed the influence of the process parameters on the ultimate lap shear force and established a predictive analytical model, via a full-factorial design of experiments and analysis of variance (ANOVA). For a recent and comprehensive overview of friction-based joining processes for polymer-metal hybrid structures, please refer to Reference [6].

The present investigation focuses on evaluating the global mechanical performance of joints produced by friction riveting (FricRiveting), using polyetherimide (PEI) and AA2024-T351. Friction riveting was patented by Helmholtz-Zentrum Geesthacht [7] as a technique to produce both similar and dissimilar, polymer and hybrid polymer or composite-metal overlapping connections. The process has been reported to have successfully joined several material combinations. Initial studies on AA2024-T351/PEI joint formation and mechanical performance were performed by Amancio-Filho et al. [8], who produced and mechanically tested the joints by a quasi-static rivet pullout setup, observing several distinct types of failure. Failure throughout the rivet was achieved for some of the joining conditions tested [9]. Similar results were reported by Rodrigues et al. [10] for AA2024-T351/polycarbonate joints. By assessing joint formation measurements, they established a volumetric ratio for the plastically deformed rivet tip, plotted along with the maximum tensile force obtained from the quasi-static testing prior to failure. This analysis resulted in a relatively good correlation between the volumetric ratio and the load achieved. The increase of the former led also to an increase tendency displayed by the latter. This ratio, earlier introduced by Blaga et al. [11], establishes a simplified ratio between the plastically deformed rivet tip and the polymeric volume above it offering mechanical resistance to a rivet-pullout solicitation. In both works, this determined ratio had considerable scatter against the joint ultimate tensile force (UTF). These derived from the limitations of this ratio when a wide range of deformed rivet tip geometries is considered.

In the first part of the present work, by Cipriano et al. (Part I) found in Reference [3], the AA2024-PEI joints were produced, using a force-controlled, time-limited process variant of friction riveting. The resulting joint formation—the plastically deformed shape of the metallic rivet tip—was studied. Correlations between the joining process parameters and the resulting joint formation were established. Predictive statistical models were developed and reported for the following responses: rivet penetration depth; maximum width of the deformed rivet tip; and rivet anchoring depth. Building on this knowledge, the present work (Part II) aimed to evaluate the global mechanical properties of the exact same joints. A response surface methodology was used to statistically evaluate the response object of study, the UTF, and establish a predictive analytical model, with the objective of determining the expected mechanical behavior based on the joining process parameters. The mechanical energy input used to produce the joints, was evaluated along with the quasi-static joint mechanical performance and a concept of energy efficiency was established. Furthermore, an updated volumetric ratio calculation was proposed, to better take into consideration the wide range of rivet plastic deformation shapes and anchoring performance. This ratio was the basis to estimate joint global mechanical performance, based solely on joint formation. Finally, an optimized range of process parameters was defined for maximizing the UTF, while aiming to minimize the energy used.

2. The Process

Friction riveting (FricRiveting) is an alternative friction-based mechanical fastening method, combining principles from both conventional mechanical fastening and friction welding. FricRiveting can be performed using several setup configurations, such as single rivet and single polymeric plate (point-on-plate joints), and polymer–polymer or polymer–metal overlap joints [8]. The metallic rivet can be used either with a plain featureless surface or with different profiles, such as threaded [8] and hollow rivets [12]. The main connection mechanism of this process is mechanical interlocking, achieved between the plastically deformed rivet tip and the polymeric component enveloping it (i.e., through rivet anchoring). The rotating rivet is pressed into the polymer/composite, and given the local temperature increase during the process, it plastically deforms, assuming an axisymmetric anchor-shaped geometry and consolidating under pressure. A more detailed process description is given in Part I [3]. For this work, the user-defined process parameters are: rotational speed (RS); friction time (FT); friction force (FF); forging time (FoT); and forging force (FoF). The friction parameters are applied during the friction phase of the process, while the rivet is rotating and being inserted. After this friction phase the rotation is reduced to zero and a forging phase may take place, being defined by the forging parameters, force and time. Both friction and forging forces are axial forces applied to the rivet. Further detailed descriptions of the process and its configurations can be found in the literature [6,8] and in Part I of this work [3].

3. Materials and Methods

3.1. Base Materials

The materials used in the present work were polyetherimide (PEI) and AA2024-T351. Polyetherimide is a high-performance thermoplastic developed by Wirth et al. [13]. It is characterized by an elevated glass transition temperature (T_g) at 215 °C [14]. Its mechanical behavior is in accordance with Hooke's Law, having an elastic modulus that decreases by about 50% when at temperatures from 170 °C to 190 °C [15]. This engineering thermoplastic also meets automotive and aircraft industries' specific requirements regarding flame resistance and smoke evolution [16]. Table 1 shows some of the properties characterizing this material.

Table 1. Summarized polyetherimide (PEI) properties [17].

Property	Value
$R_{0.2}$ (MPa)	129
E (MPa)	3500
Glass Transition Temp. (°C)	215
Thermal Conductivity (W/m·K)	0.24

The polymeric joining parts, 70 mm × 70 mm, were machined from extruded PEI plates of 13.4 mm in nominal thickness, supplied by Quadrant Engineering Plastic Products, Lenzburg, Switzerland. The plain metallic rivets used for this work were produced out of extruded AA2024-T351 rods, having a length of 60 mm and a diameter of 5 mm. This alloy is characterized by high mechanical strength and is widely used for aircraft structural and fuselage applications, as well as for mechanical fasteners, making it very attractive for process developments of the present work nature. The properties of main interest for this alloy are shown in Table 2. For a more detailed description of the materials used, please refer to Part I [3].

Table 2. Summarized AA2024-T351 properties [18].

Property	Value
R_m (MPa)	427
$R_{0.2}$ (MPa)	310
E (GPa)	72
Melting Temp. Domain (°C)	518–548
Sol. Heat Treat. Temp. (°C)	495
Annealing Temp. (°C)	256

3.2. Joining Procedure

The joints tested in this investigation were produced in a customized FricRiveting gantry equipment (RNA, H. Loitz-Robotik, Hamburg, Germany). The joining equipment had a maximum axial load capacity of 24 kN and a maximum rotational speed of 21,000 rpm. The equipment allowed process on-line monitoring and the determination of the mechanical energy being used, with integrated sensors, namely assessing position, force, and torque. The equipment is shown in Figure 1.

Figure 1. RNA custom equipment. (Photo: Helmholtz-Zentrum Geesthacht/Rasmus Lippels).

The user-set process parameters for this force-controlled variant were: rotational speed (RS); friction force (FF); forging force (FoF); friction time (FT); and forging time (FoT). Table 3 presents the joining parameter ranges used.

Table 3. Process parameter ranges.

RS [rpm]	FT [s]	FoT [s]	FF [kN]	FoF [kN]
17,000–21,000	1.4–2.2	0.5–2.5	1.5–3.5	3.3–5.7

The joining parameter combinations were set by Cipriano et al. in Part I [3] via a central composite design. The selection of the joining parameters was intended to promote a wide range of plastic deformation on the metallic rivet tip, aiming for providing an understanding of the energy ranges necessary to achieve a certain level of rivet mechanical anchoring in the polymeric part. Hence, correlating the energy input range and resulting rivet plastic deformation, with the global mechanical performance assessed in Part II of the work.

3.3. Non-Destructive Testing of Joint Formation

The joint formation (i.e., the plastically deformed rivet tip geometry) was investigated in Part I [3], through X-ray tomography, exemplified in Figure 2.

Previous studies demonstrated the correlation between a volumetric ratio and the global mechanical performance of the joint [6,8,9]. The volumetric ratio establishes a simplified quotient between the volume of the plastically deformed rivet and the volume of polymer offering mechanical resistance to a rivet-pullout action. The volumetric ratio (VR) is determined by Equation (1):

$$VR = \frac{(H - B) \times \left(W^2 - D^2\right)}{H \times W^2}, \ [0-1] \tag{1}$$

where H is the penetration depth, B the deformed tip height (a dimension measured from the beginning of changes in the original rivet diameter, D, until the bottom of the deformed rivet tip, Figure 2), W the maximum deformed width of the rivet tip, and D the original rivet diameter.

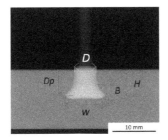

Figure 2. X-ray tomography joint formation measurements: rivet penetration depth (H); maximum width of the deformed rivet tip (W); depth until the maximum width of the rivet tip, or anchoring depth, (Dp); the height of the deformed rivet tip (B); and with original rivet diameter displayed (D).

In the present work, an improved volumetric ratio assessment is proposed and compared with the previous approach. For distinguishing purposes, the updated volumetric ratio will be referred to as VR(U). This modification arose from the need to better assess the differences observed in joint formation and rivet tip shape, over a wide range of parameters reported in Part I [3] and further discussed in the results chapter. The VR(U) is expressed by Equation (2),

$$VR(U) = \frac{\left(W^2 - D^2\right) \times D_p}{H \times W^2}, \; [0 - 1] \tag{2}$$

where the new term Dp is used, representing the anchoring depth (i.e., the depth until the maximum width of the rivet tip), differing from the measure previously used based on B. Figure 3 schematically illustrates the limitation of the previous VR calculation procedure. For bell-shaped deformations of the rivet tip, using the B parameter leads to a considerable reduction of the polymeric interaction volume being considered. While by using Dp in the proposed VR(U) equation, a closer to reality and more robust estimation across a wide range of rivet tip deformations and geometries can be achieved, since Dp corresponds to the depth up to the maximum width of the deformed rivet tip. The limit cases where VR and VR(U) are equal to zero, entails that no rivet deformation has occurred, i.e., no interaction volume is present (Figure 3), and W has the value of the original rivet diameter, D. For both VR and VR(U) to achieve a value of one, some limit conditions must be met. The initial value of the diameter, D, would necessarily tend to the value of zero, with a W higher than D, for both ratios. For VR a B value close to zero would also need to be observed. In the case of VR(U), Dp would also tend to the same value as H.

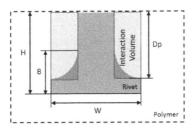

Figure 3. Schematic representation of joint formation geometrical measurements on a bell-shaped deformed rivet tip.

3.4. Mechanical Performance

To evaluate the global mechanical performance of the specimens produced, a quasi-static pullout tensile testing set-up was used (adapted from ISO 6892 [19]). The tests were conducted at room temperature using a Zwick/Roell 1478 universal testing machine (Zwick/Roell, Ulm, Germany) equipped with a 100 kN load cell. A customized clamping adapter, illustrated in Figure 4, was used to distribute the load over the polymeric plate. The specimens were tested at a rate of 1 mm/min and room temperature conditions, with a grip distance L_0 of 22 mm.

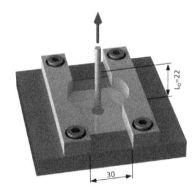

Figure 4. T-Pull testing set-up schematic representation (dimensions in millimeters).

3.5. Energy Input

The energy input values used to produce the specimens for this work were calculated and reported by Cipriano et al. in Part I [3], using Equation (3). This equation considers the total mechanical energy input, E_M, applied for friction-based processes, involving both metallic material [20] and thermoplastic [21].

$$E_M = E_f + E_d = \int M \cdot \omega \cdot dt + \int F \cdot \vartheta \cdot dt \; [\text{J}] \tag{3}$$

The first term refers to the frictional energy (E_f) resulting from torque (M) and rotational speed (ω). The second estimates the deformational component (E_d), from axial force (F) and plunging rate of the metallic rivet (ϑ). The results previously reported on the energy input (Part I [3]) will sustain correlations and discussions between the energy used and the obtained global mechanical performance.

3.6. Statistical Analysis of the Mechanical Performance Results

By using a design of experiments (DoE), Cipriano et al. (Part I) [3] determined the joining parameter combinations expected to yield a wide range of joint formation, and so, resulting in a large range of UTF. A central composite design (CCD) was used in Part I [3] to define the joining parameter test matrix. This is a second order design capable of generating response surfaces [22,23]. In the present work, the influence of the process parameters (RS, FT, FoT, FF, and FoF) on the UTF response was quantified and a predictive reduced regression model was established. This regression model was generated with a stepwise backward elimination procedure, considering an alpha-to-remove value of 0.05. By this method, all the potential terms of the model are considered at first, being the least significant term eliminated on each step; this iteration process is carried out up to the point at which no factor has a p-value above the defined alpha (i.e., being statistically significant). The model was validated by producing and testing additional joints with different parameter sets from the original design points, within the same parameter window.

4. Results and Discussion

4.1. Volumetric Ratio Assessment

As described in Section 3.3, the volumetric ratios, VR and VR(U), were determined by making use of the measurements on joint formation, published in Part I [3]. The calculated values are shown in Table 4. As previously discussed, VR gives an indication of the expected mechanical performance (UTF) of a given joint [10,11].

Table 4. Volumetric ratios of the produced joints.

Condition	VR	VR(U)	Condition	VR	VR(U)	Condition	VR	VR(U)
1	0.14	0.28	13	0.33	0.62	25	0.30	0.62
2	0.23	0.39	14	0.42	0.60	26	0.36	0.63
3	0.32	0.51	15	0.44	0.54	27	0.29	0.50
4	0.27	0.66	16	0.38	0.58	28	0.39	0.60
5	0.19	0.31	17	0.29	0.49	29	0.23	0.38
6	0.21	0.45	18	0.35	0.62	30	0.48	0.56
7	0.21	0.55	19	0.44	0.64	31	0.36	0.56
8	0.37	0.61	20	0.38	0.62	32	0.36	0.62
9	0.38	0.58	21	0.31	0.54	33	0.18	0.32
10	0.34	0.60	22	0.31	0.60	34	0.20	0.43
11	0.38	0.56	23	0.31	0.48	35	0.40	0.57
12	0.40	0.52	24	0.37	0.62	36	0.28	0.63

The joints which yielded both the lowest and the highest VR(U), Conditions 1 (VR = 0.14/VR(U) = 0.28) and 4 (VR = 0.27/VR(U) = 0.66) are shown in Figure 5. It is clear that relevant differences in rivet tip deformation were achieved. These conditions were produced with different joining parameters, which resulted in different total energy inputs (Condition 1: E_M = 24 J; Condition 4: E_M = 77 J). The influence of the energy input on joint formation will be addressed in the following sections.

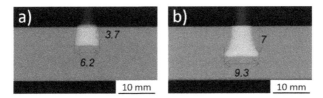

Figure 5. X-ray tomography of: (**a**) Condition 1 (E_M = 24 J; RS = 18,000 rpm; FT = 1.6 s; FoT = 1 s; FF = 2000 N; FoF = 5100 N); (**b**) Condition 4 (E_M = 77 J; RS = 20,000 rpm; FT = 2 s; FoT = 1 s; FF = 2000 N; FoF = 5100 N).

4.2. Global Mechanical Performance

The global mechanical performance of the joints was assessed by the procedure described in Section 3.4. The UTF and mechanical energy input, E_M [3], values achieved during testing are presented in Table 5.

Table 5. Mechanical testing ultimate tensile force (UTF) results.

Condition	E_M (J)	UTF (N)	Condition	E_M (J)	UTF (N)	Condition	E_M (J)	UTF (N)
1	24	1776	13	78	8251	25	68	7741
2	46	4943	14	86	8046	26	71	8461
3	53	5427	15	120	9106	27	51	5689
4	77	9619	16	208	8996	28	83	9049
5	29	2202	17	63	7290	29	36	3166
6	36	3897	18	76	9304	30	136	8643
7	65	6256	19	74	8824	31	64	9098
8	57	7829	20	73	9033	32	73	9029
9	60	6391	21	56	6068	33	38	1096
10	83	9004	22	59	7663	34	159	7864
11	106	8192	23	47	5041	35	59	6811
12	155	9362	24	67	8701	36	86	9668

The highest UTF was achieved for Condition 36 (E_M = 86 J), with a value of 9668 N. The lowest UTF value was obtained for Condition 33 (E_M = 38 J), 1096 N. The latter condition is characterized by a very small rivet tip plastic deformation inside the polymer, consequence of the smaller E_M. Hence, a lower strength mechanical anchoring resulted between the plastically deformed rivet tip and the polymeric plate. As can be seen in Figure 6a, this joining condition induced only a slight change of the rivet diameter at the tip (W = 6.5 mm) in comparison to the original rivet diameter (5 mm).

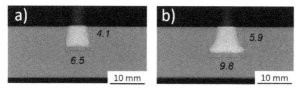

Figure 6. X-ray tomography of: (**a**) Condition 33 (RS = 19,000 rpm; FT = 1.8 s; FoT = 1.5 s; FF = 1500 N; FoF = 4500 N); (**b**) Condition 36 (RS = 19,000 rpm; FT = 1.8 s; FoT = 1.5 s; FF = 2500 N; FoF = 5700 N).

As opposed to what is seen in Figure 6a, Condition 36 joined with higher FF and FoF (refer to Figure 6 caption or Table 2 in Part I [3]) in Figure 6b, yielded the highest UTF. In this case, the observed deformation sustained by the rivet is considerably higher, resulting in a bell-shaped rivet tip. The mechanical anchoring of the deformed rivet tip inside the polymer increases the UTF by an 8.8 factor, when compared with Condition 33, from 1096 N to 9668 N. There is a significant increase in the deformed rivet tip diameter (W = 9.8 mm), while the rivet penetrates deeper into the polymer (H = 5.9 mm). Consequently, a greater polymeric interaction volume resists the pullout mechanical solicitation during testing. The higher interaction volume is demonstrated by the increase of VR(U) for Condition 36 (0.63) by a factor of 1.97 from that of Condition 33 (0.32). From this example, one might consider that by increasing the energy input used, it would invariably result in a higher VR(U) and consequently in a higher mechanical performance of the joint. Nonetheless, after a certain energy level is reached, the increasing plastic deformation will result in a decrease of VR(U). In the coming sections, the corroborated effect of energy input and other factors, such as geometrical shape and features of the anchoring zones, on the anchoring performance will be discussed.

Different joint failure types were observed for the tested specimens. Figure 7 schematically represents the current classification of the several failure modes reported in the literature [10] for metallic-insert friction riveted joints.

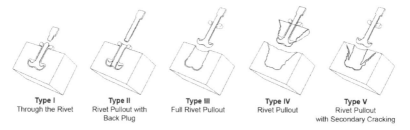

Type I	Type II	Type III	Type IV	Type V
Through the Rivet	Rivet Pullout with Back Plug	Full Rivet Pullout	Rivet Pullout	Rivet Pullout with Secondary Cracking

Figure 7. Current failure modes of friction riveted joints reported in the literature (Reprinted from *J. Mater. Process Technol.* [10]).

The fractures of the conditions tested in this work were in accordance with those previously reported in the literature [8,10,24] and are summarized in Table 6.

Table 6. Types of fracture obtained for the tested joints.

Failure Type	Condition	UTF Range [N]
Rivet pullout with back plug (Type II)	12, 19, 21, 23, 26, 30, 35	5041–9362
Full Rivet Pullout (Type III)	1, 2, 3, 5, 6, 7, 8, 9, 10, 11, 17, 18, 20, 22, 24, 25, 27, 29, 33	1096–9049
Rivet Pullout (Type IV)	4, 13, 14, 15, 16, 28, 31, 32, 34, 36	7864–9668

Although an early initial ductile necking of the exposed rivet was verified in Condition 36, none of the tested conditions displayed a Type I failure mode. Both full rivet pullout (Type III) and rivet pullout (Type IV) failures, occur when the polymer is not capable of sustaining the mechanical solicitation [8]. The difference between these two failure types is that, in Type III, there is no fractured polymer from the polymeric interaction volume being removed with the rivet, although the expelled flash does stay attached to the rivet shaft, as seen in Figure 8a (Condition 7, $E_M = 65$ J). Here, the low deformation of the rivet tip allows it to be pulled by radially deforming the polymeric interaction volume, as it slides out. In failure Type II (rivet pullout with back plug), the interaction volume can sustain the mechanical solicitation. In this case the failure takes place on the rivet deformed tip, leaving a back plug of metal inside the polymer. This occurs when the resistance of the transition metallic area between main rivet body and the deformed tip is inferior to that offered by the polymeric interaction volume above it [10]. An example of Type II is seen in Figure 8b, for Condition 30 ($E_M = 136$ J). Rivet pullout (type IV) corresponds to the joints which yielded the highest UTF in this study. In these cases, the deformed rivet tip can withstand the solicitation and not fail on the metal, hence, not leaving the back plug observed in failure Type II. The deformation for these rivet pullout cases, is sufficient to promote a good mechanical anchoring inside the polymer, forcing it to bare the mechanical solicitation up to final failure. Figure 8c,d, represent the rivet pullout failure observed for Condition 13 ($E_M = 78$ J).

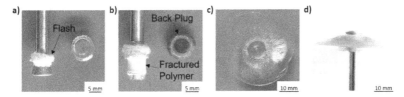

Figure 8. Examples of failure modes observed: (**a**) Condition 7 (RS = 18,000 rpm; FT = 2 s; FoT = 2 s; FF = 2000 N; FoF = 5100 N), full rivet pullout failure; (**b**) Condition 30 (RS = 19,000 rpm; FT = 2.2 s; FoT = 1.5 s; FF = 2500 N; FoF = 4500 N), rivet pullout with back plug; (**c**) Condition 13 (RS = 18,000 rpm; FT = 1.6 s; FoT = 2 s; FF = 3000 N; FoF = 5100 N), polymeric plate, rivet pullout failure; (**d**) Condition 13, side view of rivet and detached polymer, rivet pullout failure.

From the volumetric ratio assessment in the previous section, the VR(U) of Conditions 1 and 4 (0.28 and 0.66, respectively) are in accordance with the expected indication they give on UTF, as Condition 1 yielded a UTF of 1776 N and Condition 4 of 9619 N. The same was not observed for the rivet mechanical anchoring performance assessed by VR. For instance, Condition 4 (UTF = 9619 N), with a calculated VR of 0.27, was far from the maximum VR value observed of 0.48 for Condition 30, although the latter has a smaller UTF (8643 N). These results suggest that the state-of-the-art VR equation has limitations when comparing different deformation magnitudes. This is clearer when comparing Conditions 6 ($E_M = 36$ J) and 7 ($E_M = 65$ J), despite having the same VR of 0.21, demonstrate different VR(U), 0.45 and 0.55, respectively. As can be seen from X-ray tomography images (Figure 9), although the overall geometry is similar in both joints, both the rivet penetration and deformation of Condition 7 are greater than that of Condition 6. In this comparison, calculated VR(U) values are proportional to UTF, whereby Condition 7 is stronger than Condition 6 (UTF = 6256 N and UTF = 3897 N, respectively). Therefore, the modified rivet mechanical anchoring estimation by VR(U) (Equation (2)) seems to allow for a better fitting with the joint mechanical performance.

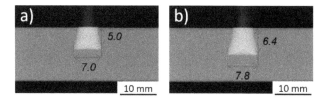

Figure 9. X-ray tomography of: (**a**) Condition 6 (RS = 20,000 rpm; FT = 1.6 s; FoT = 2 s; FF = 2000 N; FoF = 5100 N); (**b**) Condition 7 (RS = 18,000 rpm; FT = 2 s; FoT = 2 s; FF = 2000 N; FoF = 5100 N).

The correlation between both VR and VR(U), with the global mechanical performance (UTF) of the joints produced, can be seen in Figure 10.

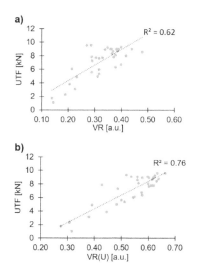

Figure 10. UTF—volumetric ratio plots: (**a**) VR; (**b**) VR(U).

Although the data demonstrates the tendency of linear proportionality of the volumetric ratio with the UTF, as reported in the literature for the VR [10], an improvement to this direct correlation (based on the value of the correlation performance parameter R^2) is observed when considering VR(U). This further supports the assumption that the VR(U) is a more accurate method of assessing the rivet mechanical anchoring and estimating joint mechanical performance, as it better takes into consideration the variations in shape/geometry of the rivet tip. Thus, for the remainder of the analysis, only the VR(U) will be considered.

4.3. Energy Efficiency

Energy input during friction riveting has been addressed in the literature [25], with some correlations being established with the joining parameters used. Nonetheless, no correlation between the energy input and mechanical performance has been analyzed. Therefore, a notion of energy efficiency, concerning the joint quasi-static mechanical performance, is then necessary. This could minimize the energy input and reduce costs (e.g., reduce power consumption, joining time.) when producing joints with higher mechanical performance. Hence, the total energy inputs (E_M), previously published for the present conditions in Part I, were evaluated in terms of UTF. Figure 11 presents the correlation between the total energy input and the respective UTF values.

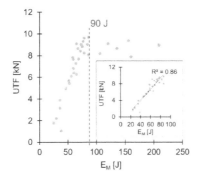

Figure 11. Correlation between mechanical performance and total energy input (E_M). In detail, the correlation for the energy efficient range ($E_M \leq 90$ J).

A relatively linear initial tendency of increasing UTF with the increase of the total energy input is evident. Also, relatively clear, is the level of energy input at which this correlation ceases to be valid ($E_M \approx 90$ J), with UTF reaching a relative plateau. As mentioned in Part I, above a certain level of energy input, the resultant deformation of the rivet tip is considered over-deformation. This is characterized by a small Dp, resulting from a premature increase of W (detailed in Figure 20, Part I [3]). Condition 15 (E_M = 120 J), Figure 12a, illustrates a small amount of over-deformation, contrasting with the bell-shaped plastically deformed rivet tip seen in Figures 5b and 6b. Figure 12b shows Condition 12 (E_M = 155 J), exemplifying a considerably over-deformed rivet tip. In these particular cases of excessive deformation, VR was more sensitive to plastic deformation changes than VR(U). Despite this fact, as shown in Figure 10, the accuracy of VR(U) remains higher than that pf VR, across the rivet plastic deformation range observed in this study. This is further accentuated when the energy efficient threshold is imposed (90 J), Figure 11.

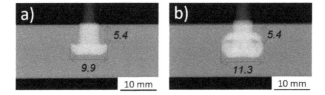

Figure 12. X-ray tomography of: (**a**) Condition 15 (RS = 18,000 rpm; FT = 2 s; FoT = 2 s; FF = 3000 N; FoF = 3900 N); and (**b**) Condition 12 (RS = 20,000 rpm; FT = 2 s; FoT = 1 s; FF = 3000 N; FoF = 3900 N).

Over-deformation of the rivet tip is considered negative since it does not inherently lead to a higher joint mechanical performance. By the correlation established in Figure 11, the UTF of Condition 12 (9362 N) could be achieved by a joint produced with a much lower energy input ($E_M \approx 80$ J). Figure 13 shows an energy efficiency perspective over the process before any mechanical testing, by assessing VR(U). Similar to the discussion regarding UTF, an energy efficient joint formation threshold (regarding VR(U)) can also be established. Therefore, using energy inputs higher than the defined thresholds means unnecessary consumption of resources. Therefore, this should be taken into consideration when defining joining parameters with a targeted UTF value, to minimize production costs.

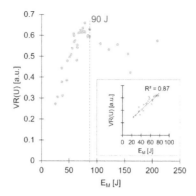

Figure 13. Correlation between improved volumetric ratio, VR(U), and total energy input (E_M). In detail, correlation for the energy efficient range ($E_M \leq 90$ J).

4.4. Influence of the Process Parameters on Mechanical Performance

The quasi-static mechanical performance (UTF) of the produced joints was statistically investigated. Response surface methodology was used to determine the influence joining process parameters have on this mechanical response, as described in Section 3.6.

The first order parameters present in the reduced statistical model were RS, FT and FF. The second order parameters were FF × FF and FT × FT. Finally, the interaction FT × FF is also considered. The respective *p*-values of these parameters are presented in Table 7.

Table 7. Statistical significance (p-values) of reduced model factors.

Parameter	*p*-Value	Parameter	*p*-Value
RS	0	**FF × FF**	0
FT	0	**FT × FT**	0.017
FF	0	**FT × FF**	0.011

The individual contributions of the terms present in the model and its total error are shown in Figure 14. The largest contribution (32%) to the achieved UTF comes from a linear term, the FF parameter. One quadratic term, FF × FF, also plays an important role with 11.6%.

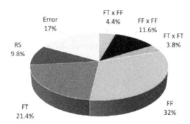

Figure 14. Relative contributions of the model factors to the response UTF.

From the statistical analysis, FoF and FoT are not part of the model, having *p*-values larger than 0.05 (Table 7). This behavior may relate to the investigated joining parameters windows, as these may be narrow for FoF and FoT to promote considerable variance on the mechanical performance across the entire selected range, independently of the relatively wide range of resulting rivet plastic deformation in this work.

The reduced regression equation obtained for this predictive model is shown below (Equation (4)) in parameter-coded levels [−2; 2].

$$UTF = 8016 + 887\,RS + 1310\,FT + 1602\,FF - \\ (478\,FT \times FT + 835\,FF \times FF + 726\,FT \times FF) \tag{4}$$

The model-predicted values for UTF were correlated with those obtained experimentally in Figure 15. In this validation plot, it is visible that the majority of the data points fall within the prediction limit lines (solid grey), within which the model can predict a single response observation [26]. A set of 13 additional validation joints supported this trend.

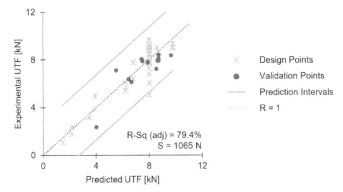

Figure 15. Validation diagram for the reduced model of UTF.

The explanatory power of the UTF model—the adjusted R-sq—was 79.4%. Moreover, this model shows a predicted R-sq = 77.9% and standard error, S, of 1065 N.

Figure 16 displays the influence the joining parameters have on UTF, using the main effects plots.

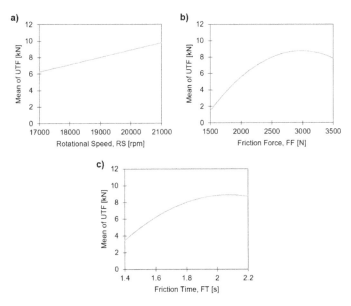

Figure 16. Main effects plots of linear model terms for the UTF response, with: (**a**) Rotational Speed; (**b**) Friction Force; and (**c**) Friction Time.

The only parameter that does not present complex effects is RS, with its increase resulting in higher UTF, given its linearly increasing contribution to the energy input. In other words, the RS promotes a higher rivet penetration, H, (refer to Figure 10a in Part I [3]), without reducing the polymeric interaction volume or negatively affecting the anchoring depth, Dp, as presented in Figure 19a, Part I. Both FF and FT display relatively similar curves over the studied range. In both cases the maximum UTF value is achieved at the upper quarter of the parameter range. Altmeyer et al. [25], have found that for friction riveting of titanium grade 3 with short-fiber-reinforced polyether-ether-ketone (PEEK), the UTF increased mostly due to the increase of RS, FT, and forging pressure (FoP) [27]. The high contribution of FF has been reported also in Part I of this investigation. Both FT and FF effects on the UTF become negative when close to the upper limits of the investigated parameter ranges. This can be explained by the occurrence of over-deformation on the metallic rivet tip, also reported in Part I, which is counterproductive towards the mechanical performance of the joint and not energy efficient, as demonstrated in Section 4.3.

The two-way interaction part of the statistical model (FT × FF) is depicted in the surface and contour plots of Figure 17. In order to assess this interaction, the remaining parameters (RS, FoT and FoF) were set at their respective middle range values [23].

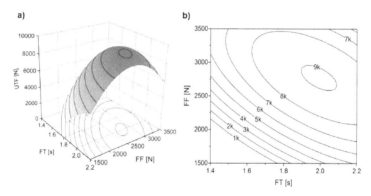

Figure 17. Effect of FT × FF two-way parameter interaction on UTF (in newton), (**a**) surface and (**b**) contour plots. RS set at 19,000 rpm, FoF at 4500 N, and FoT at 1.5 s.

It seems that only a small area (peak of the surface in Figure 17a) of both FT and FF ranges can maximize the UTF. This roughly elliptic area is located around FF values of 2750 N and FT around 2.0 s. Given the orientation of the curves (Figure 17b), smaller variations of FF than those of FT may result in UTF values outside the peak and optimal response region. This behavior was also seen in the main effects plots (Figure 16b,c), where effect of FF displayed a more pronounced curvature than FT. At low levels of both parameters, the resulting low energy input will not promote sufficient plastic deformation on the rivet tip to resist the pullout solicitation, hence the low UTF for this left lower quarter parameter region (e.g., Condition 1, seen in Figure 5, with a VR(U) = 0.28 and E_M = 24 J). In Figure 17b, following a 1:1 correlation between FF above 3000 N and FT higher than 2.0 s the UTF begins to gradually decrease to around 6000 N for maximum values of FF and FT. Since high levels of these parameters tend to produce over-deformation on the rivet tip, e.g., Condition 15, seen in Figure 12a. This is also in accordance to the proposed threshold of energy efficiency of 90 J (see Figures 11 and 12 for reference).

4.5. Summary of the Findings

In Part I of this work, the influence of the process parameters on the plastic deformation of the tip of the rivet was investigated. The energy input during the production of the joints was calculated and predictive reduced statistical models were established for the geometrical features of joint formation:

rivet penetration depth, maximum width of the deformed rivet tip, and anchoring depth. An initial optimized range of parameters for joint formation was established with the aim of improving the mechanical performance of the joints. In the present Part II, the mechanical performance of the joints was assessed. Based on the UTF and the energy input, the energy efficiency of the joints was investigated. The anchoring efficiency estimation by volumetric ratio (VR) was amended and the proposed updated model was validated (VR(U)). The energy efficiency and UTF were then correlated with the joint formation, using VR and VR(U), with an improved accuracy in the case of the latter.

In Part I [3], resulting from the reduced statistical models, Figure 22 illustrated the influence of FT and FF on H, W, and Dp. A similar approach was now used for VR(U), across the ranges of these parameters (Figure 18).

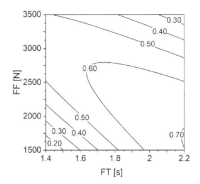

Figure 18. Contour plot for VR(U) correlated with FT and FF ranges. RS set at 21,000 rpm, FoT at 1.5 s, and FoF at 4500 N.

This plot shows how the use of maximum values for both FT and FF (i.e., higher energy input) leads to a VR(U) lower than 0.30. This is almost as low as the VR(U) resulting from using minimum values of those same parameters (VR(U) < 0.20). The decline in VR(U) observed when using energy input values beyond the energy efficiency threshold (Figure 13) is a result of rivet over-deformation, characterized by a decrease of the polymeric interaction volume. This effect has been discussed in Section 4.3 (Figure 12) and in more detail in Part I (Section 4.3.3; Figure 20) [3] It is directly correlated with the notion of energy efficiency, as using an excessive energy input (E_M > 90 J) tends to result in a decrease of the mechanical performance of the joints. An example of this effect summarized in Table 8, is the correlation between VR(U), UTF, and E_M between Conditions 25 (RS = 19,000 rpm; FT = 1.8 s; FoT = 1.5 s; FF = 2500 N; FoF = 4500 N) and 34 (RS = 19,000 rpm; FT = 1.8 s; FoT = 1.5 s; FF = 3500 N; FoF = 4500 N), with the only different parameter being FF.

Table 8. Joint performance comparison.

Condition	VR(U)	UTF [N]	E_M [J]
25	0.62	7741	68
34	0.43	7864	159

The total energy input calculated for Condition 25 is 43% of that used to produce Condition 34. The UTF of both conditions are in accordance with Figure 17b, for the respective FT and FF parameters. For both conditions, the plotted UTF values are close to reach the ellipsoidal 8000 N contour line. This demonstrates the energetic inefficiency of Condition 34, as the remnant 57% of the energy input used did not contribute to a significant improvement of the mechanical anchoring performance of the joint (UTF).

As shown in the previous section, RS has a linear increasing effect on the UTF (Figure 16a). Given this fact, in order to maximize the UTF response, Figure 19 displays a contour plot analogue to that of Figure 17b, now with RS set to its maximum (21,000 rpm). This allows to investigate how this increase of RS influenced the contour lines across the ranges of both FT and FF. The remaining parameters (FoT and FoF) were set to their central values (1.5 s and 4500 N, respectively), considering that these did not demonstrate a statistically significant effect on the UTF response.

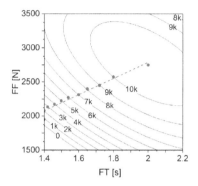

Figure 19. Contour plot for UTF (in Newton) correlated with the ranges of FT and FF. RS set at 21,000 rpm, FoT at 1.5 s, and FoF at 4500 N.

As expected, the peak region where the UTF is maximized remains centered in the vicinity of the same point (FT = 2 s and FF = 2750 N), given the mentioned linear effect RS has on UTF (Figure 16a). However, this region increased both in area and in UTF, from 9000 N $\leq$ UTF < 10,000 N to 10,000 N $\leq$ UTF < 11,000 N.

From these discussions, an energetically efficient approach toward producing a strong joint with this combination of materials, can be accomplished by using the highest value of RS from the investigated range (RS = 21,000 N), central values of both FoT and FoF (FoT = 1.5 s; and FoF = 4500 N), with FT and FF being chosen along the marked dashed line in Figure 19 (FF = 1189.8 × FT + 403.6, SI units). This correlation between FF and FT has been determined by linear regression from the points (seen as red circles in Figure 19) which represent the local minimums of the respective contour lines and also the predicted maximum (FT = 2 s and FF = 2750 N). These points identify a minimum combination of FT and FF values, which yield the respective UTF. In this manner, the energy usage is optimized (i.e., minimized), while maximizing the corresponding mechanical performance.

5. Conclusions

The global mechanical performance of hybrid connections produced using force-controlled and time-limited friction riveting, was investigated in this second and final part of the study into the fundamentals of this process variant. The joints previously produced (using AA2024-T351 and polyetherimide) and studied in Part I [3] of the work—assessment of joint formation—were mechanically tested in Part II. The ultimate tensile force (UTF) of the joints (rivet pullout solicitation) was determined, ranging between 1096 and 9668 N. The knowledge on joint formation from Part I [11] allowed the assessment of the anchoring efficiency, using the previously established volumetric ratio (VR) and a revised improved calculation (VR(U)). The latter was demonstrated to have a more accurate correlation with the mechanical performance, across the observed deformations and respective VR(U) range (0.28–0.66). The influence and contributions of the process parameters, their quadratic effects and interactions, on the mechanical performance were assessed using response surface methodology and statistical analysis of variance. Friction force and friction time parameters displayed complex behavior across their ranges showing a curvature related to over-deformation of the rivet tip. Increasing rotational speed promoted a linear increase of the mechanical performance. Forging parameters did not display a statistically significant effect on the performance response for the investigated range of parameters.

The wide range of plastic deformation experienced by the rivet tip, led to a wide range of mechanical performance and different joint failure types: full rivet pullout; rivet pullout with back plug; and rivet pullout. The highest values of VR(U) (above 0.60) yielded the highest mechanical performances (9619 N), in joints with the deformed rivet tip having a characteristic overall bell-shaped geometry (e.g., Condition 36, Figure 6b). A maximum threshold of energy efficiency was established at 90 J. Above this value, the energy used no longer contributes toward the increase of mechanical performance, instead promoting a counterproductive over-deformation of the rivet tip, with decreasing anchoring efficiency. Bellow this threshold, the energy input was found to have good linear correlations both with the new proposed volumetric ratio (VR(U)), reaching an R-sq = 0.87, and the ultimate tensile force, reaching an R-sq = 0.86. The highest contributions to the UTF originated from the friction parameters: force (FF = 32.0%) and time (FT = 21.4%). Both demonstrating the influence of higher order effects. Neither forging force (FoF) nor forging time (FoT) were found to be statistically significant for the investigated joining range of parameters. The region of maximum mechanical performance was found to be centered on 2750 N for friction force and 2 s for friction time, yielding ultimate tensile forces above 10,000 N. An optimized correlation capable of maximizing the mechanical performance and simultaneously minimizing energy input, across the parameter ranges, was established (FF = 1189.8 × FT + 403.6, SI units). This allows the production of joints with pre-determined mechanical properties, without unnecessary expenditure of energy and material.

The conclusions of the present work, with the knowledge from Part I [3], allow for an estimation of the expected global mechanical performance, of friction riveted AA2024/polyetherimide hybrid point-on-plate joints, based on process parameters and mechanical energy input. Furthermore, the proposed volumetric ratio amendment, VR(U), improves the assessment of the anchoring efficiency.

Author Contributions: G.P.C. designed and performed the experiments and analyzed all collected data; L.A.B., P.V., and J.F.d.S. contributed with discussions on the experimental results; S.T.A.-F. determined the structure of the manuscript; All authors contributed to the preparation and revision of the manuscript.

Funding: The authors would like to acknowledge the financial support provided by the Helmholtz Association, Germany (Grant No. VH-NG-626), the Austrian aviation program TAKE OFF, and BMVIT-Austrian Ministry for Transport, Innovation and Technology.

Conflicts of Interest: The authors declare no conflict of interest.

References

1. Amancio-Filho, S.T.; Abibe, A.B.; Dos Santos, J.F. Joining: Mechanical Fastening of Polymers, Composites, and Polymer–Metal Hybrid Structures. In *Wiley Encyclopedia of Composites*; Nicolais, L., Borzacchiello, A., Eds.; John Wiley & Sons, Inc.: Hoboken, NJ, USA, 2012; ISBN 9781118097298.
2. Amancio-Filho, S.T.; Dos Santos, J.F. Joining of polymers and polymer-metal hybrid structures: Recent developments and trends. *Polym. Eng. Sci.* **2009**, *49*, 1461–1476. [CrossRef]
3. Pina Cipriano, G.; Blaga, L.; F. dos Santos, J.; Vilaça, P.; Amancio-Filho, S. Fundamentals of Force-Controlled Friction Riveting: Part I—Joint Formation and Heat Development. *Materials (Basel)* **2018**, *11*, E2294. [CrossRef] [PubMed]
4. Abibe, A.B.; Amancio-Filho, S.T.; dos Santos, J.F.; Hage, E. Mechanical and failure behaviour of hybrid polymer–metal staked joints. *Mater. Des.* **2013**, *46*, 338–347. [CrossRef]
5. Goushegir, S.M.; dos Santos, J.F.; Amancio-Filho, S.T. Influence of process parameters on mechanical performance and bonding area of AA2024/carbon-fiber-reinforced poly(phenylene sulfide) friction spot single lap joints. *Mater. Des.* **2015**, *83*, 431–442. [CrossRef]
6. Amancio-Filho, S.T.; Lucian-Attila Blaga, L.-A. *Joining of Polymer-Metal Hybrid Structures: Principles and applications*, 1st ed.; John Wiley & Sons: Hoboken, NJ, USA, 2018; ISBN 9781119429807.
7. Amancio-Filho, S.; Beyer, M.; Santos, J. Method for Connecting a Metallic Bolt to a Plastic Piece. U.S. Patent Application No. 7,575,149 B2, 18 August 2009.

8. Amancio-Filho, S.T.; dos Santos, J.F. Henry Granjon Prize Competition 2009 Winner Category A: "Joining and Fabrication Technology" Friction Riveting: Development and Analysis of a New Joining Technique for Polymer-Metal Multi-Material Structures. *Weld. World* **2011**, *55*, 13–24. [CrossRef]

9. Amancio-Filho, S.T.; Dos Santos, J.F. FricRiveting: A new technique for joining thermoplastics to lightweight alloys. Proceedings of Annual Technical Conference of the Society of Plastic Engineers—ANTEC, Milwaukee, WI, USA, 4–8 May 2008.

10. Rodrigues, C.F.; Blaga, L.A.; dos Santos, J.F.; Canto, L.B.; Hage, E.; Amancio-Filho, S.T. FricRiveting of aluminum 2024-T351 and polycarbonate: Temperature evolution, microstructure and mechanical performance. *J. Mater. Process. Technol.* **2014**, *214*, 2029–2039. [CrossRef]

11. Blaga, L.; Bancilă, R.; dos Santos, J.F.; Amancio-Filho, S.T. Friction Riveting of glass–fibre-reinforced polyetherimide composite and titanium grade 2 hybrid joints. *Mater. Des.* **2013**, *50*, 825–829. [CrossRef]

12. Borges, M.F. Desenvolvimento de nova geometria de rebite para uso em estruturas híbridas compósito-metal obtidas através do processo de rebitagem por fricção. Ph.D. Thesis, Federal University of Rio Grande do Sul, Porto Alegre, Brazil, 2013.

13. Wirth, J.G. Discovery and Development of Polyetherimides. In *High Performance Polymers: Their Origin and Development*; Kirshenbaum, G.S., Ed.; Springer Netherlands: Dordrecht, The Netherlands, 1986; pp. 195–205.

14. Johnson, R.O.; Burlhis, H.S. Polyetherimide: A new high-performance thermoplastic resin. *J. Polym. Sci. Polym. Symp.* **2007**, *70*, 129–143. [CrossRef]

15. Fukuhara, M. Temperature dependency of elastic moduli and internal dilational and shear frictions of polyetherimide. *J. Appl. Polym. Sci.* **2003**, *90*, 759–764. [CrossRef]

16. Thomas, S.; Visakh, P.M. *Handbook of Engineering and Specialty Thermoplastics*; Scrivener Publishing LLC: Salem, MA, USA, 2012; Volume 4, ISBN 978-111-822-906-4.

17. Duratron U1000 PEI; Quadrant Plastics. 2011. Available online: https://www.quadrantplastics.com/de/produkte/technische-kunststoffe/temperatur-160-220-c/duratronr-pei/?r=1 (accessed on 19 March 2018).

18. Military Handbook—MIL-HDBK-5H: Metallic Materials and Elements for Aerospace Vehicle Structures. Available online: https://app.knovel.com/web/toc.v/cid:kpMHMILH61/viewerType:toc (accessed on 24 August 2017).

19. *Metallic Materials—Tensile Testing—Part 1: Method of Test at Room Temperature*; ISO 6892-1:2009; International Organization for Standardization: Geneva, Switzerland, 2009.

20. Ma, T.J.; Li, W.; Yang, S.Y. Impact toughness and fracture analysis of linear friction welded Ti–6Al–4V alloy joints. *Mater. Des.* **2009**, *30*, 2128–2132. [CrossRef]

21. Crawford, R.J.; Tam, Y. Friction welding of plastics. *J. Mater. Sci.* **1981**, *16*, 3275–3282. [CrossRef]

22. Montgomery, D.C. *Design and Analysis of Experiments*, 5th ed.; John Wiley and Sons: New York, NY, USA, 2001. [CrossRef]

23. Myers, R.H.; Montgomery, D.C.; Anderson-Cook, C.M. *Response Surface Methodology: Process and Product Optimization Using Designed Experiments, 3rd ed*; John Wiley & Sons: New York, NY, USA, 1995; ISBN 0471581003.

24. Amancio-Filho, S.T. Friction Riveting: Development and analysis of a new joining technique for polymer-metal multi-materials structures. Ph.D. Thesis, Technische Universität Hamburg-Harburg, Hamburg, Germany, 1 July 2007.

25. Altmeyer, J.; dos Santos, J.F.; Amancio-Filho, S.T. Effect of the friction riveting process parameters on the joint formation and performance of Ti alloy/short-fibre reinforced polyether ether ketone joints. *Mater. Des.* **2014**, *60*, 164–176. [CrossRef]

26. Montgomery, D.C.; Runger, G.C. *Applied statistics and probability for engineers*, 3rd ed.; John Wiley & Sons: New York, NY, USA, 2003; ISBN 0-471-20454-4.

27. Amancio-Filho, S.T.; Dos Santos, J.F. Preliminary analytical modeling of heat input in friction riveting. In Proceedings of the Annual Technical Conference—ANTEC, Indianapolis, IN, USA, 23–25 May 2016.

Article

The Influence of Clamping Pressure on Joint Formation and Mechanical Performance of Ti6Al4V/CF-PEEK Friction-Riveted Joints

Natascha Z. Borba [1,2], Jorge F. dos Santos [1] and Sergio T. Amancio-Filho [3,*]

[1] Helmholtz-Zentrum Geesthacht, Centre for Materials and Coastal Research, Institute of Materials Research,
    Materials Mechanics, Solid State Joining Processes, 21502 Geesthacht, Germany;
    natascha.zocoller@hzg.de (N.Z.B.); jorge.dos.santos@hzg.de (J.F.d.S.)
[2] Hamburg University of Technology, Institute of Polymer and Composites, 21073 Hamburg, Germany
[3] Graz University of Technology—TU Graz, Institute of Materials Science, Joining and Forming,
    BMVIT Endowed Professorship for Aviation, Kopernikusgasse 24/1, 8010 Graz, Austria
*   Correspondence: sergio.amancio@tugraz.at; Tel.: +43-316-873-1610; Fax: +43-316-873-7184

Received: 18 February 2019; Accepted: 28 February 2019; Published: 4 March 2019

Abstract: This work aims at investigating the influence of pre-set clamping pressure on the joint formation and mechanical strength of overlapping direct-friction-riveted joints. A pneumatic fixture device was developed for this work, with clamping pressure varying from 0.2 MPa to 0.6 MPa. A case study on overlapping joints using Ti6Al4V rivets and woven carbon fiber-reinforced polyether-ether-ketone (CF-PEEK) parts were produced. Digital image correlation and microscopy revealed the expected compressive behavior of the clamping system and the continuous pressure release upon the joining process owing to the rivet plastic deformation and the polymer squeezing flow. Two preferential paths of material flow were identified through the alternate replacement of the upper and lower composite parts by a poly-methyl-methacrylate (PMMA) plate—the composite upward and squeezing flow between the parts which induced their separation. The ultimate lap shear forces up to 6580 ± 383 N were achieved for the direct-friction-riveted CF-PEEK overlap joints. The formation of a gap to accommodate squeezed polymer between the composite parts during the process had no influence on the joint mechanical performance. The increase in the clamping pressure for joints produced with a low friction force did not affect the joint-anchoring efficiency and consequently the joint strength. On the other hand, the combined effect of a high-friction force and clamping pressure induced the inverted bell shape of the plastically deformed rivet tip, a lower anchoring efficiency, and the delamination of the composite, all of which decrease the mechanical strength by 31%. Therefore, the higher the friction force and clamping pressure, the more defects would be generated in the composite parts and the more changes in the shape of the plastically deformed rivet tip, leading to a lower level of quasi-static mechanical performance. All the joints failed by initial bearing of the composite and final rivet pull-out. The findings of this work can contribute to further improvement of the clamping design for industrial application.

Keywords: Friction Riveting; clamping influence; joint formation; mechanical properties

---

1. Introduction

New concepts and designs of high-performance lightweight structures in a wide range of engineering applications, such as the transportation industry, wind power, and infrastructure, increasingly demand the development of cost-effective, fast, and precise manufacturing and post-processing techniques. The examples include machining [1–3], welding [4,5], and joining [6–8]. Recently, Saint Jean Industries, a global supplier of parts and subassemblies for automotive and aeronautic industries, has developed a lightweight suspension knuckle made of carbon fiber reinforced polymer (CFRP) and aluminum to increase the part's stiffness [9]. The joining technology was required to improve and automate the whole manufacturing cycle while guaranteeing the required properties [9]. In such metal–polymer hybrid structures, the post-processing of joining or welding poses challenges due to the high dissimilarities among the properties of the materials. The optimization of such post-processing is, therefore, critical for providing a high quality of components and structures, high productivity, and reproducibility. A typical variable in machining, welding, and joining is the clamping system, which has been reported as a relevant factor to avoid any undesirable distortion and defects and hence a loss of structural integrity [10–14].

The influence of clamping on machining processes is relatively well understood for several materials [15–18] including fiber-reinforced polymers [10,11,19]. Klotz et al. [11] investigated the influence of the clamping system during the drilling of carbon-fiber-reinforced plastics. The planar specimens were clamped by three and four points as well as by a ring clamping system. The results showed that the distance from the drill axis to the fixed points of the composite significantly influence the process of reactive forces and workpiece quality. By increasing the distance of the clamping points, the workpieces are deflected, leading to typical delamination at the upper composite side, namely "peel-up," and at the underside, namely "push-out".

For welding processes of metals, clamping systems have been designed to reduce buckling as well as bending and angular distortions. However, there is still limited literature available on the influence of the clamping on the weld properties. Weidinger et al. [12] investigated the influence of different clamping conditions on laser weld formation and weld strength. The rigid clamping conditions strongly affected the local shrinkage during the weld pool solidification, thereby reducing the solidification cracking and improving the weld quality and strength. According to Richter-Trummer et al. [13], high clamping forces in the order of 2500 N led to better quasi-static mechanical properties of friction stir butt welds of AA2198-T851. Although higher clamping forces induced less distortion and more uniform residual stress distribution through the plate thickness, higher residual stresses were observed in the case of more rigidly clamped parts. The authors also identified a decrease in the degree of separation between the parts during welding by increasing the clamping forces, which may contribute to weld sealing. Shahri et al. [14] reported the influence of clamping on the fatigue life of friction stir welds of AA6005; they showed that the clamping induced local plastic deformation on the crack tip, leading to tensile residual stresses that accelerate the crack initiation during dynamic loading.

Recently, alternative joining technologies suitable for hybrid structures have been developed due to the increasing replacement of conventional metallic materials by polymer composites in aircraft and automotive applications. Such technologies aim to overcome or reduce the drawbacks mainly related to the manufacturing time of traditional techniques such as adhesive bonding and mechanical fastening. Facing this reality, single lap shear joint geometries produced by different innovative joining technologies have been widely explored. However, no previous study has investigated the effect of the clamping system on the joint formation and mechanical performance of composite–composite overlap joints. Goushegir et al. [7] reported the use of a clamping system during and after the friction spot joining (FSpJ) process of AA2024-T3 and carbon-fiber-reinforced polyphenylene sulfide overlap joints. They addressed the importance of clamping to ensure intimate contact between the joining parts and to avoid their separation during the cooling phase as result of different coefficients of thermal expansion of the materials. However, no systematic study has been performed to evaluate the influence of the clamping force on the FSpJ joint properties. A similar study was carried out by Feistauer et al. [6] for ultrasonic joints of Ti6Al4V metal injection molded parts and glass-fiber-reinforced polyetherimide laminates. Although the clamping pressure applied by the sonotrode was shown to influence the joint formation, there is no detailed investigation performed on the correlation between clamping pressure and joint strength. Wagner et al. [20] used a clamping system for the ultrasonic welding of aluminum alloy and CFRP to control the welding force during the joining process, leading to improved joint reproducibility and stable mechanical properties.

Friction Riveting (FricRiveting) is also an alternative joining technology to produce metal-composite overlap joints. The technology relies on the principles of mechanical fastening and friction welding [21]. This technique uses frictional heat and pressure to plasticize and deform a cylindrical metallic rivet into polymer composite parts. In previous publications, the feasibility of the process has been shown on glass- and carbon-fiber-reinforced composites joined with AA6056-T6 [22], commercially pure titanium grade 2 [23], titanium grade 3 [24], and Ti6Al4V [25] rivets. In these works, the main characteristic of the process and the effects of the process parameters on the joint microstructure and mechanical properties were addressed. Amanico-Filho [21] produced friction-riveted overlap joints of the AA2024-T351 rivet and unreinforced polyetherimide (PEI) using a clamping device. Owing to the relatively low strength of AA2024-T351 (tensile strength of 495 MPa [26]), the equilibrium between joining (up to 4.5 kN) and reactive forces during the joining process was not critical, thus resulting in a plastically deformed rivet without any separation of the overlapped PEI parts [21]. Accordingly, no systematic study has been carried out to evaluate the influence of clamping forces on the joint formation and quasi-static mechanical strength. However, by increasing the strength of the rivet base material, higher joining forces (forces up to 20 kN [27]) are needed to achieve sufficient rivet plastic deformation and consequently strong joints. Thus, improved clamping is required to compensate the higher reactive forces and to avoid parts separation [13].

This work aims at investigating the influence of pre-set clamping pressure on the joint formation and mechanical strength of friction-riveted composite overlap joints. A pneumatic fixture device was designed to allow clamping pressure levels up to 1.0 MPa. A case study on overlap joints was produced using an aircraft-applied material combination of Ti6Al4V rivets and woven carbon-fiber-reinforced polyether-ether-ketone (CF-PEEK) plates. The process-related microstructural changes, plastic deformation of the rivet, and the material flow were evaluated using optical and scanning electron microscopy, digital image correlation method, and X-ray computed micro-tomography. The quasi-static mechanical behavior of the friction-riveted joints was evaluated by lap shear testing.

2. Principles of Friction Riveting

In Friction Riveting, frictional heat is generated by rivet rotation and insertion into one or more parts, leading to plastic deformation of the metallic rivet tip and its mechanical anchoring. Different joint geometries are possible, including metallic inserting (i.e., rivet insertion into a single polymer part) and overlapping joints (i.e., overlapped parts of unreinforced polymers, reinforced polymers and/or metal). For the overlap geometry, the rivet can be inserted through the upper part with a through-hole and then deformed into the lower part or directly joined within the overlapped parts without holes. For the latter, the process variant is called Direct-Friction Riveting [21,27], which was selected for the present work. Details of the conventional Friction Riveting configuration can be found in [23,28].

Direct-Friction Riveting controlled by force was adopted for this work, with joining phases limited by spindle displacement. Figure 1 depicts the joining phases based on a schematic drawing of the process. After the positioning step (Figure 1I), the rotating rivet reaches a pre-set rotational speed and moves toward the surface of the upper part by applying a constant force (Friction Phase I). Frictional heat is generated, which softens or melts a polymeric layer in the rivet surroundings (Figure 1II). Owing to the continuous insertion of the rivet into the upper part, the softened or molten polymer is expelled as flash outward the joining area (Figure 1II). The second stage of the Friction Phase follows (Figure 1III), in which the rivet is inserted into the lower part at the same rotational speed and higher axial force. The distribution of joint internal stress leads to changes in the material flow, thereby promoting the polymeric squeezing flow (Figure 1III) between the overlapped parts. With constant increase in temperature, the viscosity of the polymer from the lower part decreases concomitantly and the rivet displacement rate increases until the heating phase ends. By this moment, the local temperature at the rivet tip reaches the plasticizing temperature of the metal. The plasticized rivet tip is pressed against the cold polymeric layer underneath it. This provides the required resistance to plastically deform the metal and increases the rivet diameter, thereby anchoring the rivet tip into the lower part. At the end of the Friction Phase II, the rotational speed becomes null, while no further axial force is applied. The joint consolidates by cooling under pressure (Figure 1IV) to avoid the relaxation effects upon cooling, which, in turn, could lead to dimensional changes of the joining parts.

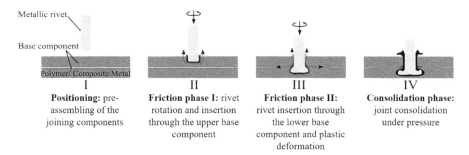

I	II	III	IV
Positioning: pre-assembling of the joining components	**Friction phase I:** rivet rotation and insertion through the upper base component	**Friction phase II:** rivet insertion through the lower base component and plastic deformation	**Consolidation phase:** joint consolidation under pressure

Figure 1. Schematic description of the Direct-FricRiveting process.

3. Materials and Methods

Extruded plane rivets of Ti6Al4V (Henschel KG, Munich, Germany) with a diameter of 5 mm and length of 60 mm were selected. This alloy is widely used for bolts, rivets, and screws in aircraft and devices for the oil and gas industry due to the high specific strength, good corrosion, and creep resistance [29]. Table 1 lists the experimentally determined chemical composition of the titanium alloy. The main properties of this titanium alloy are summarized in Table 2.

Table 1. Chemical composition of Ti6Al4V alloy rivets.

Weight (wt.%)	N	H	O	Fe	Al	V	Ti
	0.002	0.003	0.107	0.217	6.2	4.5	Bal.

The 4.34-mm nominal thickness carbon-fiber-reinforced poly-ether-ether-ketone (CF-PEEK) laminates (Toho Tenax Europe, Wuppertal, Germany) with 58 wt.% nominal fiber content were used as the composite part. The composite laminate consists of 14 plies of carbon-fibers in a stacking sequence of $[[(0,90)/(\pm45)]_3/(0,90)]_s$. CF-PEEK is a high-performance semi-crystalline thermoplastic composite, which is mainly used in primary and secondary aircraft structures because of its high strength, chemical resistance, and resistance to fatigue failure over aging [30,31]. The main properties of CF-PEEK are summarized in Table 2.

Table 2. Properties of the investigated materials.

	Ti6Al4V [29]	CF-PEEK [32]
Tensile/ Shear strength [MPa]	940–1180/550	963 (warp, 0°)/186
E-Modules [GPa]	114	60 (warp, 0°)
Thermal transition [°C]	1655 (Tm)	143 (Tg)/343 (Tm)
Thermal conductivity [W/m K]	17.5	2.0
CLTE [μm/m °C]	9.7 (20–650)	30 (≤ Tg)

Friction-riveted single-lap joints were produced using an automated FricRiveting gantry system (RNA, H.Loitz-Robotik, Hamburg, Germany). A pneumatic clamping system built out of low carbon steel with two actuators (DZF-50-25-P-A, FESTO, Islandia, NY, USA), each with a maximum capacity of 1.0 MPa, was used as a sample holder to fix the overlapped composite parts. Figure 2a show the clamping system, while Figure 2b highlights the dimensions of the upper clamping element. A circular fixation diameter of 16 mm was selected to homogeneously distribute the clamping force and reduce the superficial damages of the composite (according to common practices for drilling procedures of fiber reinforced polymers [10]). The selected joining conditions used in this work are listed in Table 3. The combination of joining parameters was obtained from a 2^3-full-factorial design of experiments with an additional centre point. Owing to the good exploratory power of the regression models acquired for the ultimate lap shear force and the volumetric ratio (R^2_{adj} = 88% and R^2_{adj} = 81%, respectively), the assumption of linear dependence between joining parameters and responses was validated. Therefore, in this work, only the maximum and minimum levels of tested joining parameters range were selected, with focus on the effect of internal forces on the joint formation and properties. The individual contribution of the clamping pressure under different joining forces were investigated through two levels of clamping pressure (0.2 and 0.6 MPa) and two levels of friction force (10 and 15 kN), while the rotational speed was constant (15,000 rpm). The results of process optimization and the influence of all process parameters on the joint formation and mechanical strength of friction-riveted joints are not within the scope of this work and will be published elsewhere.

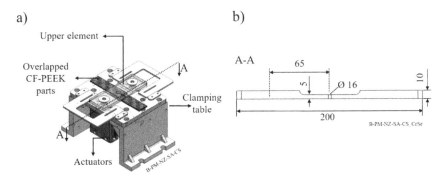

Figure 2. (a) Schematic illustration of the pneumatic clamping system and its main elements; (b) cross-sectional view of the upper element used to transfer the clamping load. All dimensions are in millimeters.

Table 3. Selected joining conditions of Direct-Friction Riveting.

Rotational Speed, RS [rpm]	Friction Force, FF [kN]	Displacement at Friction, DF [mm]	Clamping Pressure, CP [MPa]
15,000	10.0, 15.0	7.5	0.2, 0.6

The surface displacement of the clamping device and the specimen during the Friction Riveting process was measured by the digital image correlation (DIC) system (ARAMIS-4m, GOM, Braunschweig, Germany). The displacement and deformation measurements can be used to indicate regions of material under different stress fields—i.e., under compression or tension. The required stochastic speckle pattern on the clamping device and specimen surfaces were prepared using black ink spray paint deposited on a white background. Figure 3a depicts the DIC areas of analysis along with an example of the recorded initial frame (i.e., t = 0 s) which shows the displacement distribution in the Y-axis direction (Figure 3b). An incoherent light source was used to illuminate the DIC areas. A digital camera equipped with 50 mm focal length lens placed perpendicular to the DIC areas was used to record the images. A frame rate of 7 Hz, a facet frame of 15 pixels, and a facet step of 13 pixels, giving an overlap of 2 pixels, were set up in accordance with the image resolution required for accurate results.

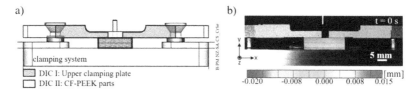

Figure 3. (**a**) Overview of the clamping system showing the areas of analysis for the digital image correlation (DIC) method; (**b**) displacement distribution through the upper clamping plate and the joining parts in the Y-axis direction.

Light optical microscopy (LOM; DM IR microscope, Leica, Wetzlar, Germany), scanning electron microscopy (SEM; Quanta™ FEG 650 equipment, FEI, Hillsboro, OR, USA), and X-ray micro-computed tomography, X-ray µ-CT (Y. Cougar- FineFocus X-ray system, YXLON, Hamburg, Germany) were performed to analyze the microstructure of the joints and the fracture surfaces after mechanical testing. The mid-cross-section of the joints was analyzed by LOM to reveal the joint microstructure along with the geometric aspects of the plastic-deformed rivet tip. SEM was used to reveal detailed joint microstructural features and the fracture surface. The samples were prepared following standard materialography procedures. The joints were sectioned through the center of the rivet, embedded in cold resin, ground and polished to obtain a smooth surface finishing. For SEM analysis, the conductivity of the sample surfaces was increased via gold sputtering using a Q150R ES equipment (Quorum Technologies Ltd., Lewes, UK) for 15 s with a current of 65 mA.

From the LOM images, the rivet penetration depth (H), rivet tip width (W), anchoring depth (Dp), and the separation between the composite parts (S) were measured according to Figure 4 and summarized in Table 4. H, W, and Dp were used to calculate the volumetric ratio (VR) (Equation (1)) by adopting the analytical model proposed by Pina et al. [33]. The volumetric ratio uses the interaction volume of the remaining composite material over the deformed rivet tip to represent the anchoring efficiency of the friction-riveted joints.

$$VR = \frac{Dp \times (W^2 - D^2)}{H \times W^2} \, [a.u] \tag{1}$$

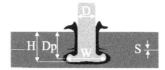

Figure 4. Schematic illustration of a single overlap friction-riveted joint showing geometrical features of the anchoring zone (H, Dp, and W) as well as the separation between the composite parts (S).

Table 4. Geometrical features (penetration depth, H; rivet tip width, W; anchoring depth, Dp) of friction-riveted joint measured to calculate the volumetric ratio and the separation (S) between the composite plates.

Joining Condition	H [mm]	W [mm]	Dp [mm]	S [mm]
FF – 10 kN CP – 0.2 MPa	7.6 ± 0.2	6.9 ± 0.1	5.9 ± 0.4	0.3 ± 0.1
FF – 10 kN CP – 0.6 MPa	6.9 ± 0.01	7.2 ± 0.05	4.4 ± 0.3	0.3 ± 0.05
FF – 15 kN CP – 0.2 MPa	7.3 ± 0.2	6.2 ± 0.3	6.2 ± 0.1	0.6 ± 0.1
FF – 15 kN CP – 0.6 MPa	7.5 ± 0.2	5.7 ± 0.2	6.1 ± 0.6	0.6 ± 0.06

Non-destructive evaluation of friction-riveted joints via X-ray μ-CT was carried out to assess the joint formation over joining time. An operating voltage of 60 kV, a current of 95 μA, and no filters were used for the analyses. The evolution of the geometry of the plastically deformed rivet tip and material flow were investigated by the stop-action procedure. Therefore, joints from four different process steps were produced and evaluated.

Single-lap shear testing was carried out to analyze the quasi-static joint mechanical performance. The joint strength was evaluated in accordance with ASTM D5961 [34] by using a universal testing machine (model 1478, Zwick Roell, Ulm, Germany) with a load capacity of 100 kN. The transverse test speed was 2 mm/min. Three replicates for each processing condition described in Table 1 were tested at room temperature (21 °C). Figure 5 shows the joint geometry and sample dimensions used in this work. The tightening torque of 5 Nm was applied together with the M5 stainless steel nut and washer to pre-load the joints in order to eliminate any through-thickness failure and to increase the joint load capacity [35]. The stainless steel material for the nut and washer had been selected due to its low static coefficient of friction (μ_e) when in contact with Ti6Al4V (μ_e = 0.36) [36], thereby increasing the pre-load transferability and consequently the tightening efficiency.

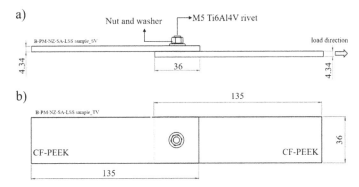

Figure 5. Schematic illustration of single lap shear specimen geometry along with the dimensions and load direction: specimen (**a**) side view and (**b**) top view. All dimensions are in millimeters.

4. Results and Discussion

4.1. Analytical Description of Clamping Force Effect

Figure 6 illustrates the theoretical principle of the clamping concept based on a simplified equilibrium of forces. FF is the friction force, Σf_i is the sum of internal forces (f_i) released during the joining process (indicated by the downward arrows), F_{cl} is the clamping force applied by the two actuators, and F_r is the resultant force of the distributed reaction over the clamped area (f_r (x)). The shear and friction components were neglected for simplifications purposes.

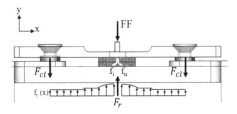

Figure 6. Schematic representation of the forces acting during joint clamping (simplified equilibrium of internal forces).

During the joining process, a friction force (FF) is applied to allow the penetration of a rotating metallic rivet through the overlapped composite parts and to contribute to the plastic deformation of the rivet tip. According to Amancio-Filho and dos Santos [37], the distribution of such force over the friction area significantly influences the viscous dissipation in Friction Riveting, which is the main mechanism of heat generation. The friction force is, however, partially lost ($\sum f_i$) due to the process-related physical changes in the materials, including a decrease in the polymer viscosity and metal plasticizing [24,28]. The reactive load (F_r) can be expressed using the equilibrium of forces, as analytically presented by Equation (2). Such reaction is responsible mainly for the deformation of the plasticized metal [21] and indirectly for the outward flow of the low viscous polymer from the joining area.

$$F_r = FF - \sum_{i=1}^{n} f_i \tag{2}$$

The polymer flow from the lower composite plate and rivet deformation can induce the separation of the composite overlapped parts, which is not restricted by any externally applied forces. Figure 7 shows a typical cross-section of a friction-riveted joint produced without the external clamping device. It can be seen that a significant amount of material, which is squeezed between the composite parts, creates a significant gap between the parts. Moreover, further separation of the composite parts is expected due to the surface delamination evidenced by the fiber peel-up and push-out effects (highlighted by dashed-line squares in Figure 7, a commonly reported phenomenon in the drilling of composites [10,11]. As reported by Matsuzaki et al. [38], this lack of joint sealing can compromise the corrosion behavior and loading capacity of bolted composite joints by creating eccentricities. For butt-friction-stir-welds, the gap between the welded parts leads to differential plate distortion through the welding line, resulting in less ductile welds under tensile and three-point bending loading, as reported by Richter-Trummer et al. [13]. Therefore, any undesirable separation of the joined composite parts should be minimized or avoided.

Figure 7. Typical cross-section of a Ti6Al4V/carbon fiber-reinforced polyether-ether-ketone (CF-PEEK) friction-riveted joint produced without the application of external clamping pressure. (Joining parameters: RS: 15,000 rpm, FF: 15 kN, DF: 7.5 mm).

The effect of F_r on the separation of the composite parts is expected to be attenuated by applying external clamping forces (F_{cl}) during the Friction Riveting of overlap joints. The resultant force of a distributed clamping load transferred to the joining parts must be equal or superior to the reactive forces from the joining process (Equation (3)) to constrain the upward polymer flow and, consequently, the separation of any plate.

$$2F_{cl} \geq F_r \tag{3}$$

Additionally, the clamping scheme may also influence the final shape of the plastically deformed rivet tip and consequently the joint mechanical performance, as will be discussed in Section 4.3. Thus, an optimized balance of the internal and external forces of the Friction Riveting process and the clamping system must be achieved to allow the best compromise between joint formation, quality, and joint mechanical properties. Owing to the complexity of quantifying internal and reaction forces, only the theoretical basis was addressed in this work. Further analysis using the finite element method (FEM) must be carried out to quantitatively prove the established concept.

4.2. Evolution of Clamping Displacement and Joint Formation during Direct-FricRiveting

Figure 8 shows a typical evolution of the clamping and joint displacement at different joining times by the digital image correlation (DIC) method along with the joint formation through X-ray micro-computed tomography. The displacement in the Y-axis provides qualitative evidence of stresses fields through the clamping system and joining parts. In the initial position (t = 0 s, Figure 3b), the clamping system and overlapped composite parts were at 0 mm. As soon as the rivet was inserted into the upper composite part (Figure 8a), the system underwent a compression regime, leading to a negative displacement of the upper clamping element and the composite parts. No initial separation of the composite parts is observed at this stage (Figure 8e). The compression field imposed by the clamping element was maintained over the joining process (Figure 8b,c), decreasing at t = 1.1 s (Figure 8d) when the rivet was released by the chuck, the spindle retracted, and the process finished. This effect is evidenced by brighter colored areas depicted by the dashed-line rectangles in Figure 8d. By this time, the plasticized rivet tip was highly deformed and widened, as shown in Figure 8h. Moreover, throughout the whole joining cycle a localized region in the upper composite plate, in the vicinities of the rivet insertion path, was progressively submitted to a tension field, resulting in a local positive displacement (Figure 8a–d). As previously reported by Altmeyer et al. [24], in the Friction Riveting of CF-PEEK, the process temperatures (415–460 °C) are above the melting temperature of the polymer matrix (T_m = 334 °C) and thus melts a thin layer of polymer in the rivet surroundings. This material presents low viscosity and easily flows while the rivet penetrates the composite parts. Therefore, in the initial stages (Figure 8e,f), the molten polymer flowed mainly upwards and thereby formed the so-called flash. Such flow pattern seems to induce the tension field in the rivet surroundings and perhaps an upward bending of the upper composite plate.

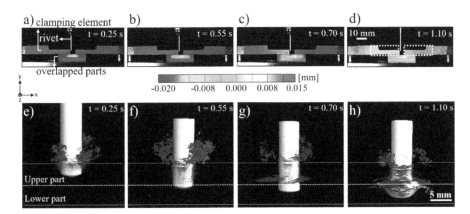

Figure 8. Evolution of the displacement distribution through the clamping system and joint parts (**a**–**d**) along with the joint formation (**e**–**h**) over the process time. (Joining parameters - RS: 15,000 rpm, FF: 15 kN, DF: 7.5 mm, CP: 0.2 MPa).

Figure 9a show the neutral plane of the upper clamping element used to evaluate the displacement evolution over its length and indirectly the compression fields of the DIC areas at different joining times. From Figure 9b, it is clear that partial loss of the clamping compression took place along with the tension created at the surroundings of the hole in the clamping system. Over the joining time, the whole span of the upper clamping element was negatively displaced relative to the Y-axis, reaching a displacement of around −0.02 mm at t = 0.7 s. At this process stage, the distribution of displacement through the length of the clamping element was non-symmetrical to the center. This can be explained by the discontinuous and irregular composite squeezing flow between the composite parts, as presented in Figure 9d. Upon the maximum rivet tip plastic deformation (at t = 1.1 s), the clamping system recovered approximately 50% of the negative displacement and reached values of about −0.009 mm.

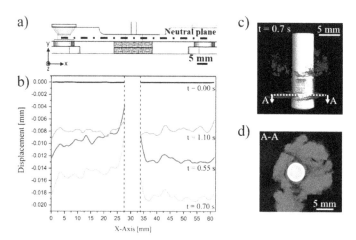

Figure 9. (**a**) Schematics showing the neutral line of the upper clamping element. (**b**) Displacement distribution through the neutral line of the upper clamping element at different joining times. (**c**) X-ray micro-computed tomography showing the side view of the friction-riveted joint at the joining time of t = 0.7 s (A-A is the plane between the composite parts). (**d**) Upper view of the A-A plane that displays the composite squeezing flow between the composite parts (Joining parameters—RS: 15,000 rpm, FF: 15 kN, DF: 7.5 mm, CP: 0.2 MPa).

To assess the influence of the stress fields presented in Figures 9 and 10 on the flow of the molten polymer layer, the lower composite part was substituted by a transparent poly-methyl-methacrylate (PMMA) plate. This approach allowed a better observation of the expelled flash material and squeezing flow evolution. Figure 10a shows an overview of the joining area in which the upward flow of the composite is predominant, as indicated by arrows. The SEM image of the PMMA-metal interface (indicated by the dotted-line square in Figure 10a) is depicted in Figure 10b. Figure 9c schematically displays a possible bending of the upper composite plate due to the upward composite flow, promoting localized tension field in the rivet insertion direction, as presented in Figure 9b.

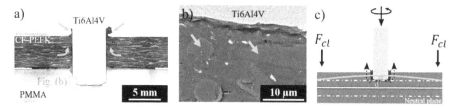

Figure 10. (**a**) Cross-section of the friction-riveted joint with upper CF-PEEK and lower poly-methyl-methacrylate (PMMA) parts. (**b**) Detail of the metal-PMMA interface showing broken fiber embedded in PMMA in the rivet surroundings (**c**) Schematics of the initial joining stage showing possible bending of the upper composite plate and the upward material flow. (Joining parameters—RS: 15,000 rpm, FF: 15 kN, DF: 7.5 mm, CP: 0.2 MPa).

Although the molten composite flowed mainly upward in the initial joining stage, broken fibers embedded into the lower PMMA part were detected underneath and around the rivet tip (arrows in Figure 10b). This clearly indicates that a small amount of the damaged composite from the upper part was transported into the lower part during the initial rivet insertion. Bearing in mind the phenomenological similarities between Friction Riveting and Friction Stir Welding (FSW), the frictional regime of sticking between the welding tool and the plasticized metal being stirred [39,40] may explain the observation. Upon the initial stages of rivet insertion in the upper composite part, the shear stresses at the rivet tip-composite interface may induce a flow of low viscous molten polymer at the same rotational speed as the rivet. This effect leads to composite sticking on the rotating rivet surface, similarly to the metal sticking on the FSW tool [40], driving the upper composite into the lower part. As reported by Schneider et al. [41], such flow can be a complex rigid body rotation, assuming a vortex-ring or a uniform translation pattern. Further investigation using X-ray micro-computed tomography must be carried out to understand such flow patterns for friction-riveted joints. The shear stresses along with the axial joining forces may also lead to the breakage of the superficial composite plies at the overlapped area, thus pushing the solid-damaged composite from the upper to the lower part.

The composite flow during the rivet insertion through the lower composite plate is shown in Figure 11. Figure 11a illustrates the cross-section of a joint in which the upper composite part was replaced by PMMA. As it can be observed in Figure 11a and detailed in Figure 11b, broken fibers were detected all over the rivet shaft in the PMMA upper part. Owing to the external restriction imposed by the clamping forces, the molten material from the lower composite plate was mainly driven upward. This flow pattern was absent in the joints produced without any external clamping, whereby the molten material is mainly squeezed out between the overlapped parts (see Figure 7). Although the clamping device restricts the squeezing flow, the rivet plunge and plastic deformation of the rivet tip imposed a positive displacement on the clamping element, as shown at the end of the joining process (Figure 8d). Such a tension field may cause slight bending of the composite parts (see Figure 11c) leading to a material squeeze between the composite parts, the formation of a reconsolidated composite layer, and consequent plate separation. One may assume that the separation of the parts is proportional to the thickness of the squeezed layer. Therefore, it is reasonable to expect that the higher the external clamping force, the more constrained the squeezing flow and the thinner the squeezed layer.

Figure 11. (**a**) Cross-section of friction-riveted with upper PMMA and lower CF-PEEK parts. (**b**) Detail of the metal-PMMA interface showing broken fibers embedded in PMMA in the rivet surroundings. (**c**) Schematics of the final joining stage showing a possible bending of the lower composite plate and the squeezing flow (Joining parameters—RS: 15,000 rpm, FF: 15 kN, DF: 7.5 mm, CP: 0.2 MPa).

4.3. Influence of Clamping Pressure on the Plastically Deformed Rivet Tip and Joint Quasi-Static Mechanical Performance

4.3.1. Process-Related Changes in the Rivet Tip Shape and Joint Microstructural Features

Figure 12 shows the effect of the clamping pressure on the plastic deformation regime of the rivet tip by X-ray micro-computed tomography. The joints produced with low (Figure 12a) and high (Figure 12b) friction force and constant rotational speed (15,000 rpm) were selected for this purpose. As discussed in Section 4.1, the clamping efficiency depends mainly on the compromise between the internal reactive forces arising from the friction force and the clamping force. Thus, for a lower friction force (FF = 10 kN), less deformation of the rivet tip was evidenced and the effect of clamping pressure did not substantially affect the anchoring zone (i.e., penetration, widening, and shape of the plastically deformed rivet tip). However, when joining with a higher friction force (FF = 15 kN), the increase in clamping pressure from 0.2 MPa to 0.6 MPa induced a higher level of plastic deformation and changes in the rivet tip shape by which the rivet-anchoring zone assumed an inverted bell shape.

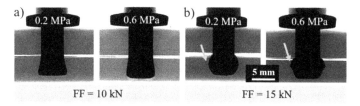

Figure 12. X-ray micro-computed tomography analysis of the joints produced with (**a**) low (10 kN) and (**b**) high (15 kN) friction forces, as well as the influence of clamping pressure on the rivet tip shape. (Joining condition—RS: 15,000 rpm, DF: 7.5 mm).

The rivet-anchoring efficiency was calculated based on the volumetric ratio (Equation (1), Section 3). These results are shown in Figure 13a. By increasing clamping pressure, the volumetric ratio decreases by approximately 34% for higher friction force joints and 9% for lower friction force joints. The combined effect of a higher level of clamping pressure and friction force decreased the composite interaction volume above the deformed rivet tip, thereby decreasing the macro-mechanical interlocking. Therefore, a reduction in the load-carrying capacity can be expected.

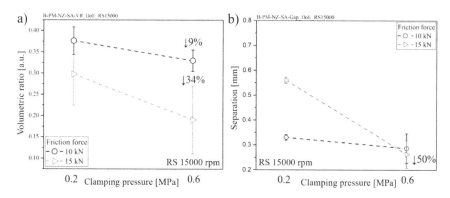

Figure 13. Effect of the clamping pressure on the (**a**) volumetric ratio and (**b**) separation of the composite parts. The hatched upper area in (**b**) represents the usual range of the sealant and adhesive thickness used for hybrid bolted-bonded joints in aircraft structures [42–44].

Figure 13b shows the influence of clamping pressure on the thickness of the squeezing flow and therefore on the separation of the upper and lower parts. The separation values from 0.20 mm to 0.57 mm were achieved. Such levels are inferior to the common range of adhesive thicknesses (0.5 to 0.8 mm) used in hybrid bonded-bolted composite lap joints for aircraft application [42–44]. The squeezing flow between the composite parts in Friction Riveting is assumed to behave similarly to adhesives in hybrid-joining processes, thus contributing to the global joint mechanical performance. As reported by Kelly [44], the hybrid-joining process with flexible adhesives can produce a higher level of joint strength and extend the fatigue life due to improved load transfer distribution through the joint parts.

A 50% decrease in the CF-PEEK plate's separation was observed for a friction force of 15 kN when the clamping pressure increased from 0.2 MPa to 0.6 MPa (Figure 13b). Under higher clamping pressure, the movement of the joint parts due to high plastic deformation and squeezing flow is constrained and consequently the joining parts are less separated. Such effect is more pronounced for the joints produced under higher friction force (15 kN) towards higher plastic deformation at the rivet tip (see Figure 12) and more composite flow. For a friction force of 10 kN, no significant change in the separation of parts' was observed by increasing the clamping pressure. In this case, one can assume that the clamping pressure of 0.2 MPa is sufficient to constrain the reduced material flow, inhibiting the movement of the joint parts.

Figure 14 shows the process-related delamination in the lower composite part of joints produced with higher friction force (FF = 15 kN) and clamping pressures of 0.2 MPa (Figure 14a,c) and 0.6 MPa (Figure 14b,d,e). The delamination propagates from the joining area when the clamping pressure is increased. As previously explained, the equilibrium between internal reactive and external forces restricts the flow and plastic deformation of the joint materials, imposing preferential paths to the displacement of materials. By increasing clamping pressure, less room for plastic deformation of the rivet tip in the formed hole and between the joining parts is expected. Therefore, the plasticized metal deformed between the bundles of carbon-fiber (highlighted by arrows in Figure 14b and detailed in Figure 14d). Such metal entrapment induces fiber-to-matrix debonding and delamination throughout the lower composite part (Figure 14e). According to Nixon-Pearson and Hallett [45], composite delamination plays a critical role in the quasi-static and cyclic mechanical behavior of conventional bolted composite joints by interacting with bolt clamp-up forces and decreasing the joint structural integrity. Therefore, such process-related defects should be avoided by optimizing the external clamping pressure applied during Friction Riveting, which, nonetheless, is required to minimize the separation of the joining parts and to promote joint sealing.

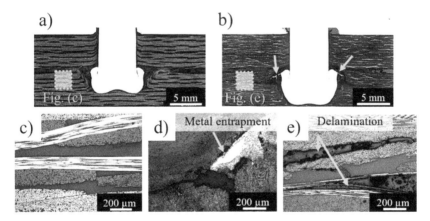

Figure 14. Typical cross-section of joints produced with (**a**) low (CP = 0.2 MPa) and (**b**) high (CP = 0.6 MPa) clamping pressures. (**c**) Detail of the lower composite part where delamination was absent for low CP joints. (**d**) Plasticized metal entrapped between fiber bundles. (**e**) Detail of process-related delamination on the lower composite part for high CP joints. (Joining parameters—RS: 15,000 rpm, DF: 7.5 mm, FF: 15 kN).

4.3.2. Joint Quasi-Static Mechanical Performance

The combined effect of clamping pressure and friction force (FF) on the friction-riveted joint strength is shown in Figure 15. At low FF (FF = 10 kN), increasing the clamping pressure from 0.2 MPa to 0.6 MPa does not display a significant change in the ultimate lap shear force (ULSF) (6580 ± 383 N to 6038 ± 802 N), while a 31% decrease in the ULSF (5660 ± 860 N to 3903 ± 462 N) took place for high FF (FF = 15 kN) joints. As discussed in Section 4.3.1, the increase of clamping pressure (CP) for low FF joints did not affect the volume and geometry of the plastically deformed rivet tip and therefore anchoring efficiency, providing similar joint strength. On the other hand, for high FF joints, changes of CP led to an inverted bell-shape rivet tip and thus a lower level of anchoring efficiency. The shape of the deformation and the low level of anchoring efficiency, along with delamination in the composite part, resulted in weaker joints. Although the separation between joined parts is influenced by CP (see Figure 13), the process-related defects in the composite and the shape and volume of the plastically deformed rivet tip are more compelling for the quasi-static mechanical performance.

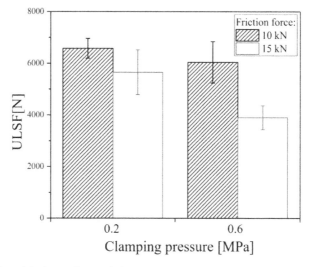

Figure 15. Effect of the friction force and clamping pressure on the ultimate lap-shear force (ULSF) of friction-riveted joints. (Joining parameters - RS: 15,000 rpm, DF: 7.5 mm).

Figure 16a illustrates a typical fracture surface of direct friction-riveted joints. All joints failed by initial composite bearing followed by partial rivet pull-out. Adhesive failure over the reconsolidated composite layer was also identified and is shown in Figure 16b. In such interlayer, fiber tearing impressions (Figure 16c) can be an indication of out-of-plane forces due to secondary bending. Additionally, featureless regions and elongated fibrils (Figure 16d) indicate complex failure micro-mechanisms combining brittle and ductile fractures. Furthermore, Figure 16e depicts the attachment of broken fiber and reconsolidated polymer on the rivet tip surface. Such feature is reported in the literature for friction spot joints (FSpJ) [7,46] as micro-mechanical interlocking, which contributes to the joint mechanical performance. Therefore, one may expect this phenomenon to improve the strength of friction-riveted joints.

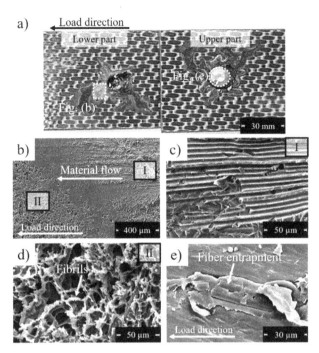

Figure 16. Typical fracture surface of friction-riveted joint. (**a**) General overview of the overlapped area from the lower and upper composite parts. (**b**) Squeezed composite at the surface of the lower composite part, showing the adhesive failure of the reconsolidated composite layer; (**c**) Impressions of fiber tearing in the reconsolidated composite layer; (**d**) Polymer fibrils, indicating ductile fracture of the reconsolidated composite layer. (**e**) Surface of the rivet tip, showing broken fiber entrapment. (Joining parameters—RS: 15,000 rpm, DF: 7.5 mm, FF: 10 kN, CP: 0.2 MPa).

5. Conclusions

The main goal of the current investigation was to assess the influence of external clamping pressure during the Friction Riveting process on the joint formation and the strength of Ti6Al4V/CF-PEEK single lap joints. The balance of internal and external forces induced by the joining process and clamping system was shown to be relevant to a compromise between joint quality (i.e., minimum defects such as delamination and separation of parts) and high joint strength. The compression imposed by the clamping system varied upon the joining time being partially released at the end of the process when the rivet tip widened and the molten polymer flowed outward the joining area. This compression was also not homogeneously distributed over the span of the clamping element owing to discontinuous and irregular squeezed material between the composite parts. Two preferential paths of the material flow were identified: the composite upward flow, which forms the flash, and squeezing flow between the composite parts, leading to their separation. As expected, by increasing clamping pressure from 0.2 MPa to 0.6 MPa, the squeezing flow was restricted and decreasing the separation of the composite parts was decreased by 50%. Ultimate lap shear forces ranging from 3903 ± 462 N to 6580 ± 383 N were achieved. Despite a 50% decrease in the separation of CF-PEEK parts due to the increasing clamping pressure, no correlation with the quasi-static mechanical performance was observed. A higher level of friction force along with a threefold increase of clamping pressure induced the delamination of the composite part and the inverted bell shape of the plastically deformed rivet tip. These effects led to a 34% loss of the joint-anchoring efficiency and a 31% decrease in joint strength compared to the joints produced under low friction force. All joints failed by initial composite bearing and final rivet pull-out.

Considering the similarities between Friction Riveting and the post-processing of composite laminates, the findings of this work may be adopted to further improve and develop the quality and strength of metal-composite overlap hybrid structures through clamping device optimization.

Author Contributions: S.T.A.-F. conceived the structure of the manuscript; N.Z.B. designed and performed most of the experiments and analyzed all experimental data; J.F.d.S. contributed with the discussions of experimental results. All authors contributed in the preparation and review of the manuscript.

Funding: This research was funded by CNPq, Brazil (process number 304169/2014-5), and the Austrian aviation program TAKE OFF, and BMVIT-Austrian Ministry for Transport, Innovation and Technology.

Acknowledgments: This work was supported by the Helmholtz Association.

Conflicts of Interest: The authors declare no conflict of interest.

References

1. Chavoshi, S.Z.; Goel, S.; Morantz, P. Current trends and future of sequential micro-machining processes on a single machine tool. *Mater. Des.* **2017**, *127*, 37–53. [CrossRef]
2. Klimchik, A.; Ambiehl, A.; Garnier, S.; Furet, B.; Pashkevich, A. Efficiency evaluation of robots in machining applications using industrial performance measure. *Robot. Comput. Integr. Manuf.* **2017**, *48*, 12–29. [CrossRef]
3. Li, L.; Li, C.; Tang, Y.; Yi, Q. Influence factors and operational strategies for energy efficiency improvement of CNC machining. *J. Clean. Prod.* **2017**, *161*, 220–238. [CrossRef]
4. Dos Santos, J.F.; Olea, C.A.W.; Coelho, R.S.; Kostka, A.; Paglia, C.S.; Ghidini, T.; Donne Eads, C.D. 11 - Metallurgy and weld performance in friction stir welding. In *Friction Stir Welding*; Woodhead Publishing Series in Welding and Other Joining Technologies; Woodhead Publishing: Sawston, UK, 2010; pp. 314–410, ISBN 978-1-84569-450-0.
5. Goebel, J.; Reimann, M.; Norman, A.; dos Santos, J.F. Semi-stationary shoulder bobbin tool friction stir welding of AA2198-T851. *J. Mater. Process. Technol.* **2017**, *245*, 37–45. [CrossRef]
6. Feistauer, E.E.; Guimarães, R.P.M.; Ebel, T.; dos Santos, J.F.; Amancio-Filho, S.T. Ultrasonic joining: A novel direct-assembly technique for metal-composite hybrid structures. *Mater. Lett.* **2016**, *170*, 1–4. [CrossRef]
7. Goushegir, S.M.; dos Santos, J.F.; Amancio-Filho, S.T. Influence of process parameters on mechanical performance and bonding area of AA2024/carbon-fiber-reinforced poly(phenylene sulfide) friction spot single lap joints. *Mater. Des.* **2015**, *83*, 431–442. [CrossRef]
8. Amancio-Filho, S.T.; dos Santos, J.F. Joining of polymers and polymer–metal hybrid structures: Recent developments and trends. *Polym. Eng. Sci.* **2009**, *49*, 1461–1476. [CrossRef]
9. Gardiner, G. Hybrid Carbon Fiber/Aluminum Suspension Knuckle. Available online: http://www.compositesworld.com/articles/hybrid-carbon-fiberaluminum-suspension-knuckle (accessed on 14 July 2017).
10. Klotz, S.; Lepold, A.; Zanger, F.; Schulze, V. Experimental Investigation of Clamping Systems and the Resulting Change of Cutting Conditions While Drilling Carbon Fiber Reinforced Plastics. *Procedia CIRP* **2017**, *62*, 15–20. [CrossRef]
11. Klotz, S.; Gerstenmeyer, M.; Zanger, F.; Schulze, V. Influence of Clamping Systems During Drilling Carbon Fiber Reinforced Plastics. *Procedia CIRP* **2014**, *13*, 208–213. [CrossRef]
12. Weidinger, P.; Günther, K.; Fitzel, M.; Logvinov, R.; Ilin, A.; Ploshikhin, V.; Hugger, F.; Mann, V.; Roth, S.; Schmidt, M. Testing of New Materials and Computer Aided Optimization of Process Parameters and Clamping Device During Predevelopment of Laser Welding Processes. *Phys. Procedia* **2014**, *56*, 487–496. [CrossRef]
13. Richter-Trummer, V.; Suzano, E.; Beltrão, M.; Roos, A.; dos Santos, J.F.; de Castro, P.M.S.T. Influence of the FSW clamping force on the final distortion and residual stress field. *Mater. Sci. Eng. A* **2012**, *538*, 81–88. [CrossRef]
14. Mahdavi Shahri, M.; Sandström, R.; Osikowicz, W. Critical distance method to estimate the fatigue life time of friction stir welded profiles. *Int. J. Fatigue* **2012**, *37*, 60–68. [CrossRef]
15. Venkatesan, K. The study on force, surface integrity, tool life and chip on laser assisted machining of inconel 718 using Nd:YAG laser source. *J. Adv. Res.* **2017**, *8*, 407–423. [CrossRef] [PubMed]
16. Liu, H.; Zhao, L.; Li, T.; Hou, B.; Wang, Y.; Ma, Y.; Jia, Z. Multi-point Clamping with Automatic Collision Avoidance for Aircraft Structural Parts Machining. *Procedia Manuf.* **2016**, *6*, 33–38. [CrossRef]

17. Hatt, O.; Crawforth, P.; Jackson, M. On the mechanism of tool crater wear during titanium alloy machining. *Wear* **2017**, *374–375*, 15–20. [CrossRef]

18. Feng, P.; Wang, J.; Zhang, J.; Zheng, J. Drilling induced tearing defects in rotary ultrasonic machining of C/SiC composites. *Ceram. Int.* **2017**, *43*, 791–799. [CrossRef]

19. Hejjaji, A.; Zitoune, R.; Crouzeix, L.; Roux, S.L.; Collombet, F. Surface and machining induced damage characterization of abrasive water jet milled carbon/epoxy composite specimens and their impact on tensile behavior. *Wear* **2017**, *376–377*, 1356–1364. [CrossRef]

20. Wagner, G.; Balle, F.; Eifler, D. Ultrasonic Welding of Aluminum Alloys to Fiber Reinforced Polymers. *Adv. Eng. Mater.* **2013**, *15*, 792–803. [CrossRef]

21. Amancio-Filho, S.T. Henry Granjon Prize Competition 2009 Winner Category A: "Joining and Fabrication Technology" Friction Riveting: Development and analysis of a new joining technique for polymer-metal multi-material structures. *Weld. World* **2011**, *55*, 13–24. [CrossRef]

22. Proença, B.; Blaga, L.; Canto, L.B.; Dos Santos, J.F.; Amancio-Filho, S.T. Force controlled Friction Riveting of glass fiber reinforced polyamide 6 and aluminum alloy 6056 hybrid joints. In Proceedings of the ANTEC 2015, Orlando, FL, USA, 23–25 March 2015.

23. Blaga, L.; dos Santos, J.F.; Bancila, R.; Amancio-Filho, S.T. Friction Riveting (FricRiveting) as a new joining technique in GFRP lightweight bridge construction. *Constr. Build. Mater.* **2015**, *80*, 167–179. [CrossRef]

24. Altmeyer, J.; Suhuddin, U.F.H.; dos Santos, J.F.; Amancio-Filho, S.T. Microstructure and mechanical performance of metal-composite hybrid joints produced by FricRiveting. *Compos. Part B Eng.* **2015**, *81*, 130–140. [CrossRef]

25. Borba, N.Z.; Afonso, C.R.M.; Blaga, L.; dos Santos, J.F.; Canto, L.B.; Amancio-Filho, S.T. On the Process-Related Rivet Microstructural Evolution, Material Flow and Mechanical Properties of Ti-6Al-4V/GFRP Friction-Riveted Joints. *Materials* **2017**, *10*, 184. [CrossRef] [PubMed]

26. Rodrigues, C.F.; Blaga, L.A.; dos Santos, J.F.; Canto, L.B.; Hage, E.; Amancio-Filho, S.T. FricRiveting of aluminum 2024-T351 and polycarbonate: Temperature evolution, microstructure and mechanical performance. *J. Mater. Process. Technol.* **2014**, *214*, 2029–2039. [CrossRef]

27. Borba, N.Z.; Blaga, L.; dos Santos, J.F.; Amancio-Filho, S.T. Direct-Friction Riveting of polymer composite laminates for aircraft applications. *Mater. Lett.* **2018**, *215*, 31–34. [CrossRef]

28. Altmeyer, J.; dos Santos, J.F.; Amancio-Filho, S.T. Effect of the friction riveting process parameters on the joint formation and performance of Ti alloy/short-fibre reinforced polyether ether ketone joints. *Mater. Des.* **2014**, *60*, 164–176. [CrossRef]

29. Welsch, G.; Boyer, R.; Collings, E.W. *Materials Properties Handbook: Titanium Alloys*; ASM International: Almere, The Netherlands, 1993; ISBN 978-0-87170-481-8.

30. Avanzini, A.; Donzella, G.; Gallina, D.; Pandini, S.; Petrogalli, C. Fatigue behavior and cyclic damage of peek short fiber reinforced composites. *Compos. Part B Eng.* **2013**, *45*, 397–406. [CrossRef]

31. Schambron, T.; Lowe, A.; McGregor, H.V. Effects of environmental ageing on the static and cyclic bending properties of braided carbon fibre/PEEK bone plates. *Compos. Part B Eng.* **2008**, *39*, 1216–1220. [CrossRef]

32. Toho Tenax, Teijin. *Tenax®-E TPCL PEEK-HTA40 Product Data Sheet*; Teijin: Tokyo, Japan, 2018.

33. Pina Cipriano, G.; Blaga, L.A.; dos Santos, J.F.; Vilaça, P.; Amancio-Filho, S.T. Fundamentals of Force-Controlled Friction Riveting: Part II—Joint Global Mechanical Performance and Energy Efficiency. *Materials* **2018**, *11*, 2489. [CrossRef] [PubMed]

34. *ASTM D5961 Standard Test Method for Bearing Response of Polymer Matrix Composite Laminates*; ASTM: West Conshohocken, PA, USA, 2017.

35. Khashaba, U.A.; Sallam, H.E.M.; Al-Shorbagy, A.E.; Seif, M.A. Effect of washer size and tightening torque on the performance of bolted joints in composite structures. *Compos. Struct.* **2006**, *73*, 310–317. [CrossRef]

36. Lempert, G.D.; Tsour, A. Reduction of static friction between surfaces of Ti-6Al-4V and between surfaces of Ti-6Al-4V and Al-7075. *Surf. Coat. Technol.* **1992**, *52*, 291–295. [CrossRef]

37. Amancio-Filho, S.T.; dos Santos, J.F. Preliminary analytical modeling of heat input in Friction Riveting. In Proceedings of the ANTEC, Indianapolis, IN, USA, 23–25 May 2016; pp. 1361–1368.

38. Matsuzaki, R.; Shibata, M.; Todoroki, A. Improving performance of GFRP/aluminum single lap joints using bolted/co-cured hybrid method. *Compos. Part Appl. Sci. Manuf.* **2008**, *39*, 154–163. [CrossRef]

39. An Analytical Model for the Heat Generation in Friction Stir Welding (PDF Download Available). Available online: https://www.researchgate.net/publication/231054655_An_analytical_model_for_the_heat_generation_in_friction_stir_welding (accessed on 20 June 2017).

40. Yuan, W.; Mishra, R.S.; Carlson, B.; Verma, R.; Mishra, R.K. Material flow and microstructural evolution during friction stir spot welding of AZ31 magnesium alloy. *Mater. Sci. Eng. A* **2012**, *543*, 200–209. [CrossRef]

41. Schneider, J.; Beshears, R.; Nunes, A.C. Interfacial sticking and slipping in the friction stir welding process. *Mater. Sci. Eng. A* **2006**, *435–436*, 297–304. [CrossRef]

42. Bodjona, K.; Lessard, L. Hybrid bonded-fastened joints and their application in composite structures: A general review. *J. Reinf. Plast. Compos.* **2016**, *35*, 764–781. [CrossRef]

43. Chowdhury, N.M.; Wang, J.; Chiu, W.K.; Chang, P. Static and fatigue testing bolted, bonded and hybrid step lap joints of thick carbon fibre/epoxy laminates used on aircraft structures. *Compos. Struct.* **2016**, *142*, 96–106. [CrossRef]

44. Kelly, G. Quasi-static strength and fatigue life of hybrid (bonded/bolted) composite single-lap joints. *Compos. Struct.* **2006**, *72*, 119–129. [CrossRef]

45. Nixon-Pearson, O.J.; Hallett, S.R. An experimental investigation into quasi-static and fatigue damage development in bolted-hole specimens. *Compos. Part B Eng.* **2015**, *77*, 462–473. [CrossRef]

46. André, N.M.; Goushegir, S.M.; dos Santos, J.F.; Canto, L.B.; Amancio-Filho, S.T. Friction Spot Joining of aluminum alloy 2024-T3 and carbon-fiber-reinforced poly(phenylene sulfide) laminate with additional PPS film interlayer: Microstructure, mechanical strength and failure mechanisms. *Compos. Part B Eng.* **2016**, *94*, 197–208. [CrossRef]

 *materials*

Article

Evaluation of Joint Formation and Mechanical Performance of the AA7075-T6/CFRP Spot Joints Produced by Frictional Heat

Natalia Manente André [1], Jorge F. dos Santos [1] and Sergio T. Amancio-Filho [2],*

[1] Department of Solid State Joining Processes, Institute of Materials Research, Materials Mechanics, Centre for Materials and Coastal Research, Helmholtz-Zentrum Geesthacht, 21502 Geesthacht, Germany; natalia.manente@hzg.de (N.M.A.); jorge.dos.santos@hzg.de (J.F.d.S.)

[2] Institute of Materials Science, Joining and Forming, Graz University of Technology–TU Graz, BMVIT Endowed Professorship for Aviation, Kopernikusgasse 24/1, 8010 Graz, Austria

* Correspondence: sergio.amancio@tugraz.at; Tel./Fax: +43-316-871-610

Received: 26 February 2019; Accepted: 14 March 2019; Published: 17 March 2019

Abstract: The development of lightweight hybrid metal–polymer structures has recently attracted interest from the transportation industry. Nevertheless, the possibility of joining metals and polymers or composites is still a great challenge. Friction Spot Joining (FSpJ) is a prize-winning friction-based joining technique for metal–polymer hybrid structures. The technology is environment-friendly and comprises very short joining cycles (2 to 8 s). In the current work, aluminum alloy 7075-T6 and carbon-fiber-reinforced polyphenylene sulfide (CF-PPS) friction spot joints were produced and evaluated for the first time in the literature. The spot joints were investigated in terms of microstructure, mechanical performance under quasi-static loading and failure mechanisms. Macro- and micro-mechanical interlocking were identified as the main bonding mechanism, along with adhesion forces as a result of the reconsolidated polymer layer. Moreover, the influence of the joining force on the mechanical performance of the joints was addressed. Ultimate lap shear forces up to 4068 ± 184 N were achieved in this study. A mixture of adhesive–cohesive failure mode was identified, while cohesive failure was dominant. Finally, a qualitative comparison with other state-of-the-art joining technologies for hybrid structures demonstrated that the friction spot joints eventually exhibit superior/similar strength than/to concurrent technologies and shorter joining times.

Keywords: Friction Spot Joining; aluminium alloys; fibre reinforced composites; friction; mechanical properties

---

1. Introduction

Interest has grown in the transport industry to use fiber-reinforced polymers aiming at reducing weight and fuel consumption in vehicles [1]. Glass- and carbon-fiber-reinforced polymers present optimal specific strength and stiffness, along with improved corrosion properties when compared with conventional materials such as steel [2]. Most of the time, the manufacturing of monolithic structures is not feasible due to technical and economic concerns [2]. Therefore, there is a growing trend of combining lightweight metal alloys with advanced fiber-reinforced polymers in the development of metal–polymer hybrid structures.

Over the past 30 years, aircraft manufacturers have been increasing the use of polymer composites in their products. Some well-known examples include the Boeing 787 (50% in weight composed of composites) [3], the Airbus A350 (53% in weight composed of composites) [4], and recently, the Embraer KC-390 that used polymer composites as a ballistic solution in a military model [5].

Mechanical fastening and adhesive bonding are the traditionally applied techniques to join metal–polymer hybrid structures in production lines [6]. However, there have been disadvantages related to stress concentration and additional process steps (for mechanical fastening) and long curing times (for adhesive bonding) which urged the development of alternative joining technologies [7]. Ultrasonic [8,9], resistance [10], induction [11], and laser [12] welding have been studied in the past years as advanced joining methods for metal–polymer hybrid structures. The present work considers frictional heat as the heat source for joining such dissimilar materials and presents Friction Spot Joining as a joining solution for metal–polymer hybrid structures.

Friction Spot Joining (FSpJ) is a friction-based method for joining metals to polymers or composites [13]. FSpJ produces high-quality joints relying on short joining cycles (2 to 8 s) and absence of filler material and post-joining treatment. Low-cost machinery and easy reparability are other advantages of this process. The feasibility of FSpJ has been demonstrated for several combinations of materials such as AZ31-O/glass-fiber- and carbon-fiber-reinforced polyphenylene sulfide (GF- and CF-PPS) [14] and AA6181-T4/CF-PPS [15] for automotive applications, and AA2024-T3/CF-PPS [16] for aerospace applications. Recently, the process was also demonstrated for carbon nanotube polycarbonate nanocomposites/AA6082-T6 single-lap joints for indirect heating of polymeric parts and electrostatic painting of metal–polymer hybrid parts in the automotive industry [17].

In the current study, AA7075-T6/CF-PPS friction spot joints were produced and evaluated for the first time in the literature. This combination of materials is strategic for aerospace applications due to the improved stress–corrosion cracking resistance of AA7075-T6 when compared with other aluminum alloys like AA2024-T3 [18]. The fundamentals of joint formation and the influence of the joining force on the mechanical performance of AA7075-T6/CF-PPS friction spot joints were addressed. The joint interface and bonding mechanisms were analyzed by optical and confocal laser scanning microscopy. The mechanical performance of the joints produced with three different joining forces was evaluated under quasi-static loading by using a lap shear test. A qualitative comparison of the quasi-static mechanical performance for metal–polymer or composite structures produced with different methods was also presented. Finally, the failure micro-mechanisms of the joints were briefly discussed.

2. Friction Spot Joining (FSpJ)

Friction Spot Joining uses a non-consumable tool composed of three pieces: a pin and a sleeve which rotate and move axially, and a stationary clamping ring [14]. The three pieces are mounted coaxially and have independent movements. The parts to be joined are aligned in an overlap configuration and then clamped between the backing plate and the clamping ring to ensure intimate contact during the process.

The joining process can be divided into three steps. In the first step, the sleeve starts to rotate and plunges into the upper sheet (a metal sheet in this work, Figure 1A). Note, that to avoid the thermal–mechanical degradation of the polymer matrix and damage to the fiber reinforcement of the composite, the plunge of the sleeve is restricted to the metal part. The motion of the rotating sleeve in contact with the metal part generates frictional heat. Consequently, a volume of metal near the tool is softened and plastically deformed due to a local increase in temperature [15,16]. Concurrently with the sleeve plunging event, the pin is retracted forming a reservoir, which is filled with the softened metal (Figure 1A). In the second step of the process, the sleeve and pin move back to the metal surface. Thus, the softened metal is forced back into the metal part by the pin movement, thereby closing the keyhole left by the sleeve plunging (Figure 1B). In the third and final step, the tool is retracted from the surface of the metal part and the joint is kept clamped to consolidate under pressure (Figure 1C). The main process parameters of FSpJ are: the rotational speed of the tool (RS), the plunge depth of the sleeve into the metal part (PD), plunging and retracting time of the sleeve combined as the joining time (JT), and the joining force applied to the clamping ring during the process (JF) [19].

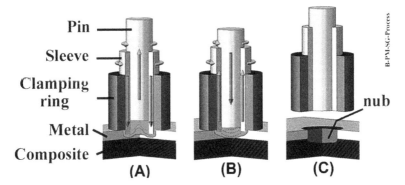

Figure 1. Description of the FSpJ process in three steps: (**A**) sleeve plunging, softening and deformation of the metal part; (**B**) spot refilling; (**C**) retraction of the tool and joint consolidation. (Adapted from Reference [14]).

3. Materials and Methods

3.1. Aluminum Alloy 7075-T6

Aluminum alloy 7075 in the T6 temper condition (2-mm thick rolled sheets) was used in the current study. As the main alloying element, zinc provides high strength to this aluminum alloy through precipitation hardening. The addition of chromium improves the stress–corrosion cracking resistance of this alloy when compared with the 2XXX alloys [20]. The nominal chemical composition of the AA7075-T6 is presented in Table 1. A selection of relevant physical and mechanical properties of the alloy used in this work are listed in Table 2.

Table 1. Nominal chemical composition of AA7075-T6 [20].

Element	Zn	Mg	Cu	Fe	Si	Mn	Cr	Ti	Al
Wt.%	6.1–5.1	2.1–2.9	1.2–2.0	0.50	0.40	0.30	0.18–0.28	0.2	Bal.

Table 2. Selected physical and mechanical properties of AA7075-T6 [21].

Tensile Strength (TL * direction) (MPa)	Yield Strength (TL * direction) (MPa)	Elongation (%)	Incipient Melting Temperature (°C)	Thermal Conductivity (W m^{-1} K^{-1})	Coefficient of Thermal Expansion, 20–300°C (µm m^{-1} °C^{-1})
538	469	8	477	130	25.2

* TL: transverse to lamination.

3.2. Carbon-Fiber-Reinforced Polyphenylene Sulfide (CF-PPS)

Carbon-fiber-reinforced polyphenylene sulfide (CF-PPS), a quasi-isotropic laminate, was used as the composite part in this work. Moreover, 2.17-mm-thick sheets with 43 wt.% carbon fiber-woven fabric (5H satin configuration) were selected. The carbon fiber fabric reinforcement is stacked as seven plies in the [(0.90)/(±45)]3/(0.90) sequence. CF-PPS is a high-performance thermoplastic composite that presents a continuous service temperature around 100 °C [22]. It was produced by TenCate (Netherlands). Several aerospace applications, such as the "J-Nose" subframe wings of Airbus A380 and the engine pylon cover of Airbus A340-500/600 are addressed for this material [22]. Here a selection of relevant physical and mechanical properties of CF-PPS is listed in Table 3.

Table 3. Selected physical and mechanical properties of CF-PPS [22].

Tensile Strength (warp/weft) (MPa)	In-Plane Shear Strength (MPa)	Glass Transition Temperature—T_g (°C)	Melting Temperature—T_m (°C)	Thermal Conductivity (W m^{-1} K^{-1})	Coefficient of Thermal Expansion, 23–300 °C (μm m^{-1} °C^{-1})
790/750	119	120	280	0.19	52.2

3.3. Experimental Procedure

3.3.1. Joining Procedure

Before the joining process, the aluminum part was sandblasted to increase its surface roughness. As reported in previous investigations [16,23], such mechanical surface pre-treatment improves the adhesion between aluminum and composite. Corundum (Al$_2$O$_3$) was used as a blasting medium with an average particle size of 100–150 μm. The samples were sandblasted for 10 s at a distance of 20 cm and an incidence angle of 45° of the blasting pistol. An average roughness (Ra) of 6.7 ± 0.4 μm was achieved.

Single overlap joints were produced using an FSp-joining equipment (RPS 200 Harms&Wende, Hamburg, Germany). The configuration and dimensions of the joints are shown in Figure 2.

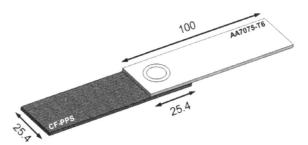

Figure 2. Configuration and dimensions of the joints (in mm).

The joining parameters used to produce the joints in this study are presented in Table 4. These joining parameters were obtained from the statistical analysis (full factorial design of experiments combined with analysis of variance) applied to maximize the ultimate lap shear force of the joints. Although the details of the statistical analysis for process optimization will be published in a separate document, the process parameter range used in the design of the experiments for the study to determine the range of optimal joining parameters of the current manuscript was: rotational speed—1900 to 2900 rpm; plunge depth—0.8 to 1.0 mm; joining time—4 to 8 s; and joining force—4 to 8 kN. To address the influence of the JF on the mechanical performance of the joints, RS, PD and JT were kept constant and a range of JF was investigated in this work.

Table 4. Joining parameters used in the current study.

Condition	Rotational Speed (rpm)	Plunge Depth (mm)	Joining Time (s)	Joining Force (kN)
C1	1900	0.8	4	4
C2	1900	0.8	4	6
C3	1900	0.8	4	8

The temperature evolution on the aluminum surface was monitored during the joining process using an infrared thermo-camera (High-end Camera Series ImageIR, Infratech GmbH, Dresden, Germany). The measurement was set within the range of 150–700 °C with a frequency of 20 Hz. The specimens were covered with a black and high-temperature-resistant paint prior to the joining process to avoid deviations regarding the emissivity of the aluminum alloy. Figure 3 shows a schematic example of the set-up for infrared thermography. The peak process temperature was considered as the maximum temperature identified on the aluminum surface.

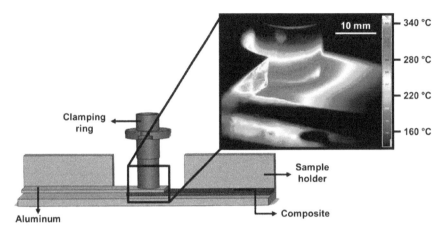

Figure 3. Schematic illustration of the set-up for infrared thermography and an example of the snapshot during the measurement.

3.3.2. Microstructural Analysis

The joints were cut close to the middle of the spot and prepared for microstructural analysis, following standard grinding and polishing procedures. Optical (DM IR microscope, Leica, Wetzlar, Germany) and confocal laser scanning (VK-9700, Keyence, Osaka, Japan) microscopy were employed to investigate the microstructure and interface of the joints.

3.3.3. Mechanical Testing

Lap shear testing under tensile loading was used to assess the quasi-static mechanical performance of the joints. The mechanical testing was performed according to the ASTM D3163-01 standard procedure by using a universal testing machine Zwick/Roell 1478 (Zwick Roell, Ulm, Germany). The cross-head speed of 1.27 mm min^{-1} was selected and the tests were performed at room temperature. Specimens with dimensions of 100 × 25.4 mm and 645.2 mm^2 of overlap area were tested (Figure 2). The average ultimate lap shear force (ULSF) of the joints was evaluated based on three replicates for each joining condition. The strength of these joints was calculated by using the area of the external sleeve diameter (9 mm) as the nominal bonded area of the joints.

3.3.4. Fracture Surface Analysis

The fractured surfaces of the joints were gold-sputtered and analyzed by scanning electron microscopy (SEM) (FEI, QUANTA FEG 650, Hillsboro, OR, USA). A voltage of 5 kV and a working distance of 17 mm were utilized. Confocal laser scanning microscopy (Keyence, Japan) was also used to generate 3D images of the fracture surface of the joints to estimate the volume of the composite entrapped into the aluminum part after the joining.

4. Results and Discussion

4.1. Temperature Evolution

Figure 4 presents a representative curve of the temperature evolution on the aluminum surface during the FSpJ process. Considering the parameters used in this study, the maximum aluminum surface temperature achieved during the joining process was 331 ± 4 °C. On the one hand, such temperature represents about 77% of the incipient melting point of the AA7075-T6 [20]. Therefore, the metallic part of the joint is not expected to melt. Nevertheless, metallographic phenomena, such as recovery and dynamic recrystallization, are likely to occur due to the combination of the high temperature ($0.77T_m$) and the shear rate applied by the rotating sleeve, as commonly observed in the friction-based welding processes [14,24]. On the other hand, the maximum temperature achieved is well above the T_g (120 °C) and T_m (280 °C) of the PPS matrix of the composite. Thus, it is expected that a thin layer of the PPS matrix close to the joint's interface is melted during the joining process. The onset temperatures for the cross-linking (500 °C [25]) and chain scission (550° [25]) of PPS were not reached during the FSpJ process in this study. Therefore, extensive thermo-mechanical degradation of the polymeric part is not expected.

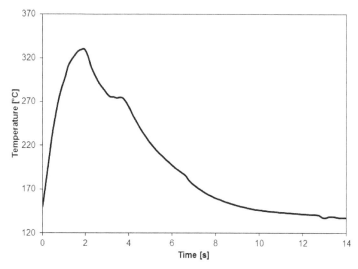

Figure 4. A representative curve of the temperature evolution on the aluminum surface during the FSpJ process (RS: 1900 rpm, PD: 0.8 mm, JT: 4 s, JF: 6 kN).

4.2. Joint Formation

Figure 5A,B show a typical AA7075-T6/CF-PPS single lap joint along with its top view. Excellent surface finishing was achieved. The area where the sleeve plunge occurred has a bright and flat surface, as shown in Figure 5B.

A representative example of the cross-section of the joints is shown in Figure 5C. One notes that at the center of the joint a certain volume of the aluminum, which softened during the joining process, has symmetrically plastically deformed into the composite part because of the axial movement of the tool. This metallic undercut, known as the "metallic nub", is responsible for the macro-mechanical interlocking between aluminum and composite. The metallic nub is a characteristic of FSp joints which was also observed in other combination of materials; it leads to macro-mechanical interlocking as one of the main bonding mechanisms in friction spot joints [14–16,26].

A detailed analysis of the joint's interface also revealed the sites of micro-mechanical interlocking between the crevices of aluminum and the consolidated composite matrix. As previously discussed, a thin layer of the PPS matrix close to the joint's interface is melted during the joining process. The molten PPS is displaced from the center to the edges of the joint due to the axial force applied by the tool and the plastic deformation of the metal. Such displacement of the PPS matrix exposes some carbon fibers at the center of the joints to be in intimate contact with the aluminum surface. Figure 6A shows the presence of these fibers anchored by the irregularities of the sandblasted aluminum surface.

The entrapment of the PPS matrix into the crevices of the aluminum surface was also identified, as shown in Figure 6B. It is possible to note that an effective micro-mechanical interlocking was achieved because the PPS matrix took the shape of the irregularities of the aluminum surface, while some fibers were entrapped into the crevices.

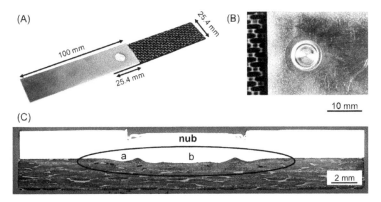

Figure 5. (**A**) Example of an AA7075-T6/CF-PPS friction spot joint along with typical (**B**) top view and (**C**) cross-section of the joints. The metallic nub is indicated with an ellipse in (**C**). The details of regions a and b are presented in Figure 6. (RS: 1900 rpm, PD: 0.8 mm, JT: 4 s, JF: 6 kN).

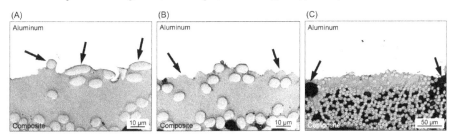

Figure 6. (**A**) Fiber anchoring (region a in Figure 5C), (**B**) PPS matrix entrapment (region b in Figure 5C) by the aluminum surface, and (**C**) volumetric defects in the composite part close to the joint's interface (region b in Figure 5C).

Figure 6C shows the presence of volumetric defects in the composite part close to the joint's interface. It is believed that such defects are micro-voids generated by air entrapment due to the outflow of the molten matrix during the joining process. Some of these voids may also be correlated with the differential shrinkage between the metal and the composite matrix during joint consolidation [19]. The presence of microvoids was also addressed for AA2024-T3/CF-PPS friction spot joints by Goushegir et al. [16]. As mentioned previously, the maximum process temperature achieved for the joints in this study was $331 \pm 4\,^\circ$C. This temperature is far below the onset degradation temperature of PPS (for cross-linking 500 °C). Therefore, it is not expected that such voids are the result of the thermo-mechanical degradation of the composite part.

As previously discussed, the generated frictional heat is conducted through the aluminum surface and melts a thin layer of the polymer matrix close to the joint's interface. Owing to the axial force applied by the tool, the molten polymer is displaced from the center of the joint toward the edges of the overlap area (Figure 7). The layer of molten polymer reconsolidates during the cooling phase of the process, thereby establishing adhesion forces between the aluminum and composite. The bonding area in the friction spot joints can be determined by the perimeter of the reconsolidated molten polymer layer, as indicated by the dashed line in Figure 7.

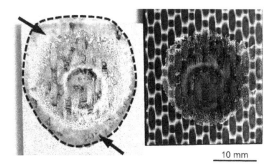

Figure 7. A representative example of the fracture surface of a friction spot joint. The arrows indicate the layer of the reconsolidated molten PPS.

Therefore, three main bonding mechanisms can be identified for AA7075-T6/CF-PPS friction spot joints: macro- and micro-mechanical interlocking and adhesion forces. Similar mechanisms were addressed for AA2024-T3/CF-PPS [16] and AA6181-T6/CF-PPS [15] friction spot joints.

4.3. Quasi-static Mechanical Performance

It can be seen that the ULSF of the joints does not show a linear correlation with the applied joining force (Figure 8). The strongest joint was obtained with intermediate joining force (JF: 6 kN; ULSF: 4068 ± 184 N). The joint produced with a low joining force resulted in a ULSF that is about 40% lower (JF: 4 kN; ULSF: 2456 ± 60 N), while the joint produced with a high joining force showed an approximately 24% lower ULSF (JF: 8 kN; ULSF: 3102 ± 199 N) than the ULSF obtained for with intermediate joining force.

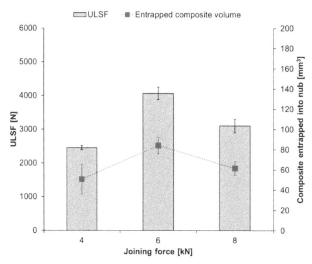

Figure 8. Average ultimate lap shear force of the joints along with the volume of the composite entrapped into the nub by using different joining forces (constant joining parameters RS: 1900 rpm, PD: 0.8 mm, JT: 4 s).

The cross-section of the joints produced by using various joining forces are presented in Figure 9. Furthermore, the fracture surface and respective 3D images of the metallic nub (obtained from the fracture surface of the joints on the aluminum side) are also presented in Figure 10. Different geometries of the metallic nub can be identified in the images. In the joint produced with low joining force (4 kN), the deformation of the aluminum into the composite was very shallow (the metallic nub, Figure 9A). Thus, the macro-mechanical interlocking between the aluminum and the composite is less effective. In this case, the volume of the composite entrapped into the nub was 51 ± 15 mm^3 (Figure 10A) and the joints reached the lowest ultimate lap shear force (2456 ± 60 N) for the joining conditions studied in this work. The joint produced with the intermediate joining force (6 kN) presented a more pronounced deformation of the aluminum into the composite (Figure 9B). In this case, the deformation of the aluminum into the composite retained the shape of two rings (ellipses in Figure 10B). This geometry provides two sites of macro-mechanical interlocking between the aluminum and composite, thereby maximizing the volume of the composite entrapped into the nub (84 ± 8 mm^3). Therefore, the highest mechanical performance of the joints (4068 ± 184 N) was achieved in this study. The aluminum deformation in the joint produced with high joining force (8 kN) resulted in the shape with only one wide ring (Figure 9C). Such geometry provides only one site for the macro-mechanical interlocking between the aluminum and the composite (Figure 10C). Moreover, the volume of the composite entrapped into the nub was 62 ± 7 mm^3. Therefore, a decrease in the ULSF was observed for the joint produced with 8 kN (3102 ± 199 N) compared to those produced with 6 kN.

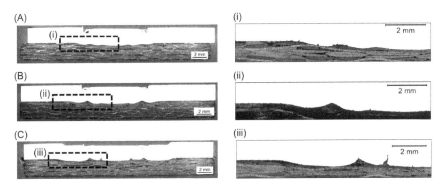

Figure 9. Cross-sections of friction spot joints produced with (**A**) 4 kN, (**B**) 6 kN, and (**C**) 8 kN. Details of the metallic nubs are given in (**i**), (**ii**) and (**iii**) for the joints produced with 4, 6 and 8 kN respectively (constant joining parameters RS: 1900 rpm, PD: 0.8 mm, JT: 4 s).

It is worth noting, that for all the investigated joints, a layer of the reconsolidated molten PPS was formed and remained attached to the aluminum surface (Figure 10), providing adhesion forces. Additionally, signs of fiber and matrix entrapment on the aluminum surface were also observed in all cases (black arrows in Figure 10). These results indicate the importance of the nub geometry and its influence on the macro-mechanical interlocking between the joining parts and hence the mechanical performance of the friction spot joints. Further investigation using the finite element method (FEM) may help to better understand the influence of the geometry of the metallic nub on the mechanical strength of the friction spot joints.

A qualitative comparison between the state-of-the-art welding-based joining technologies for metal–polymer hybrid structures is given in Figure 11. Induction welding (IW) [11], resistance welding (RW) [7], ultrasonic welding (UW) [8], and laser welding (LW) [27] were included in the comparison. Joints with similar materials (metals and carbon-fiber-reinforced polymers), configuration (overlap), surface pre-treatments, thicknesses, and failure mechanisms to friction spot joints were chosen. Figure 11 shows that the friction spot joints presented comparable or superior quasi-static strength to those provided by the concurrent technologies. Another advantage of FSpJ is the process time. The friction spot joints are produced in a single-step joining cycle, which is performed in a few seconds (4 s in this study). However, for example, the induction welding process lasts about 1 min [11], while the resistance welding process can take from 30 s up to 5 min [7]. The ultrasonic welding also has a joining cycle similar to FSpJ (3.5 s) [8].

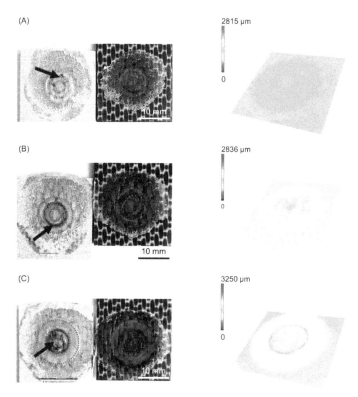

Figure 10. Fracture surface and 3D image of the deformation on the aluminum part (nub region) for the joints produced with (**A**) 4 kN, (**B**) 6 kN and (**C**) 8 kN of joining force (constant joining parameters RS: 1900 rpm, PD: 0.8 mm, JT: 4 s).

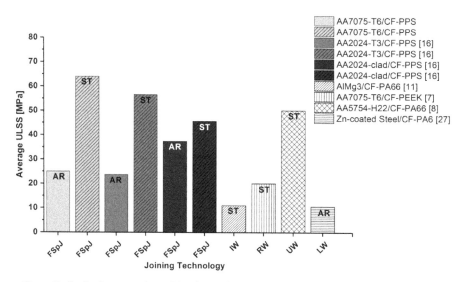

Figure 11. Qualitative comparison of the ultimate lap shear strength (ULSS) of the state-of-the-art and concurrent joining technologies for hybrid structures (AR: as received, ST: surface treatment).

4.4. Fracture Mechanisms

The fracture mechanisms of the joints were investigated through a detailed SEM analysis of their fracture surface after lap shear testing. Three bonding zones were identified: Plastically Deformed Zone (PDZ), Transition Zone (TZ), and Adhesion Zone (AZ), as previously described by Goushegir et al. [16]. Figure 12 shows a typical fracture surface of AA7075-T6/CF-PPS friction spot joints along with the defined bonding zones.

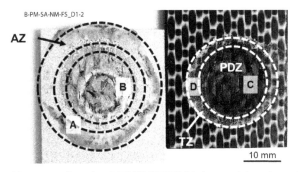

Figure 12. Typical fracture surface of AA7075-T6/CF-PPS friction spot joints along with the defined bonding zones. The regions analyzed by SEM are indicated as A–D.

AZ is the external region of the bonding area originated from the layer of reconsolidated molten polymer expelled from the center of the joint during the joining process. In this zone, the main bonding mechanism is the adhesion forces provided by the reconsolidation of the molten polymer matrix in contact with the aluminum surface. Figure 13A shows a featureless fracture surface of the AZ (reconsolidated molten PPS). It indicates that the failure occurred in this zone due to the detachment of the reconsolidated molten PPS from the composite surface, thus characterizing an adhesive failure mode.

PDZ is the central region of the bonding area where the metallic nub is formed. In this zone, the highest process temperatures are achieved due to the proximity to the tool. The plastic deformation of the metal into the composite displaces a volume of the softened/melted composite's matrix, thus exposing the carbon fibers on the surface of the composite. Therefore, micro-mechanical interlocking (in the form of PPS and carbon-fiber entrapment into the aluminum surface) was identified in this region as previously discussed (Figure 6A,B). Figure 13B shows that the carbon fibers and the PPS matrix remained attached to the aluminum surface after the failure of the joint by mechanical testing. This feature indicates an effective micro-mechanical interlocking in this zone between the aluminum and composite. Additionally, this residual composite material on the aluminum surface indicates that the crack propagated in this zone through the first plies of the composite part instead of at the interface. Figure 13C shows that the fibrils of the PPS originated from the large plastic deformation of the composite's matrix during failure. Therefore, the failure occurred in the PDZ through a cohesive failure mode with a predominantly ductile micro-mechanism of failure. Such a ductile micro-mechanism was also reported for metal–composite hybrid joints welded by Resistance Welding [10] and Ultrasonic Welding [8].

TZ is the transition region between AZ and PDZ. This zone is characterized by the presence of air bubbles formed during the displacement of the molten matrix from the center to the edge of the overlap area during the joining process (see discussion in Section 4.2). Figure 13D shows the air bubbles in this zone on the composite surface. The white arrows indicate plastic deformation sites and tearing of the PPS around the bubbles. It suggests that the cohesive failure mode in the TZ is predominant and that a mixture of brittle and ductile micro-mechanisms of failure occurred. A similar fracture micro-mechanism was also observed for AA2024-T3/CF-PPS friction spot joints in [28].

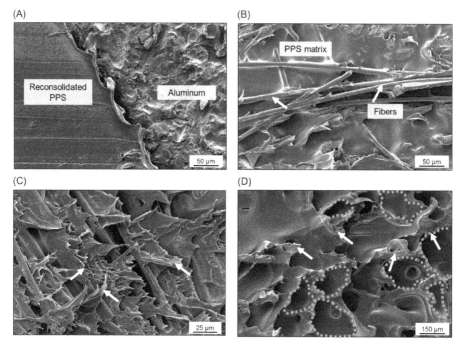

Figure 13. Detailed SEM images of the bonding zones in a representative AA7075-T6/CF-PPS friction spot joint. (**A**) The transition between AZ and TZ. (**B**) The PDZ on the aluminum surface. (**C**) The PDZ and (**D**) the TZ on the composite surface.

5. Conclusions

Friction spot joints of aluminum alloy 7075-T6 and carbon-fiber-reinforced polyphenylene sulfide (CF-PPS) were produced and evaluated for the first time in the literature. The main conclusions drawn from this work are:

- Three main bonding mechanisms were identified at the metal–composite interface: macro- and micro-mechanical interlocking and adhesion forces. The macro-mechanical interlocking was provided by the plastic deformation of the aluminum (metallic nub) into the composite part. The micro-mechanical interlocking at the metal–composite interface was provided by the entrapment of the PPS matrix and carbon fibers into the aluminum surface. Additionally, the reconsolidated molten PPS matrix led to the adhesion forces between the joining parts.

- Ultimate lap shear force of up to 4068 ± 184 N was achieved in this study. The joining force showed a significant influence on the nub geometry and hence on the ULSF of the joints. Intermediate joining force (6 kN in this study) originated a metallic deformation in the shape of two rings inserted into the composite part. This geometry effectively interlocked the aluminum and the composite part, thereby maximizing the volume of the composite entrapped into the nub (84 ± 8 mm^3) and consequently the ULSF of the joint.

- A qualitative comparison with other state-of-the-art joining technologies for hybrid structures demonstrated that the friction spot joints exhibit superior/similar strength than/to the concurrent joining technologies for hybrid structures.

- The fracture surface of the joints showed that the bonding area could be divided into different zones. Three bonding zones were identified as the following: Plastically Deformed Zone (PDZ), Transition Zone (TZ), and Adhesion Zone (AZ), as previously reported in the literature for other combinations of materials joined with FSpJ.

- A mixture of adhesive–cohesive failure mode was identified, while cohesive failure was dominant. A combination of brittle and ductile micro-mechanisms of failure was observed by SEM analysis.

In face of the findings of this work, further investigations regarding the influence of the nub geometry on the mechanical performance of the joints, as well as the assessment of the fatigue performance of such structures for the transportation industry are required. This will be the focus of the coming publications of the group.

Author Contributions: N.M.A. and S.T.A.-F. designed the experiments; N.M.A. performed the experiments, analyzed the results, and structured the manuscript; S.T.A.-F. and J.F.d.S. contributed with the discussions of experimental results. All authors contributed in the review of the manuscript.

Funding: The authors would like to acknowledge the financial support provided by the Helmholtz Association, Germany (Grant No. VH-NG-626), CNPq, Brazil (process number 200694/2015-4), and the Austrian aviation program TAKE OFF, and BMVIT-Austrian Ministry for Transport, Innovation and Technology.

Conflicts of Interest: The authors declare no conflict of interest.

References

1. Arakaki, F.K.; Gonçalves, W.G. Embraer composite material application. In Proceedings of the 16th International Conference of Composite Materials, Kyoto, Japan, 8–13 July 2007.
2. Mallick, P.K. *Materials, Design and Manufacturing for Lightweight Vehicles*, 1st ed.; Woodhead Publishing Limited: Cambridge, UK, 2010.
3. Boeing 787: From the Ground Up. Available online: www.boeing.com/commercial/aeromagazine/articles/qtr_4_06/article_04_2.html (accessed on 12 May 2017).
4. Faivre, V.; Morteau, E. Damage tolerant composite fuselage sizing, characterization of accidental damage threat. *Airbus Tech. Mag. FAST* **2011**, *48*, 10–16.
5. TenCate Advanced Armour will provide ballistic solutions for the Embraer KC-390. Available online: http://www.compositesworld.com/news/tencate-advanced-armour-will-provide-ballistic-solutions-for-the-embraer-kc-390 (accessed on 12 May 2017).
6. Chaves, F.J.P.; Da Silva, L.F.M.; De Moura, M.F.S.F.; Dillard, D.A.; Esteves, V.H.C. Fracture mechanics tests in adhesively bonded joints: A literature review. *J. Adhes.* **2014**, *90*, 955–992. [CrossRef]
7. Marinelli, J.M.; Lambing, C.L.T. Advancement in welding technology for composite-to-metallic joints. *J. Adv. Mater.* **1994**, *25*, 20–27.
8. Balle, F.; Emrich, S.; Wagner, G.; Eifler, D. Improvement of ultrasonically welded aluminum/carbon fiber reinforced polymer-joints by surface technology and high resolution analysis. *Adv. Eng. Mater.* **2013**, *15*, 814–820. [CrossRef]
9. Feistauer, E.E.; Guimarães, R.P.M.; Ebel, T.; Dos Santos, J.F.; Amancio-Filho, S.T. Ultrasonic joining: A novel direct-assembly technique for metal-composite hybrid structures. *Mater. Lett.* **2016**, *170*, 1–4. [CrossRef]
10. Ageorges, C.; Ye, L. Resistance welding of metal/thermoplastic composite joints. *J. Thermoplast. Compos. Mater.* **2001**, *14*, 449–475. [CrossRef]
11. Mitschang, P.; Velthuis, R.; Didi, M. Induction spot welding of metal/CFRPC hybrid joints. *Adv. Eng. Mater.* **2013**, *15*, 804–813. [CrossRef]
12. Cheon, J.; Na, S.-J. Relation of joint strength and polymer molecular structure in laser assisted metal and polymer joining. *Sci. Technol. Weld. Join.* **2014**, *19*, 631–637. [CrossRef]
13. Amancio-Filho, S.T.; Dos Santos, J. Method for joining metal and plastic workpieces. European Patent 2329905B1, 30 May 2012.
14. Amancio-Filho, S.T.; Bueno, C.; Dos Santos, J.F.; Huber, N.; Hage, E., Jr. On the feasibility of friction spot joining in magnesium/fiber-reinforced polymer composite hybrid structures. *Mater. Sci. Eng. A* **2011**, *528*, 3841–3848. [CrossRef]
15. Esteves, J.V.; Goushegir, S.M.; Dos Santos, J.F.; Canto, L.B.; Hage, E., Jr.; Amancio-Filho, S.T. Friction spot joining of aluminum AA6181-T4 and carbon fiber-reinforced poly(phenylene sulfide): Effects of process parameters on the microstructure and mechanical strength. *Mater. Des.* **2015**, *66*, 437–445. [CrossRef]

16. Goushegir, S.M.; Dos Santos, J.F.; Amancio-Filho, S.T. Friction spot joining of aluminum aa2024/carbon-fiber reinforced Poly(phenylene sulfide)composite single lap joints: Microstructure and mechanical performance. *Mater. Des.* **2014**, *50*, 196–206. [CrossRef]

17. Junior, W.S.; Amancio-Filho, S.; Abetz, V.; Dos Santos, J.F. Verfahren zum Herstellen einer leitfähigen Verbindung zwischen einem Metallbauteil und einem Nanokomposit-Bauteil. European Patent 2993029 B1, 30 November 2016.

18. American Society for Metals. *Metals Handbook*; Metals Park: Russel Township, Geauga County, OH, USA, 1981; Volume 2.

19. Goushegir, S.M. Friction spot joining (FSpJ) of aluminum-CFRP hybrid structures. *Weld. World* **2016**, *60*, 1073–1093. [CrossRef]

20. Alcoa Mill Products. Technical datasheet of AA7075-T6. 2009. Available online: http://www.calm-aluminium.com.au/Documents/alloy7075techsheet.pdf (accessed on 17 March 2019).

21. ASM International. *ASM Handbook. Properties and Selection: Nonferrous Alloys and Special-Purpose Materials*; ASM International: Russell Township, Geauga County, OH, USA, 1992; Volume 2.

22. Tencate Advanced Composites; Technical data sheet of CETEX® PPS. 2009. Available online: https://www.tencatecomposites.com/media/221a4fcf-6a4d-49f3-837f-9d85c3c34f74/0EEq4g/TenCate%20Advanced%20Composites/Documents/Product%20datasheets/Thermoplastic/UD%20tapes,%20prepregs%20and%20laminates/TenCate-Cetex-TC1100_PPS_PDS.pdf (accessed on 17 March 2019).

23. Esteves, J.V.; Dos Santos, J.F.; Hage, E., Jr.; Goushegir, S.M.; Canto, L.B.; Amancio-Filho, S.T. Friction Spot Joining of aluminum 6181-T4 and carbon fiber reinforced poly(phenylene sulfide). In Proceedings of the ANTEC 2012, Orlando, FL, USA, 2–4 April 2012; pp. 418–422.

24. Amancio-Filho, S.; Camillo, A.P.C.; Bergmann, L.; Dos Santos, J.F.; Kury, S.E.; Machado, N.G.A. Preliminary investigation of the microstructure and mechanical behaviour of 2024 aluminium alloy friction spot welds. *Mater. Trans.* **2011**, *52*, 985–991. [CrossRef]

25. Gavalyan, V.B.; Zhuravleva, I.V.; Pavlova, S.-S.; Nedel'kin, V.I.; Sergeyev, V.A. Thermal degradation mechanism of poly-p-phenylene sulphides. *Polym. Sci. USSR* **1980**, *22*, 2327–2338. [CrossRef]

26. André, N.M.; Goushegir, S.M.; Dos Santos, J.F.; Canto, L.B.; Amancio-Filho, S.T. Friction Spot Joining of aluminum alloy 2024-T3 and carbon-fiber-reinforced poly(phenylene sulfide) laminate with additional PPS film interlayer: Microstructure, mechanical strength and failure mechanisms. *Compos. Part B Eng.* **2016**, *94*, 197–208. [CrossRef]

27. Jung, K.W.; Kawahito, Y.; Takahashi, M.; Katayama, S. Laser direct joining of carbon fiber reinforced plastic to zinc-coated steel. *Mater. Des.* **2013**, *47*, 179–188. [CrossRef]

28. Goushegir, S.M.; Dos Santos, J.F.; Amancio-Filho, S.T. Failure and fracture micro-mechanisms in metal-composite single lap joints produced by welding-based joining techniques. *Compos. Part A Appl. Sci. Manuf.* **2016**, *81*, 121–128. [CrossRef]

 *materials*

Article

Durability of Metal-Composite Friction Spot Joints under Environmental Conditions

Seyed M. Goushegir [1], Nico Scharnagl [2], Jorge F. dos Santos [1] and Sergio T. Amancio-Filho [3,*]

[1] Solid State Joining Processes, Materials Mechanics, Institute of Materials Research, Centre for Materials and Coastal Research, Helmholtz-Zentrum Geesthacht, 21502 Geesthacht, Germany; mgoushegir@gmail.com (S.M.G.); jorge.dos.santos@hzg.de (J.F.d.S.)
[2] Corrosion and Surface Technology, Magnesium Innovation Center (MagIC), Materials Mechanics, Institute of Materials Research, Centre for Materials and Coastal Research, Helmholtz-Zentrum Geesthacht, 21502 Geesthacht, Germany; nico.scharnagl@hzg.de
[3] BMVIT Endowed Professorship for Aviation, Institute of Materials Science, Joining and Forming, Graz University of Technology, 8010 Graz, Austria
* Correspondence: sergio.amancio@tugraz.at; Tel.: +43-316-8731610

Received: 2 December 2019; Accepted: 28 February 2020; Published: 4 March 2020

Abstract: The current paper investigates the durability of the single-lap shear aluminum-composite friction spot joints and their behavior under harsh accelerated aging as well as natural weathering conditions. Four aluminum surface pre-treatments were selected to be performed on the joints based on previous investigations; these were sandblasting (SB), conversion coating (CC), phosphoric acid anodizing (PAA), and PAA with a subsequent application of primer (PAA-P). Most of the pre-treated specimens retained approximately 90% of their initial as-joined strength after accelerated aging experiments. In the case of the PAA pre-treatment, the joint showed a lower retained strength of about 60%. This was explained based on the penetration of humidity into the fine pores of the PAA pre-treated aluminum, reducing the adhesion between the aluminum and composite. Moreover, friction spot joints produced with three selected surface pre-treatments were held under outside natural weathering conditions for one year. PAA-P surface pre-treated specimens demonstrated the best performance with a retained strength of more than 80% after one year. It is believed that tight adhesion and chemical bonding reduced the penetration of humidity at the interface between the joining parts.

Keywords: friction spot joining; fiber reinforced composites; aluminum alloys; aging; outdoor environmental durability; mechanical properties

---

1. Introduction

Metal-composite hybrid structures have been gaining more attention lately from the transport industry. Recently alternative joining techniques, such as Friction Spot Joining (FSpJ), have been developed to join lightweight metals with polymer composites. FSpJ was shown to be a reliable joining process for joining metals with thermoplastic-based composites [1–5]. In our previous publications, we investigated the influence of various process parameters on the mechanical performance of the FSp joints [3,5]. Moreover, the effect of different aluminums' surface pre-treatments on the lap shear strength of the aluminum alloy 2024-T3/carbon-fiber-reinforced poly (phenylene sulfide) (CF-PPS) FSp joints was recently reported [6], as well as its impact resistance [7] and corrosion properties [8] for Al-sand-blasted treatment.

In addition to initial strength, the durability of a joint, which is its ability to retain initial strength under harsh environments for long time, is particularly important for metal-composite hybrid structures [9], because engineering structures such as an airplane or car are constantly exposed to the environment. In order to select and use a specific joining method, its long-term behavior must be understood. Usually, due to time limitations, the aging of a joint is analyzed over a shorter time, but under an extremely harsh environment (high relative humidity and high temperature). This is known as accelerated aging.

It is important to understand the degradation mechanisms under accelerated aging conditions, to be able to design a durable joint. Three types of mechanisms may cause the degradation of a metal-polymer joint in a humid environment.

The first mechanism is the degradation of the metal-polymer interface [10–12]. If the metal-polymer bonding contains weak boundaries, where no intimate contact exists as a result of poor surface wetting, moisture may diffuse at the interface. Moisture can degrade the adhesion forces such as hydrogen bonds [10], leading to a reduction of joint strength and durability.

The second mechanism to consider is the influence of moisture on the polymer [13,14]. It has been suggested that humidity may degrade the properties of the polymer through plasticization [13–15] or the generation of swelling stresses [13,14]. Thus, a weakening of the polymer is another reason for the reduced durability of a joint. In addition to the humidity, ultraviolet (UV) radiation is another source of degradation for polymers and composites. It is frequently reported [16,17] that photo-oxidation, as a result of UV radiation, changes the physical properties of polymers, such as discoloration and increase in the glass transition temperature, and reduces their mechanical performance. Such behavior should also be considered when using polymers and composites in a structure.

The third mechanism suggests the degradation of the metallic part, in this case aluminum [18,19]. It is well known that aluminum oxide is prone to hydration in a humid atmosphere [19,20]. Aluminum hydroxide forms a weak layer that may be easily detached from the underlying aluminum oxide. Aluminum oxide converts into the crystalline aluminum hydroxide (AlOOH) known as boehmite [16,18]. Upon further hydration, AlOOH transforms into $Al(OH)_3$, known as bayerite [13,21]. Accordingly, the hydration of the aluminum surface also degrades the joint durability.

Sealants and paints may be used as a solution against the above-mentioned durability degradation mechanisms. To reduce the hydration of the aluminum surface, various surface pre-treatments may also be useful. Electrochemical pre-treatments showed the highest durability, followed by chemical and mechanical pre-treatments in adhesively bonded aluminum joints [22,23]. The durability of sandblasted joints was reported to be better or inferior to chemically pre-treated bonded joints in different studies reviewed in [23]. This might be attributed to the extent of the macroporosity generated on the aluminum surface and the wettability of the surface. Proper wettability is necessary for obtaining a durable joint when mechanical pre-treatment is employed. Electrochemical pre-treatments showed excellent durability as a result of the generation of a thick oxide layer, forming a barrier against humidity and corrosive environments.

Among the electrochemical pre-treatments, it is reported that phosphoric acid anodizing (PAA) offers the best durability [18]. Davis et al. explained for the first time the mechanisms of hydration inhibition by PAA pre-treatment [20]. They pointed out that a very thin layer of $AlPO_4$ is formed on top of the aluminum oxide. This layer absorbs water from humidity to form $AlPO_4 \cdot H_2O$, which inhibits the further hydration of the underlying aluminum oxide. Nevertheless, if the aluminum is exposed to a humid atmosphere sufficiently long, the $AlPO_4 \cdot H_2O$ layer starts to dissolve. This leaves the underlying oxide layer exposed to moisture and it begins to degrade.

To further protect the aluminum against hydration and corrosion, a suitable primer layer may be used. Bland et al. used an epoxy-based primer containing strontium and chromium particles on a PAA pre-treated aluminum alloy prior to adhesive bonding [22]. Their findings suggest that the primed joint had a better durability compared to PAA pre-treatment alone.

It is clear from the explanations above that a proper surface pre-treatment not only enhances the adhesion mechanisms and therefore initial joint strength but also the durability of the joint. No information could be found in the literature regarding the influence of surface pre-treatments on the accelerated aging behavior of welding-based joining techniques. A few works have been published aiming at understanding the mechanical performance of metal-polymer hybrid joints under natural outside weathering [24,25]. Didi et al. investigated the influence of different aluminum surface pre-treatments on the mechanical performance of AA5754/carbon-fiber-reinforced polyamide 66 (CF-PA66) induction welded joints after one year of weathering conditions [24]. The authors reported that degreasing and corundum blasting resulted in a very low retained lap shear strength after 12 months. By using acid etching and combined corundum blasting and acid etching, the retained strength increased to more than 50% and 60% respectively. Recently, Schricker et al. demonstrated a strength reduction of approximately 50% in AA6082 / PA66 laser joints after 12 weeks of natural weathering [25]. However, the authors claimed that the mechanical performance also depends on the selected joining speed. Such a reduction in strength was attributed to the moisture absorption and plasticization of PA66.

The current paper deals with the durability of single-lap shear (SLS) FSp joints and their behavior under harsh accelerated aging as well as natural weathering conditions. Various surface pre-treatments were applied on the surface of aluminum to investigate their influence on the failure and mechanical performance of the joints. Besides mechanical characterization, different microscopy and analytical techniques such as scanning electron microscopy (SEM), energy-dispersive X-ray spectroscopy (EDS), and X-ray photoelectron spectroscopy (XPS) were employed to analyze the surface of the joints as well as fracture surfaces after mechanical testing to evaluate the influence of the aging condition on the joints.

2. Experimental Section

2.1. Materials

Aluminum alloy AA2024-T3 rolled sheets with a 2 mm thickness (Constellium, Paris, France) were selected as the metallic part in this work. This alloy is mainly used in transport applications, particularly in aircrafts. Fatigue resistance and damage tolerance, high toughness, and a high strength to weight ratio are some of the main properties offered by AA2024-T3 [26].

As the composite part, CF-PPS laminated sheets (supplied by TenCate, Nijverdal, the Netherlands) with a 2.17 mm nominal thickness were used. The sheets consisted of five harness woven quasi-isotropic laminates with seven plies of carbon fibers [(0.90)/(±45)]3/(0.90). Furthermore, 50 vol % (42 wt %) of continuous carbon fibers was used in this composite. CF-PPS is a high-performance semi-crystalline thermoplastic composite with main applications in primary and secondary aircraft parts. It offers high strength, rigidity, chemical resistance, and low water absorption [27–29].

2.2. FSpJ Process

FSpJ was used in this work to join the parts together. The principles of the process have been explained in our previous publications [1–4,6]. Briefly, the process uses a non-consumable tool, plunging into the aluminum sheet, which was placed on top of the composite in an overlap configuration to a pre-defined position while rotating at high speed. As a result of the plunging of the rotating tool into the aluminum sheet, frictional heat is generated around the tool. Thereby, a volume of the aluminum under the tool is deformed (known as the metallic nub) and inserted into the composite due to the applied axial force by the tool. The metallic nub creates a mechanical interlocking between the joining parts, especially under shear loading. At the same time, the frictional heat is conducted to the interface between the aluminum and composite. As a result, a thin layer of the composite's matrix melts, which after solidification (during the cooling phase) generates adhesion forces between the joining parts. For more information on the process and bonding mechanisms, refer to the previous publications.

Friction spot joints were produced using position-controlled equipment (RPS 100, Harms&Wende, Hamburg, Germany). An optimized set of joining parameters (tool rotational speed: 2900 rpm, tool plunge depth: 0.8 mm, joining time: 4 s, and joining pressure: 0.3 MPa) was selected to join the single lap shear specimens based on the previous investigations [5]. Specimens from AA2024-T3 and CF-PPS were machined prior to the joining process with dimensions of 100 × 25.4 mm. An overlap area of

25.4 × 25.4 mm was selected to join the specimens. The surface of the aluminum samples was treated before joining. Four surface pre-treatments were selected; these were sandblasting (SB), stand-alone conversion coating (CC), phosphoric acid anodizing (PAA), and PAA with a subsequent application of primer (PAA-P). Although SB + CC gave a slightly higher lap shear strength than stand-alone CC in dry conditions [6,30], the CC specimen was selected for the aging experiments, in order to understand the behavior of chemical pre-treatment under environmental conditions. For a detailed explanation of each surface pre-treatment, refer to [6,30].

2.3. Accelerated Aging

To investigate the behavior of the FSp joints under harsh environments, the SLS FSp joints of the selected aluminum surface pre-treatments were placed in an artificial aging chamber (VCL 0003, Vötsch Industrietechnik, Balingen, Germany) for 28 days. The temperature of the chamber was set at 71 °C with 100% relative humidity following the recommendations given in the ASTM D3762 standard [31]. From the conditions given in the ASTM standard, the environment selected for this work was the most severe one. The humidity of the chamber during the test was constantly controlled and adjusted by pumping water into the chamber. After 28 days, the joints were removed from the chamber for further analysis. In addition to the mechanical testing and chemical composition measurements, the samples were weighed to measure the moisture uptake. The samples were first exposed to the stream of air at 40 °C for 1 h before measuring their weight.

2.4. Weathering Conditions

In addition to the accelerated aging, a set of samples with selected aluminum surface pre-treatments was held under outside natural weathering conditions (Geesthacht, Germany) for one year during the period of December 2013 to December 2014. During the exposed year, the air temperature, relative humidity, precipitation, and wind speed were monitored. The SLS specimens were removed in two intervals, after six months and one year, for further mechanical testing.

2.5. Microscopy

SEM (Quanta^{TM} FEG 650 equipment, ThermoFisher Scientific, Houston, TX, USA) was used to analyze the surface of the aluminum samples and the fracture surface of the joints after mechanical testing. To analyze the surface of the aluminum specimens, a voltage of 10 kV, spot size of 3, and a working distance of 10 mm were used. In the case of the fracture surfaces, a voltage of 5 kV, spot size of 3, and a working distance of 15 mm were set. Before analyzing non-conductive samples (e.g., all the fracture surfaces), their surfaces were gold-sputtered using a Q150R ES equipment (Quorum Technologies Ltd., Lewes, UK) for 30 s with a current of 65 mA.

2.6. EDS and XPS

EDS coupled with SEM was carried out to investigate the chemical changes on the surface of the aluminum after accelerated aging. To obtain and analyze the EDS spectra, an EDAX TEAM^{TM} software V4.0.2 (Edax Inc., Mahwah, NJ, USA) was used. Both spot and area analyses were used to characterize small features and larger areas respectively. All EDS spectra were taken with a voltage of 10 kV, spot size of 3, at a working distance of 10 mm. For the non-conductive specimens, gold sputtering was performed prior to the EDS experiments. For those specimens, a gold peak is thereby present in the respective spectra.

Furthermore, XPS was used to confirm changes of the aluminum oxide layer after the accelerated aging process. For that, a Kratos DLD Ultra Spectrometer (Kratos Analytical Ltd., Manchester, UK) with an Al-Kα X-ray source (monochromator) operated at 225 W was selected. For the region scans, a pass-energy of 40 eV was chosen. Charge neutralization was performed for all specimens. The calibration of the spectra of contamination-free surfaces was performed to a 284.8 eV binding energy of the C1s signal. CasaXPS V.2.3.16 software (Casa Software Ltd., Teignmouth, UK) was used to process the data.

2.7. Single Lap Shear (SLS) Testing

All SLS specimens after accelerated aging and weathering conditions were mechanically tested under tensile loading according to the ASTM D3163-01 standard [32], using a universal testing machine (model 1478, Zwick Roell, Ulm, Germany) with a load capacity of 100 kN. A traverse test speed of 1.27 mm/min was selected, and the tests were performed at room temperature. Five replicates were tested to obtain the average ultimate lap shear force (ULSF) of the joints.

3. Results and Discussion

The results of this work are separated in two parts. In the first part, the results obtained from the accelerated aging conditions are discussed. In the second part of the paper, the mechanical performance of the joints under outdoor weathering conditions is briefly addressed. It should also be noted that the influence of different surface pre-treatments on the bonding mechanism and mechanical performance of the FSp joints was discussed thoroughly in [30]. Briefly, SB and PAA treatment led to a rough aluminum surface, increasing the micromechanical interlocking between aluminum and the molten polymer. Conversion coating altered the chemical state of the aluminum surface on a nanoscale and enhanced the chemical (covalent) bonding. Finally, PAA-P led to strong primary bonding between the primer layer and the molten PPS.

3.1. Accelerated Aging

3.1.1. Surface Features and Chemical Composition

First of all, the joints were visually inspected as soon as they were taken out of the aging chamber. Figure 1 shows the top view of the SLS FSp joints after 28 days of the aging experiment, and Figure 2 the same joints before aging. Noticeable changes could be seen in the SB and CC pre-treated specimens on the aluminum part. Dark regions were identified both on the top and bottom surfaces of the SB and CC pre-treated aluminum. Aluminum oxide, formed on the surface of the SB and CC pre-treated specimens, interacts with the humidity in the aging chamber, which leads to the formation of a weak aluminum hydroxide layer. It is well known that an aluminum surface undergoes hydration in the presence of a high level of humidity or when immersed in water [33]. Despite the PAA and PAA-P samples having slight water stains on the aluminum, no notable changes could be identified. PAA pre-treatment is known to produce an oxide layer that is more corrosion resistant than CC [34]. This could be the reason that the PAA pre-treated specimen did not exhibit any noticeable surface changes after 28 days of aging. Moreover, phosphate ions in the $AlPO_4$ monolayer that is formed on the aluminum surface after PAA pre-treatment reduce the hydration rate of the aluminum, as reported in [20,35]. On the PAA-P specimen, the primer is a thick, corrosion resistant layer [36–38], which inhibits the interaction of the underlying aluminum oxide with humidity. That is why no visual changes could be observed on the PAA-P sample. Finally, the composite parts did not show any visual changes after 28 days of aging. This was expected, because PPS is a highly moisture-resistant polymer [29].

(a)

(b)

(c)

(d)

20 mm

B-PM-SG-AAg28 J_t

Figure 1. Top view of the SLS FSp joints after 28 days of aging; (**a**) SB, (**b**) CC, (**c**) PAA, and (**d**) PAA-P.

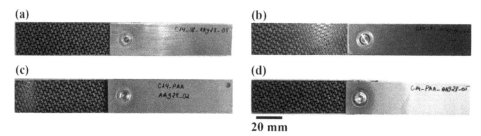

20 mm

Figure 2. Top view of the SLS FSp joints prior to aging; (**a**) SB, (**b**) CC, (**c**) PAA, and (**d**) PAA-P.

To further analyze the aluminum surfaces, high-magnification SEM images were taken from the affected areas on the specimens. Both SB and CC specimens showed compact areas consisting of the very fine nodular and flake-like structures that are related to the weak aluminum hydroxide formation (Figure 3).

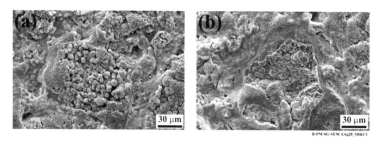

Figure 3. High-magnification SEM images of the aluminum affected areas after 28 days of aging; (**a**) SB and (**b**) CC specimens showing nodular, flake-like structures.

Table 1 shows the average chemical composition of the aluminum in the affected areas for the SB and CC pre-treated specimens, obtained from the EDS analysis. The results reveal that Al and O are the main elements present in these areas. A small amount of carbon was also detected on both specimens, which may be related to contamination in the aging environment. An even smaller amount of N was identified on the CC specimen, also from the humid environment in the aging chamber. The results showed an enormous increase in oxygen compared to the specimens before aging (see Table 2). In both cases, the oxygen content increased by more than five times after accelerated aging. This increase in oxygen was reported due to the conversion of aluminum oxide into hydroxide [19]. In contrast to the as-pre-treated specimens, other AA2024-T3 alloying elements, such as Cu and Mg, were not detected on the aged aluminum surfaces. Such an alteration of elements on the aged surfaces confirms the formation of a thick aluminum hydroxide layer on the SB and CC pre-treated specimens.

Table 1. Average chemical composition (in wt %) of the SB and CC pre-treated AA2024-T3 surface after 28 days of accelerated aging by EDS analysis.

Surface Pre-Treatment	Al	O	C	N
SB	45.7	43.2	11.1	-
CC	63.3	32.4	0.8	3.5

Table 2. Average chemical composition (in wt %) of the SB and CC pre-treated AA2024-T3 surface before aging by EDS analysis.

Surface Pre-Treatment	Al	O	C	Cu	Mg
SB	87.3	6.8	1.2	3.1	1.6
CC	88.1	5.1	1.5	3.9	1.4

Furthermore, an XPS analysis could further confirm the conversion of the oxide layer into aluminum hydroxide. Figure 4 shows a high-resolution Al 2p region of the SB specimen before and after accelerated aging. The aluminum before aging (Figure 4a) revealed two peaks at approximately 72 eV and 72.8 eV that are related to aluminum oxide [39–41] and metallic aluminum [39,42,43] respectively. After aging, the peak at 72.8 eV (related to the metallic aluminum) was still detectable, but the peak at 72 eV disappeared, and a new peak at approximately 76 eV was identified. The appearance of this peak might be due to the aluminum hydroxide formation [41]. It was reported that aluminum oxyhydroxide (AlOOH) is the most common form of aluminum hydroxide generated on the aluminum surface in the presence of humidity and at a temperature range of 25–100 °C [44–47]. However, it has also been suggested that, after further aging, the hydration of the AlOOH leads to the formation of Al(OH)$_3$ [21]. Regardless of the type of aluminum hydroxide present, the hydration of aluminum oxide was confirmed through an XPS analysis.

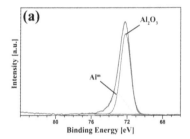 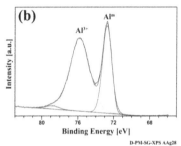

Figure 4. High-resolution Al 2p XPS region spectra of the SB specimen (**a**) before aging and (**b**) after aging.

In contrast to the SB and CC specimens, the PAA and PAA-P samples did not show any noticeable changes on the aluminum surface after aging, as visually compared in Figures 1 and 2. The SEM images of the aluminum surface, illustrated in Figure 5, appear very similar to the ones before aging (Figure 6). The PAA specimen (Figure 5a) showed an open porous structure with some coalesced pores, similar to its surface before aging (Figure 6a). The compact structure of the PAA-P specimen was also retained with the whisker-like particles of chromium and strontium oxides, as shown in Figure 5b.

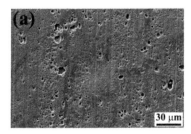 

Figure 5. SEM images of the aluminum side of the joint after 28 days of aging; (**a**) PAA and (**b**) PAA-P specimens.

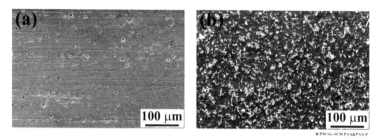

Figure 6. SEM images of the pre-treated aluminum surface (**a**) PAA and (**b**) PAA-P specimens. Reproduced with permission from [30].

As with the SB and CC specimens, an EDS analysis was performed on the PAA and PAA-P specimens. The results are listed in Table 3. In addition to Al, O, and C, in contrast with the SB and CC specimens, Cu and Mg were identified on the surface of the PAA specimen. The identified elements are very similar to those before aging (Table 4), with the exception of P, which was not detected after aging. The results reveal that the only major alteration of the PAA surface after aging is a reduction in aluminum concentration by about 7 wt % and an increase in carbon content by approximately 10 wt %. The increase in carbon content could be attributed to contamination from the aging chamber and the humid environment itself. Such an increase in carbon content as a new layer on the aluminum surface would slightly reduce the aluminum content captured by the EDS analysis. Furthermore, it was suggested that the hydration of the PAA pre-treated aluminum surface starts with a slow dissolution of the $AlPO_4$ layer, followed by the conversion of the aluminum oxide into aluminum hydroxide [20,33,48]. The absence of the P in the EDS analysis may be correlated with the early stages of the hydration process.

Table 3. Average chemical composition (in wt %) of the PAA and PAA-P pre-treated AA2024-T3 surface after 28 days of accelerated aging by EDS analysis.

Surface Pre-Treatment	Al	O	C	Cu	Mg	N	Cr	Sr
PAA	69.3	14.9	11.8	2.6	1.4	-	-	-
PAA-P	8.0	7.6	51.0	-	-	10.0	9.3	14.1

Table 4. Average chemical composition (in wt %) of the PAA and PAA-P pre-treated AA2024-T3 surface before aging by EDS analysis.

Surface Pre-Treatment	Al	O	C	Cu	Mg	P	S	Cr	Sr
PAA	76.9	14.9	2.0	3.0	1.5	1.7	-	-	-
PAA-P	0.2	17.8	76.0	-	-	-	-	2.5	3.5

The behavior of the PAA-P specimen was slightly different to the PAA sample. The EDS analysis of the PAA-P pre-treated aluminum after aging (Table 3) showed similar elements to the one before aging (Table 4), with the addition of an N peak. However, the quantification of the elements, as listed in Tables 3 and 4, revealed that the carbon content was reduced by 15 wt %, whereas the aluminum content showed an increase of approximately 8 wt %. This clearly indicates a thickness reduction of the carbon-based primer layer leading to a reduced carbon content. Moreover, the aluminum beneath the primer layer could be detected in a higher concentration due to a reduced primer thickness. In addition, a 10 wt % reduction of the oxygen content after aging was also identified. Since there were various sources of oxygen, the aluminum oxide, primer, chromium, and strontium oxides, a partial removal of the primer layer appears to have more influence on the reduction of the oxygen content. Finally, both Cr and Sr showed an increase in the content of approximately 7 wt % and 10 wt % respectively after aging. This is probably due to the partial removal of the carbon contained in the primer layer (as a result of its interaction with humidity), leading to an exposure of chromium and strontium oxides. Therefore, a higher concentration of the whisker-like oxides could be observed.

3.1.2. Mechanical Performance of the SLS Joints

The joints were mechanically tested to evaluate their lap shear strength shortly after the removal of the joints from the aging chamber (within 1 h). The obtained lap shear strengths of the SLS joints were divided by their initial strength before aging, and the results were reported as the residual strength of the joints, as illustrated in Figure 7. The SB, CC, and PAA-P specimens had only a small reduction in strength, but the PAA specimen was approximately 42% reduced, compared to their initial strength. Such results are in agreement with those reported in the literature for adhesively bonded aluminum joints, for example in [49].

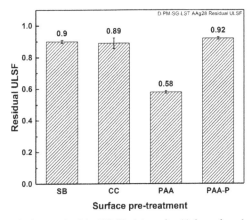

Figure 7. Residual strength of the SLS FSp joints after 28 days of accelerated aging.

It is believed that both the morphology and chemical composition of the aluminum surface play important roles in the durability of FSp joints. The SB pre-treatment generated large pores and crevices on the surface of the aluminum that could be filled almost completely by the molten PPS throughout the bonding area. Since molten PPS wet and fill such crevices, moisture cannot penetrate easily or rapidly into the interface between the aluminum and PPS, which in turn reduces the degradation kinetic of the joints. Furthermore, the chemical bonding between the aluminum and PPS, in the cases of CC and PAA-P pre-treatments [30], reduces the moisture path into the joints. In all three cases, the moisture diffusion was not completely inhibited, but the diffusion kinetic was significantly reduced. This is the reason for the small reductions in strength, compared to the initial strength of the joints. By contrast, it seems that the moisture could penetrate more easily and much more rapidly with the PAA pre-treated joint, leading to aluminum-PPS interface degradation and hence a reduction in mechanical performance. Figure 8 demonstrates the amount of moisture uptake of the FSp joints after the aging time. One observes that the PAA pre-treated joints showed the highest moisture uptake, approximately twice that of the SB pre-treated samples. The moisture was absorbed primarily at the interface between the aluminum and composite, degrading the bonding between the parts and hence the mechanical performance of the FSp joints. The larger reduction of the lap shear strength of the PAA pre-treated joints can therefore be related to the higher moisture uptake and humidity penetration into the bonding area.

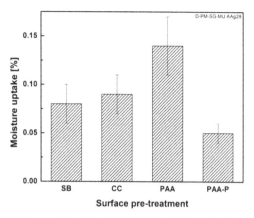

Figure 8. Moisture uptake of the FSp joints after 28 days of accelerated aging.

In the PAA pre-treated specimen, the diffusion of moisture into the interface may be related to the morphology of the oxide layer formed and the extent of pore filling by the PPS. A model with four possible situations for aluminum oxide pore filling by PPS is proposed here, as illustrated in Figure 9. The four possible pore filling cases can be summarized as follows:

(1) Complete wetting and pore filling
(2) Complete wetting, incomplete pore filling
(3) Partial wetting or pore filling
(4) No wetting or pore filling.

Incomplete pore filling (Cases 1 and 2) could still result in adequate micro-mechanical interlocking and an acceptable initial strength. The initial strength of the PAA specimens was higher than for the SB specimens (Figure 10) because of the presence of a much larger amount of pores, which could be filled (partially or completely) by the molten polymer. However, such incomplete pore filling is detrimental to the durability of the joints. According to the proposed model, while the joint is in contact with a humid atmosphere, the diffusion of the humidity into the interface depends on the pore filling situation. In Case 1 and Case 2, where the wetting between pore walls and the PPS is complete, the humidity diffusion is expected to be sluggish. By contrast, in Case 3 and particularly in Case 4 the humidity can penetrate much faster into the pores and into the interface of the aluminum-PPS. This leads to the degradation of the interface and hence the mechanical strength of the joint. These results are in agreement with the theories reported in the literature. Kinloch et al. suggested that in adhesively bonded aluminum, interfacial micro-voids in PAA pre-treated aluminum allow for the penetration of the water (or humidity) into the interface between the aluminum and adhesive [35]. The penetration of water was reported to be detrimental to the durability of the adhesive joint. Moreover, Digby and Packham stated that, in adhesive bonding, obtaining durable joints depends on the penetration of the adhesive into the aluminum oxide pores [50]. Such a penetration was considered to be dependent on several factors, such as the pore dimensions, adhesive viscosity, and the viscosity characteristic of the adhesive at a working temperature. Incomplete pore filling was reported to be the main reason for the reduced durability of the joints for specific surface pre-treatments such as PAA [50]. Therefore, it is believed that complete wetting and pore filling, as well as strong chemical bonds, are important aspects in achieving durable FSp joints.

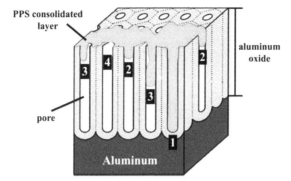

Figure 9. Schematic illustration of aluminum oxide after PAA pre-treatment, adapted from [51], and the proposed model of pore filling by the PPS. (**1**) Complete wetting and pore filling, (**2**) complete wetting, incomplete pore filling, (**3**) partial wetting and incomplete pore filling, and (**4**) no wetting and no pore filling.

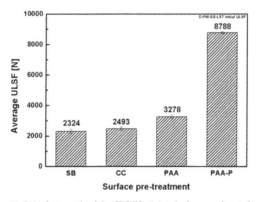

Figure 10. Initial strength of the SLS FSp joints before accelerated aging.

3.1.3. Failure and Fracture Surface Analysis

Figure 11 shows the fracture surface of the four pre-treated joints after 28 days of accelerated aging. The dark aluminum hydroxide layer can be observed on the SB and CC pre-treated specimens even very close to the consolidated molten PPS (known as the Adhesion Zone (AZ) [4,52]), as indicated by the black arrows in the figure. However, in none of the joints could any indication of aluminum hydroxide formation inside the bonding area be detected. In FSpJ, strong micro-mechanical interlocking and/or adhesion forces between the aluminum and consolidated molten PPS significantly reduce the moisture diffusion into the Plastically Deformed Zone (PDZ) [4,52], the area inside the consolidated molten PPS. Therefore, the rate of the interface deterioration is reduced, as was observed from the residual strength of the joints, shown in Figure 7. Although, the PAA specimen did not show any significant changes on the fracture surface (Figure 11c), humidity diffusion was expected to take place faster than with the other surface pre-treatments, as was also explained by the moisture uptake. The PAA-P specimen also showed very similar features to the specimen before aging (refer to [30]), such as the primer remaining attached to the composite, as indicated by the white arrows in Figure 11d.

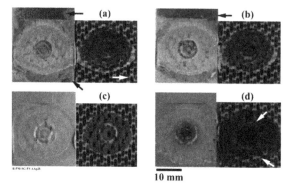

10 mm

Figure 11. Fracture surface of the SLS joints after 28 days accelerated aging; (**a**) SB, (**b**) CC, (**c**) PAA, and (**d**) PAA-P. The black arrows in (**a**) and (**b**) indicate the aluminum hydroxide formation. The white arrow in (**a**) indicates small features outside the AZ. The white arrows in (**d**) indicate the primer remaining attached to the CF-PPS.

Figure 12a shows the fracture surface of the SB specimen on the aluminum side of the joint. The image illustrates the AZ with a very smooth surface at the top of the image followed by a Transition Zone (TZ) [4,52]. The TZ shows typical features, where PPS remains attached to the aluminum as individual islands [52]. Figure 12b is a high-magnification image of the exposed SB aluminum indicated by the white rectangle in Figure 12a inside the TZ. No obvious alteration of the aluminum surface could be identified when compared to the SB surface before aging (see Figure 12c). This confirms that a large amount of moisture did not penetrate inside the bonding area, nor did it convert aluminum oxide into aluminum hydroxide in the bonding area. The same hypothesis seems to be valid for the rest of the surface pre-treatments, with the exception of PAA.

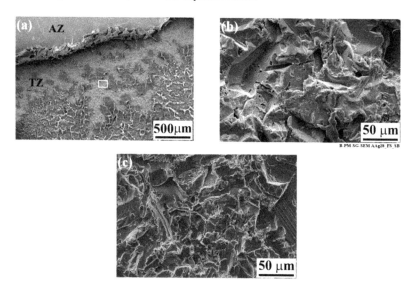

Figure 12. SEM image of the fracture surface of the SB specimen on the aluminum side after 28 days of accelerated aging. (**a**) Low-magnification image of the AZ-TZ area, (**b**) high-magnification image of the white rectangle indicated in (**a**), and (**c**) high-magnification image of the TZ area prior to aging.

As indicated by the white arrow in Figure 11a, small features could also be observed on the composite side of the fracture surfaces outside the AZ. As an example, Figure 13 shows such features on the CF-PPS of the SB specimen. Although the low-magnification image (Figure 13a) did not reveal any specific features, the high-magnification images (Figure 13b,c) show flake-like features and agglomerates of small particles. As this area on the CF-PPS corresponds to the aluminum hydroxide on the aluminum side of the joints, it is believed that these particles are the hydroxide layer removed from the aluminum and remaining attached to the composite. Despite the fact that these particles were outside the bonding area, they remained attached to the composite. This may be attributed to the weak nature of the hydroxide layer, which was easily detached from the underlying aluminum oxide as a result of frictional forces between the aluminum and composite during the lap shear testing of the joint.

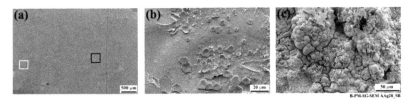

Figure 13. SEM image of the fracture surface of the SB specimen on the composite side after 28 days of accelerated aging. (**a**) Low-magnification image from the area indicated by the white arrow in Figure 11a; (**b**) high-magnification image from the black rectangle indicated in (**a**), and (**c**) high-magnification image from the white rectangle indicated in (**a**).

The EDS analysis further confirmed that both the flake-like structures and the agglomerates of particles contained Al, Cu, Mg, and O, as listed in Table 5. In both cases, the presence of aluminum and a high amount of oxygen, when compared to the as-pre-treated specimen, indicated that these particles were aluminum hydroxide. Sulfur from the underlying PPS could be detected in the case of the flake-like structures, which was an indication of the thinness of the flakes. However, because the agglomerates were larger in thickness, no sulfur from the PPS was detected in the respective EDS spectrum.

Table 5. Average chemical composition (in wt %) of the flake-like features and agglomerates on the CF-PPS by EDS analysis.

Features	Al	O	C	Cu	Mg	S
Flake-like	42.4	32.1	-	0.5	0.5	24.5
Agglomerates	38.5	42.1	18.3	0.8	0.3	-

3.2. Outdoor Natural Weathering

In addition to the accelerated aging, the SLS specimens were placed outside in natural weathering conditions for one year, as can be seen in Figure 14. Note that in this case three aluminum surface pre-treatments were selected: SB, CC, and PAA-P. PAA pre-treated specimens were not included as a result of their lower performance during accelerated aging experiments. Different climate data were recorded in this time frame, as follows [53]: an average temperature between −12.9 °C and 33 °C; a relative humidity of 3% to 100%; an average precipitation (both rain and snow) of 16.3 mm to 112.2 mm per month; an average UV index between 1 and 6; and a wind speed of 0.4 km/h to 62.6 km/h.

The aluminum/composite FSp joints were influenced both by humidity and moisture absorption as well as UV irradiation. CF-PPS showed discoloration as a result of the UV irradiation, as demonstrated in Figure 14c. It was reported by Batista et al. that such discoloration of CF-PPS is due to photolysis and photo-oxidation, resulting in an increase in the glass transition temperature [16]. Furthermore, surface embrittlement of the composite was observed as a result of the extensive cross-linking of polymer chains [16].

Figure 14. Outdoor natural weathering of the AA2024-T3/CF-PPS friction spot joints; specimens (**a**) during the first month, (**b**) during the third month, and (**c**) during the sixth month showing the discoloration of the composite.

It should also be noted that the effect of wind speed may not be neglected, since one end of the joints was not clamped and additional loads could be exerted on the specimens.

Mechanical Performance of the SLS Joints

The specimens were mechanically tested in two time intervals: six and 12 months. The obtained lap shear strengths of the SLS joints were divided by their initial strength prior to weathering, and the results were reported as the residual strength of the joints, as illustrated in Figure 15. Both SB and CC specimens showed a similar trend. In the first six months a reduction of 20–30% in the lap shear strength was observed. The trend of reduction in strength was also observed in the next six months. However, after one year both sets of joints retained more than 50% of their initial lap shear strength. These results are similar to those reported for the induction welding of the metal-composite joints after weathering conditions [24].

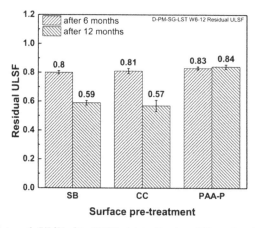

Figure 15. Residual strength (ULSF) of the SLS FSp joints after six and 12 months of outdoor weathering.

It can be argued that the moisture and humidity could penetrate slightly into the overlap area, deteriorating the bonding between the aluminum and composite, especially in the area of the consolidated molten PPS (known as AZ). Because AZ is the weakest part of the bonding area in a FSp joint [4,6,52], the penetration of the moisture inside this layer should be easier. As the fracture surface of the joints shows in Figure 16a,b, no visual changes were observed within the bonding area of SB and CC specimens after six months. Despite the lack of apparent changes on the fracture surfaces, it is valid to argue that the penetration of the moisture into the bonding area may happen slowly, which could weaken the bonds on the microscale. Moreover, one should consider the fact that the precipitation in areas near the ocean contains salty elements. Such elements have indeed a different (perhaps harsher) influence on the aluminum-polymer bonds rather than a pure humid atmosphere (as in the accelerated aging experiments). In contrast to the first six months, the fracture surfaces of the SB and CC joints after

12 months demonstrated the penetration of the moisture and humidity into the bonding area, as shown in Figure 16c,d. That is the reason for the further decrease in the residual strength of the joints.

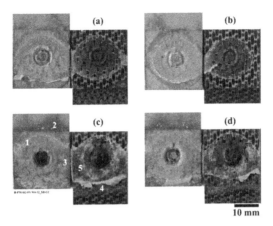

Figure 16. Fracture surface of the pre-treated joints after outdoor weathering. (**a**) SB and (**b**) CC after six months, (**c**) SB and (**d**) CC after 12 months.

The clear distinction between the fracture surface of the specimens after six and 12 months (both for SB and CC) is that after 12 months a large amount of the consolidated molten PPS remained attached to the composite. This is in contrast with the fracture surface of the joints prior to the weathering and those after six months of outdoor weathering, in which the consolidated layer was attached almost fully to the aluminum.

The SEM analysis of the fracture surface on the aluminum side reveals interesting features, as shown in Figure 17. The TZ from the unaffected region (Figure 17a) shows similar features (PPS remained attached to the aluminum as individual islands and a sandblasted aluminum surface) to the joints before weathering. However, the aluminum surface from the affected regions (Figure 17b,c) demonstrates a very cracked surface. The phenomenon is similar to the intergranular corrosion of the aluminum 2xxx alloys [54]. Since the precipitation (particularly in areas near the ocean, where this work was carried out) may contain small amounts of sodium and chloride ions [55], corrosion may have slightly occurred in these specimens.

Figure 17. SEM images of the fracture surface of the SB specimen on the aluminum side after 12 months of outdoor weathering. (**a**) TZ from the area (1) in Figure 16c; (**b**) high-magnification image from the area (2) in Figure 16c, and (**c**) high-magnification image from the area (3) in Figure 16c.

Furthermore, the SEM images from the composite side (Figure 18) show similar features as for the aluminum surface. Spherical features were observed on the composite outside the bonding area (Figure 18a), whereas a cracked surface was detected inside the bonding area (Figure 18b).

Figure 18. SEM images of the fracture surface of the SB specimen on the composite side after 12 months of outdoor weathering. (**a**) high-magnification image from the area (4) in Figure 16c, and (**b**) high-magnification image from the area (5) in Figure 16c.

The EDS analysis of the cracked surface in Figure 18b on the composite side is illustrated in Figure 19. In addition to sulfur and carbon (from the PPS), aluminum and oxygen peaks were also detected. This confirms that the cracked region is the aluminum, which remained attached to the composite. It is believed that the aluminum was slightly corroded starting outside the bonding area and penetrated beneath the PPS consolidated molten layer. One may identify the corroded/aged aluminum outside the bonding area as a weak point. During the mechanical testing, cracks may initiate from this weak corroded layer and propagate inside the aluminum in the bonding area. This is the reason why a part of the aluminum remained attached to the consolidated molten PPS on the composite side. Therefore, the lower mechanical strength of the SB and CC joints after 12 months of natural aging is believed to be the result of the weakening of the aluminum alloy rather than the bonding area.

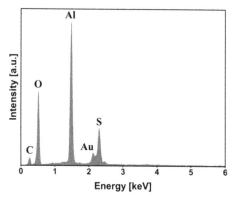

Figure 19. EDS area analysis of the fracture surface shown in Figure 18b.

In contrast to the SB and CC specimens, the PAA-P pre-treated joints showed a reduction in the lap shear strength in the first six months, while retaining their residual strength on the same level afterwards. PAA-P pre-treatment led to strong chemical carbon-carbon bonds between CF-PPS and aluminum [6,30]. It seems that moisture does not have a great influence on such chemical bonds, and the joint retained more than 80% of its initial strength. Moreover, the fracture surface of the PAA-P joints did not reveal any apparent changes as a result of the moisture penetration in the bonding area, as demonstrated in Figure 20.

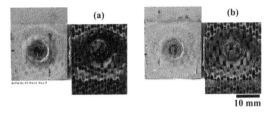

Figure 20. Fracture surface of the PAA-P pre-treated joints after (**a**) six months and (**b**) 12 months of outdoor weathering.

It is worth noting that, although CF-PPS showed discoloration due to the UV irradiation, no changes in color could be observed inside the overlap area, as illustrated in Figures 16 and 20. Therefore, it is not expected that UV irradiation had any significant effect on the deterioration of the mechanical strength of the joints.

These results suggest that a suitable surface pre-treatment not only increases the initial strength of the metal-composite joint but also enhances the long-term durability under environmental conditions.

4. Conclusions

An accelerated aging experiment was carried out on four selected surface pre-treatments: SB, CC, PAA, and PAA-P. The surface of the aluminum outside the bonding area, after 28 days of aging, showed a dark layer on the SB and CC specimens. This dark layer was determined to be $Al(OH)_3$ aluminum hydroxide, as confirmed by EDS and XPS analyses. In contrast with the SB and CC specimens, the PAA and PAA-P samples did not have any noticeable changes on the aluminum surface. Although the SB and CC specimens showed the formation of a weak aluminum hydroxide layer, the residual strength of these joints was approximately 90% of the initial dry quasi-static strength. This was comparable with the residual strength of the PAA-P pre-treated joint, which was 92% of the initial dry quasi-static strength of the respective joint. The high residual strength of the SB, CC, and PAA-P pre-treated joints was ascribed to the low level of moisture diffusion in the bonding area. Moisture diffusion was significantly decelerated due to the favorable wetting of the aluminum surface by the molten PPS. In contrast, PAA pre-treated joints resulted in a residual strength of approximately 58% after accelerated aging. This may be explained by the partial wetting and pore filling of the aluminum oxide layer by the molten PPS. A very fine structure of the pores, a high viscosity of the PPS, and a very fast cooling rate are the main causes of the partial wetting. Such partial wetting allows for moisture diffusion, degrading the aluminum-PPS interface and hence the strength of the joint.

A set of samples was also aged under natural outdoor weathering for six and 12 months. All of the joints retained more than 80% of their initial quasi-static strength. However, after one year of weathering, the ultimate lap shear strength of the joints pre-treated by SB and CC was reduced to 59% and 57% of their initial strength, respectively. The fracture surface of these joints showed that the humidity could penetrate inside the bonding area. In addition, a slight corrosion of the aluminum samples outside the bonding area may also contribute to the reduction in the strength of the joints. In the case of the SB and CC samples after 12 months of natural aging, it seems that the corrosion of the aluminum is the main reason for such a reduction in the joints' strength. The joints pre-treated with PAA-P showed, however, a retained lap shear strength of more than 80% of their initial strength even after one year of weathering. Strong carbon-carbon chemical bonds and intimate contact between the joining parts are believed to significantly reduce the diffusion of moisture into the bonding area and increase the durability of the joints.

In summary, there are two mechanisms contributing to the reduction of the joints' strength. In the case of accelerated aging for all the surface pre-treatments, penetration of humidity and hence the weakening of the interfacial bonds is the main weakening mechanism. Penetration of humidity inside the bonding area seems to remain the most important deterioration mechanism for all the joints after six months of natural aging. However, in the case of the SB and CC specimens after 12 months of natural aging, the predominant degradation mechanism changes to the weakening of the aluminum because of the occurrence of slight corrosion. For the PAA-P specimens, the main mechanism remains a slight penetration of humidity and the weakening of the bonding area.

It was also observed that natural aging had a more critical effect on the joints compared to accelerated aging. One reason was the fact that the precipitation contained chloride and other salty compounds, which are more detrimental to the aluminum and the interfacial bonds, rather than a pure humid environment. Furthermore, the free end of the joints in the natural aging experiments experienced (strong) wind that could influence the strength of the joints.

Author Contributions: Conceptualization, S.M.G. and S.T.A.-F.; methodology, S.M.G., N.S. and S.T.A.-F.; formal analysis, S.M.G.; investigation, S.M.G. and N.S.; resources, S.T.A.-F.; writing—original draft preparation, S.M.G.; writing—review and editing, S.M.G., N.S., J.F.d.S. and S.T.A.-F.; supervision, S.T.A.-F.; project administration, S.T.A.-F.; funding acquisition, S.T.A.-F. All authors have read and agreed to the published version of the manuscript.

Funding: This research was funded by Helmholtz Association through the Young Investigator Group, "Advanced Polymer Metal Hybrid Structures", grant number VH-NG-626, and the Austrian aviation program TAKE OFF, and BMVIT-Austrian Ministry for Transport, Innovation and Technology.

Conflicts of Interest: The authors declare no conflicts of interest.

References

1. Amancio-Filho, S.T.; Bueno, C.; Dos Santos, J.F.; Huber, N.; Hage, E., Jr. On the feasibility of friction spot joining in magnesium/fiber-reinforced polymer composite hybrid structures. *Mater. Sci. Eng. A* **2011**, *528*, 3841–3848. [CrossRef]

2. Andre, N.M.; Goushegir, S.M.; Dos Santos, J.F.; Canto, L.B.; Amancio-Filho, S.T. Friction Spot Joining of aluminum alloy 2024-T3 and carbon-fiber-reinforced poly (phenylene sulfide) laminate with additional PPS film interlayer: Microstructure, mechanical strength and failure mechanisms. *J. Compos. Part B* **2016**, *94*, 197–208. [CrossRef]

3. Esteves, J.V.; Goushegir, S.M.; Dos Santos, J.F.; Canto, L.B.; Hage, E., Jr.; Amancio-Filho, S.T. Friction spot joining of aluminum AA6181-T4 and carbon fiber-reinforced poly (phenylene sulfide): Effects of process parameters on the microstructure and mechanical strength. *Mater. Des.* **2014**, *66*, 437–445. [CrossRef]

4. Goushegir, S.M.; dos Santos, J.F.; Amancio-Filho, S.T. Friction Spot Joining of aluminum AA2024/carbon-fiber reinforced poly (phenylene sulfide) composite single lap joints: Microstructure and mechanical performance. *Mater. Des.* **2014**, *54*, 196–206. [CrossRef]

5. Goushegir, S.M.; dos Santos, J.F.; Amancio-Filho, S.T. Influence of process parameters on mechanical performance of AA2024/CF-PPS friction spot joints. *Mater. Des.* **2015**, *83*, 431–442. [CrossRef]

6. Goushegir, S.M. Friction spot joining (FSpJ) of aluminum-CFRP hybrid structures. *J. Weld World* **2016**, *60*, 1073–1093. [CrossRef]

7. André, N.M.; dos Santos, J.F.; Amancio-Filho, S.T. Impact resistance of metal-composite hybrid joints produced by frictional Heat. *Compos. Struct.* **2020**, *233*, 111754. [CrossRef]

8. André, N.M.; Bouali, A.; Maawad, E.; Staron, P.; dos Santos, J.F.; Zheludkevich, M.L.; Amancio-Filho, S.T. Corrosion behavior of metal–composite hybrid joints: Influence of precipitation state and bonding zones. *Corros. Sci.* **2019**, *158*, 108075. [CrossRef]

9. Borba, N.Z.; Körbelin, J.; Fiedler, B.; J dos Santos, J.F.; Amancio-Filho, S.T. Low-velocity impact response of friction riveted joints for aircraft application. *Mater. Des.* **2020**, *186*, 108369. [CrossRef]

10. Bolger, C. Acid Base Interactions between Oxide Surfaces and Polar Organic Compounds. In *Adhesion Aspects of Polymeric Coatings*; Mittal, K.L., Ed.; Plenum Press: New York, NY, USA, 1983; pp. 19–44.

11. Kerr, C.; Macdonald, N.C.; Orman, S. Effect of certain hostile environments on adhesive joints. *J. Appl. Chem.* **1967**, *17*, 62–65. [CrossRef]

12. Fowkes, F.M. Donor-Acceptor Interactions at Interfaces. *J. Adhes.* **1972**, *4*, 155–159. [CrossRef]

13. Davis, G.D. Durability of Adhesive Joints. In *Handbook of Adhesive Technology, Revised and Expanded*; Pizzi, A., Mittal, K.L., Eds.; Marcel Dekker: New York, NY, USA, 2003; pp. 273–292.

14. Davis, G.D.; Shaffer, D.K. *Handbook of Adhesive Technology*; Pizzi, A., Mittal, K.L., Eds.; Marcel Dekker: New York, NY, USA, 1994; p. 113.

15. Bjorgum, A.; Lapique, F.; Walmsley, J.; Redford, K. Anodising as pre-treatment for structural bonding. *Int. J. Adhes. Adhes.* **2003**, *23*, 401–412. [CrossRef]

16. Batista, N.L.; de Faria, M.C.M.; Iha, K.; de Oliveira, P.C.; Botelho, E.C. Influence of water immersion and ultraviolet weathering on mechanical and viscoelastic properties of polyphenylene sulfide–carbon fiber composites. *J. Thermoplast Compos. Mater.* **2015**, *28*, 340–356. [CrossRef]

17. Martínez-Romo, A.; Mota, R.G.; Bernal, J.S.; Reyes, C.F.; Candelas, I.R. Effect of ultraviolet radiation in the photo-oxidation of High Density Polyethylene and Biodegradable Polyethylene films. *J. Phys. Conf. Ser.* **2015**, *582*, 012026. [CrossRef]

18. Kinloch, A.J.; Welch, L.S.; Bishop, H.E. The Locus of Environmental Crack Growth in Bonded Aluminium Alloy Joints. *J. Adhes.* **1984**, *16*, 165–177. [CrossRef]

19. Venables, J.D. Review Adhesion and durability of metal-polymer bonds. *J. Mater. Sci.* **1984**, *19*, 2431–2453. [CrossRef]

20. Davis, G.D.; Sun, T.S.; Ahearn, J.S.; Venables, J.D. Application of surface behaviour diagrams to the study of hydration of phosphoric acid-anodized aluminium. *J. Mater. Sci.* **1982**, *17*, 1807–1818. [CrossRef]

21. Critchlow, G.W.; Yendall, K.A.; Bahrani, D.; Quinn, A.; Andrews, F. Strategies for the replacement of chromic acid anodising for the structural bonding of aluminium alloys. *Int. J. Adhes. Adhes.* **2006**, *26*, 419–453. [CrossRef]

22. Bland, D.J.; Kinloch, A.J.; Watts, J.F. The Role of the Surface Pretreatment in the Durability of Aluminium-Alloy Structural Adhesive Joints: Mechanisms of Failure. *J. Adhes.* **2013**, *89*, 369–397. [CrossRef]

23. Critchlow, G.W.; Brewis, D.M. Review of surface pretreatments for aluminium alloys. *Int. J. Adhes. Adhes.* **1996**, *16*, 255–275. [CrossRef]

24. Didi, M.; Emrich, S.; Mitschang, P.; Kopnarski, M. Characterization of Long-Term Durability of Induction Welded Aluminum/Carbon Fiber Reinforced Polymer-Joints. *Adv. Eng. Mat.* **2013**, *15*, 821–829. [CrossRef]

25. Schricker, K.; Stambke, M.; Bergmann, J.P.; Bräutigam, K. Laser-Based Joining of Thermoplastics to Metals: Influence of Varied Ambient Conditions on Joint Performance and Microstructure. *Int. J. Polym. Sci.* **2016**, *2016*. [CrossRef]

26. Davis, J.R. *Handbook of Aluminium & Aluminium Alloys*, 3rd ed.; ASM International: Cleveland, OH, USA, 1996.

27. Favaloro, M.R. *Thermoplastic composites for aerospace*; The IAPD Magazine: Overland Park, KS, USA, 2010.

28. Maruszczak, W. Advanced composite polymer for automotive—Long glass fiber linear polyphenylene sulfide. In Proceedings of the SPE ACCE Conference, Troy, MI, USA, 11–13 September 2007.

29. Spruiell, J.; Janke, C.J. *A Review of the Measurement and Development of Crystallinity and Its Relation to Properties in Neat Poly (Phenylene Sulfide) and Its Fiber Reinforced Composites*; Oak Ridge National Laboratory: Oak Ridge, TN, USA, 2004.

30. Goushegir, S.M.; dos Santos, J.F.; Amancio-Filho, S.T. Influence of aluminum surface pre-treatments on the bonding mechanisms and mechanical performance of metal-composite single-lap joints. *J. Weld World* **2017**, *61*, 1099–1115. [CrossRef]

31. ASTM. *ASTM D3762-03, Standard Test Method for Adhesive-Bonded Surface Durability of Aluminum (Wedge Test)*; ASTM International: West Conshohocken, PA, USA, 2010.

32. ASTM. *ASTM D3163-01, Standard Test Method for Determining Strength of Adhesively Bonded Rigid Plastic Lap-Shear Joints in Shear by Tension Loading*; ASTM International: West Conshohocken, PA, USA, 2008.

33. Baer, D.R. *State-of-the-art Application of Surface and Interface Analysis Methods to Environmental Material Interactions: In Honor of James, E. Castle's 65th Year*; The Electrochemical Society: Pennington, NJ, USA, 2001.

34. Juhl, A.D. Anodizing for Aerospace. 2010. Available online: http://www.metalfinishing.com (accessed on 20 December 2014).

35. Kinloch, A.J.; Little, M.S.G.; Watts, J.F. The Role of the Interphase in the Environmental Failure of Adhesive Joints. *Acta Mater.* **2000**, *48*, 4543–4553. [CrossRef]

36. Baker, A.A.; Chester, R.J. Minimum surface treatments for adhesively bonded repairs. *Int. J. Adhes. Adhes.* **1992**, *12*, 73–78. [CrossRef]

37. Rider, A.N.; Arnott, D.R. Boiling water and silane pre-treatment of aluminium alloys for durable adhesive bonding. *Int. J. Adhes. Adhes.* **2000**, *20*, 209–220. [CrossRef]

38. Rider, A.; Chalkley, P. *The Effect of FM-73 Cure Temperature on the Durability of Bonded Joints Employing BR127 Primer*; Aeronautical and Maritime Research Laboratory: Melbourne, Australia, 2000.

39. NIST. *NIST X-ray Photoelectron Spectroscopy Database*; Version 4.1; National Institute of Standards and Technology: Gaithersburg, MD, USA, 2012. [CrossRef]

40. Turner, N.H.; Single, A.M. Determination of peak positions and areas from wide-scan XPS spectra. *Surf. Interface Anal.* **1990**, *15*, 215–222. [CrossRef]

41. Kono, M. Studies of Metal-Polymer Interfaces. Ph.D. Thesis, University of British Columbia, Vancouver, BC, Canada, 2000.

42. Hauert, R.; Patscheider, J.; Tobler, M.; Zehringer, R. XPS investigation of the a-C:H/Al interface. *Surf. Sci. Lett.* **1993**, *292*, A605–A606. [CrossRef]

43. Sarapatka, T.J. Palladium-induced charge transports with palladium/alumina/aluminum interface formation. *J. Phys. Chem.* **1993**, *97*, 11274–11277. [CrossRef]

44. Chidambaram, D.; Clayton, C.R.; Halada, G.P. The role of hexafluorozirconate in the formation of chromate conversion coatings on aluminum alloys. *Electrochim. Acta* **2006**, *51*, 2862–2871. [CrossRef]

45. Stralin, A.; Hjertberg, T. Influence of surface composition on initial hydration of aluminium in boiling water. *Appl. Surf. Sci.* **1994**, *74*, 263–275. [CrossRef]

46. Alexander, M.R.; Thompson, G.E.; Beamson, G. Characterization of the oxide/hydroxide surface of aluminium using x-ray photoelectron spectroscopy: A procedure for curve fitting the O 1s core level. *Surf. Interface Anal.* **2000**, *29*, 468–477. [CrossRef]

47. Alwitt, R.S. The Growth of Hydrous Oxide Films on Aluminum. *J. Electrochem. Soc.* **1974**, *121*, 1322–1328. [CrossRef]

48. Kinloch, A.J. *Adhesion and Adhesives: Science and Technology*, 1st ed.; Springer: Cambridge, UK, 1987.

49. Butt, R.I.; Cotter, J.L. The Effect of High Humidity on the Dynamic Mechanical Properties and Thermal Transition of an Epoxy-Polyamide Adhesive. *J. Adhes.* **1976**, *8*, 11–19. [CrossRef]

50. Digby, R.P.; Packham, D.E. Pretreatment of aluminium: Topography, surface chemistry and adhesive bond durability. *Int. J. Adhes. Adhes.* **1995**, *15*, 61–71. [CrossRef]

51. Sulka, G.D. Highly Ordered Anodic Porous Alumina Formation by Self-Organized Anodizing. In *Nanostructured Materials in Electrochemistry*; Eftekhari, A., Ed.; Wiley: Weinheim, Germany, 2008; p. 8.

52. Goushegir, S.M.; dos Santos, J.F.; Amancio-Filho, S.T. Failure and fracture micro-mechanisms in metal-composite single lap joints produced by welding-based joining techniques. *J. Compos. Part A* **2016**, *81*, 121–128. [CrossRef]

53. Baschek, B.; Schroeder, F.; Brix, H.; Riethmüller, R.; Badewien, T.H.; Breitbach, G.; Brügge, B.; Colijn, F.; Doerffer, R.; Eschenbach, C.; et al. The Coastal Observing System for Northern and Arctic Seas (COSYNA). *Ocean Sci.* **2017**, *13*, 379–410. [CrossRef]

54. Davis, R.J. *Corrosion of Aluminum and Aluminum Alloys*; ASM International: Cleveland, OH, USA, 1999.

55. Neal, C.; Kirchner, J.W. Sodium and chloride levels in rainfall, mist, streamwater and groundwater at the Plynlimon catchments, mid-Wales: Interferences on hydrological and chemical controls. *Hydrol. Earth Syst. Sci.* **2000**, *4*, 295–310. [CrossRef]

MDPI

St. Alban-Anlage 66

4052 Basel

Switzerland

Tel. +41 61 683 77 34

Fax +41 61 302 89 18

www.mdpi.com

Materials Editorial Office

E-mail: materials@mdpi.com

www.mdpi.com/journal/materials

Lightning Source UK Ltd.
Milton Keynes UK
UKHW052155031122
411461UK00008B/130